C000129022

Postcard Catalogue

Fifth Edition, 1987

Stanley Gibbons Publications Ltd
London and Ringwood

Compiled by
TONIE and VALMAI HOLT

First published—September 1980
5th edition—September 1986

Published by **Stanley Gibbons Publications Ltd**
Editorial, Sales Offices and Distribution Centre:
5 Parkside, Christchurch Road, Ringwood,
Hants BH24 3SH.

© Stanley Gibbons Publications Ltd 1986

The contents of this catalogue, including the illustrations, are fully
protected by copyright. No part of this publication may be reproduced,
stored in a retrieval system, or transmitted, in any form or by any
means, electronic, mechanical, photocopying, recording or otherwise,
without the prior permission of Stanley Gibbons Publications Limited.
Requests for such permission should be addressed to the Catalogue
Editor.

This catalogue is sold on condition that it is not, by way of trade or
otherwise lent, re-sold, hired out, circulated or otherwise disposed of
other than in its complete, original and unaltered form and without a
similar condition including this condition being imposed on the
subsequent purchaser.

ISSN 0144-249X   ISBN 0 85259 142 X

Item No. 2829 (87)

Phototypeset by Input Typesetting Ltd, London
Printed in Great Britain by Whitefriars Press,
Tonbridge

CONTENTS

SECTION INDEX

THE COMPILERS

Tonie and Valmai Holt wrote their first book on picture postcards in 1971. Over the years *Picture Postcards of the Golden Age – A Collectors Guide* has become accepted as one of the standard books on the hobby. Their subsequent books have all used postcards as source material, their work contributing to the growing appreciation of the value of the postcard in studying the past, particularly social history. Their acclaimed *Till the Boys Come Home – The Picture Postcards of the First World War* (1977) was followed by *Best of Fragments from France* (1978) – a collection of Bruce Bairnsfather cartoons. *Picture Postcard Artists* (1984) covers the many artists whose landscape, animal and characters designs have appeared on postcards. Their most recent books are *In Search of the Better 'Ole'* – the first ever catalogue of 'Bairnsfatherware' and the collectables associated with the First World War cartoonist, remembered for his famous character creation 'Old Bill' and *Germany Awake!*, a lavishly illustrated work charting the rise of National Socialism in inter-war Germany.

Yet writing books, articles and giving TV and radio broadcasts is only part of the Holts' many activities. As dedicated students of the two World Wars, much of their working hours (often more than 12 a day) is spent planning and conducting military tours of famous battlefields. Their Battlefield Tours are organised jointly with British Airways and Townsend Thoresen. 1986 has been a particularly busy year for them with tours marking the seventieth anniversary of the Battle of the Somme. These regular trips abroad give Mr and Mrs Holt the opportunity of keeping in touch with postcard collectors and dealers throughout Europe, an important aspect of the work in compiling the *S.G. Postcard Catalogue*.

Copies of all of the postcard books written by Mr and Mrs Holt can be supplied by Stanley Gibbons. Inquiries to: Shop Manager, Stanley Gibbons Ltd, 399 Strand, LONDON WC2R 0LX.

ACKNOWLEDGEMENTS

As always we are pleased to record our thanks to those who have helped in the compilation of this catalogue and/or have submitted material for inclusion at a later date:

Helen Beaufort (*Artists*): G. Breach (*Literary*): Ben Chapman (*Curious/Miscellaneous*): Michael Clarke (*Artists*): David Cole (*Advertising*): Ray Collier (*Publishers*): Bill Drinkwater (*Publishers*): George Eimermann (*Artists*): Frederick G. Foley (*Modern*): J. J. Fougère (*Novelty*); Ron Griffiths (*Modern*); Ron Grosvenor (*Publishers*): Mrs Pam Hutchinson (*Publishers*): Brian Lund (*Sports*): W. F. Organ (*Publishers*): Mike Shirley (*Artists*): Helmut Stoyer (*Collections*): Mrs Angela Sturt (*Artists*): Dr Ben Swanson (*Social History*); Arthur Terry (*Military, Shipping*), Mrs L. M. Turton (*Artists*); Mrs Olwyn Walker (*Artists*), Rose Wharnsby (*Children*) and Tony Warr (*Publishers*).

We must also record our debt to Vivienne for patiently deciphering and expertly typing our impossible drafts!
Tonie & Valmai Holt

PREFACE

The last edition of this catalogue was produced in a handy pocket size which was universally welcomed; we continue with this format for this new, fifth edition.

In order to keep the retail price within sensible limits, yet at the same time publish new listings and further informative notes, Mr and Mrs Holt have skilfully revised many of the sections. Some information is now given in abbreviated form with full reference to the location of more detailed listings in earlier editions. This has enabled us to include new material and especially allow for a much expanded Modern card section. We are proud of the fact that we have had a separate listing of Modern cards since the first edition. A growing number of collectors see the division between Golden Age and Modern cards as arbitrary – there are just as many interesting and attractive cards available today as in the past.

In addition to the totally rewritten Modern section, this edition also contains fresh Commemorative, Maps and Topographical sections. All the illustrations have been changed – presenting users with another glimpse of the many fine and interesting cards in the extensive 'Holt Collection'.

Although postcard collecting differs in many ways from stamp collecting, there are similarities – for example the need for check lists of existing material. For stamps this is relatively easy in that official records exist for most issues and one can record dates of issue, numbers printed, etc. Thus stamp catalogues can list virtually every officially-issued stamp known to exist. For postcards this cannot be done so easily and in a general catalogue such as this entries can only give the type or subject of cards issued. Imagine trying to list all the cards ever produced in the U.K. The number of different cards showing popular seaside towns such as Blackpool or Margate must run into hundreds if not thousands and the resulting book would rival the London telephone directory in size.

However it is important that more detailed listings – often resulting from several years of research – should be put into print. Hence our Section Supplements which in this edition list: Dinah and Willebeek le Mair cards (Artists), Falkland Campaign cards (Military), Dalkeith Publishing Co., and J/V cards (Modern) and continue listings of David Allen Theatre cards (Collections) and the Judges London Series (Publishers).

It is obvious to all who use this catalogue that it is very much a 'team effort', collectors and dealers world-wide sending in details of cards for Mr and Mrs Holt to consider listing. It is a difficult job to decide which to include given the constraints of time, space and printing cost. If you have sent Mr and Mrs Holt details of cards and find they have not been listed in this edition, please be assured your information has not been overlooked but is held for use in a later edition. The help of those whose work appears in this edition is recorded in the Acknowledgements.

As before we request that you do not write to Mr and Mrs Holt about buying or selling cards; they cannot undertake to answer such inquiries. Please contact the Postcard Dept. of Stanley Gibbons Ltd. or one of the companies advertising in this edition.

In offering this fifth edition to you the collector, we are mindful not only of the work that has gone into it but that no catalogue can ever be definitive. However we believe we have the best catalogue currently available – we hope you will share that view. Your comments on this new edition will be most welcome and will be carefully considered.

John Holman

HOW TO USE THIS CATALOGUE

Unlike coins and postage stamps which, because of their accountability, are carefully recorded on issue, picture postcards have few birth records. Collectors have therefore created their own descriptive language in order to name and hence identify their cards. This language is explained in the GLOSSARY.

But a single picture postcard may have many names. To one collector it may be 'Comic'; to another a 'McGill'; to another, 'World War 1'; to another, 'Inter-Art', and to yet one more, 'Ethnic'.

Thus in order to consult the INDEX for a particular card, the card must first be named, and this process will be made much easier if the reader is familiar with the major collecting themes. These themes constitute the framework of this catalogue and are set out in the SECTION INDEX. The process then is simple:

1. **Name the card.**

2. **Locate that name in the index and follow the references.**

NAMING A CARD

There are three descriptive bands within which a name may be found:

1. *Artist's Name*, the signature on the card, e.g. Cassiers.

2. *Publisher*, e.g. Dietrich of Brussels.

3. *Thematic*, based upon the reason for issue or picture content of the card, e.g. COMIC, EXHIBITIONS, RAILWAYS, etc.

For this edition an index to Themes is provided. For references to artists consult the alphabetically arranged ARTISTS section.

Example 1
Name—by artist—'Tom Browne'. Consult 'Browne' in the ARTISTS section.

Example 2
Name—by theme—'Zeppelin'. Consult 'Zeppelin' in index and refer to page quoted for listing and value.

Where a card has a value because of its thematic content, that value will be increased if the picture is the work of a collected artist or publisher.

THE INDEX

The index is the key to the whole catalogue. It contains, in alphabetical order, all the major references to Themes and is placed at the back of the catalogue.

THE ILLUSTRATIONS

Each illustration is referred to in the text. Cross-reference is indicated by the sign ■. Illustrations are shown reduced size and are intended for identification purposes only.

ARTIST INFORMATION

The major portrait artists are listed in the ARTISTS section with a brief biographical account.

Where appropriate, however, lists of artists occur throughout as sub-divisions of the main sections. Those individuals with a biographical entry under ARTISTS are marked with the † sign, e.g. Barribal, W.†

THE SEVEN POSTCARD PERIODS

In the past the collecting of old picture postcards was confined to the years from about 1890 to 1918—'The Golden Age'.

Now, the extraordinary growth in popularity of the hobby has widened collecting horizons, and a cataloguing system capable of dealing with all the years from 1869 has become necessary. The 'Seven Postcard Period' system has been developed with this in view. It is now widely used by auction cataloguers, dealers and authors on postcard topics.

Period 1. 1869–1899. The first day of issue of the postcard (1 October 1869) to the last day of the 1800s (31 December 1899).

Period 2. 1900–1914. The first day of the 1900s (1 January 1900) to the last day of peace for Britain (3 August 1914).

Period 3. 1914–1918. The first day of war (4 August 1914) to the cessation of hostilities (11 November 1918).

Period 4. 1918–1939. The first day of peace (12 November 1918) to the last day of peace (2 September 1939).

Period 5. 1939–1945. The first day of war for Britain (3 September 1939) to the day of German unconditional surrender (7 May 1945).

Period 6. 1945–1969. The first day of peace (8 May 1945, VE Day) to the 100th Anniversary of the postcard (1 October 1969).

Period 7. 1969–today. From 2 October 1969 onwards.

A detailed account of each of the seven postcard periods was published in the first three editions of this catalogue.

PRICING

Intensive research into the question of postcard prices by the compilers has convinced them of the wisdom of continuing the Three-Band Pricing system used since the inception of this catalogue.

There are often considerable diversities in the retail price of any given card, due to a number of factors:

(1) *Geographic.* Certain types are more prized in different countries, or even different parts of the same country. For instance: the fine British comic cards are little collected in France, very popular in the UK. Fairly featureless postcards of Canterbury are eagerly sought after, and dearly bought, by collectors in the Canterbury area but would have virtually no value in Edinburgh. The classic *Art Nouveau* cards of the turn of the century have almost no price ceiling in the United States where there is a strong contingent of wealthy 'investor' collectors, yet they often sell in auction in Britain at well below average catalogue prices.

(2) *Fashion.* Interest is sometimes stimulated in certain types of card by a new book or article which features them. Collectors rush to buy these types, which pushes up the price, although it may then settle down again at a lower level.

(3) *Condition.* Some collectors will only buy cards in excellent condition. This will always have the effect of placing a premium on cards in virtually mint condition. Other collectors are willing to purchase a card in fairly poor condition in order to have an example of a particular artist's work (to complete a series), but usually in the hope of being able to replace that substandard card with a better example in the future. This means that there *is* a market for poor quality cards, but at a low price. In the middle is the reasonable price for a card in good, collectable condition.

(4) *Dealers Stock.* Some dealers do not change the price of cards already in their stock even though the price of those cards is generally accepted to have increased. But as they buy in new cards of the same type they mark them at the new price. Therefore in one

dealer's stock collectors often find two examples of the same card, in similar condition, at two very different prices.

(5) *Auctions.* At auction, too, prices vary enormously. If two or more potential purchasers are bidding for a card they each urgently want, an uncharacteristically high price is bound to be paid. On the other hand, normally high-priced postcards, sometimes sell in auction at well below their current average price if no-one bidding is particularly interested in them.

The Three Band Pricing System works as follows:

1. *Left Hand Band*
This is the lowest price you will probably be asked to pay for this card. It is priced thus because of a combination of the following factors:
a. It is in fairly poor condition
b. It is being sold in an area where such a card is little collected
c. The dealer selling it has had it in stock for a long time
d. The dealer selling it does not know the true value of it
e. It is an inferior example of the artist's work
f. It is poorly printed, or is not a particularly clear photograph, or is a very long distance view of the featured subject (e.g. a tram)
g. The design has been obscured by writing, postmark, etc.
h. It is a modern card

2. *Middle Band*
This what you will normally be asked to pay for this card. It is the average, reasonable, current market price that is being paid for it because of a combination of the following factors:
a. It is in good, collectable condition
b. The dealer selling it has studied the market and marked it at the current average price being paid for it
c. It is a good example of the artist's work/a good, clear, middle distance photograph/well printed
d. Any writing/postmarks do not detract from the design

3. *Right Hand Band*
This is the highest price you will probably be asked to pay for this card. It is priced so highly because of a combination of the following factors:
a. It is in virtually perfect condition
b. It is a fine/rare/early example of the artist's work/ perhaps it forms part of one of the classic *Collections*

c. It is a superb, close-up, sharp real photograph of an interesting/unusual event, building or location
d. It is a particularly early example of its type
e. It is unique or special in some way (e.g. signed by subject/artist; only very few were issued; was dropped from a balloon, etc.)

Single Price
Where one price only is printed for a card, this means:
a. It is a modern card, with a standard retail price, or
b. It is in plentiful supply in good condition, cards in poor condition are not worth collecting and would not rate the minimum valuation used in this catalogue—25p.

Prix d'Amateur (P/A)
The card concerned is so rare/attractive that its price has not been sufficiently tested at auction or in dealers' stocks and its price ceiling is only determined by the collector's desire and means.

GLOSSARY

Appliqué. Material attached to a postcard to embellish it, e.g. dried flowers, hair, velvet.

Artist drawn. Cards that originate from an artist's drawing, e.g. Tuck's 'Oilette' series, although that drawing may not have been originally or exclusively drawn for the postcard, but may be reproduced from a poster or magazine etc. They are usually printed by an ink process.

Back. That side of the postcard which carries the address.

Chromo-litho. A term used to describe high quality, lithographically printed coloured picture cards such as early Gruss Aus (*qv*) examples, where up to sixteen different colours were sometimes applied separately. Such cards are almost always from Period 1 or very early Period 2 and were ousted by the introduction of the cheaper three-colour process from around 1900.

Composite. Collective name for a number of individual picture cards that fit together to make a larger picture. Most composites consist of a dozen or less cards which may or may not be pictures in their own right.

Court size. Cards measuring approximately 115 mm × 89 mm, which were officially recognised in Britain on 21 January 1895.

Divided back. Cards where the back has been divided by a line into two sections. One is for the address, and the other for the message. The idea originated in Britain in 1902.

Front. That side of the postcard which does not carry

the address and which normally carries the picture.

Full out. A picture which covers the whole of one side of a postcard and does not share it with either the address or a message space.

Full size. Private postcards in Britain had to be the same size as the official (*qv*) postcards sold at Post Offices. On the Continent much larger cards were permitted by the UPU agreement and these allowed the rapid development of the picture card. The UPU 'full size', 140 by 89 mm (5½ by 3½ inches), became legal in Britain on 1 November 1899.

Gruss Aus. Literally 'Greetings From' in German, the term is used to describe early Continental greetings cards with vignetted pictures.

Hold-to-light. A card which, when held up to the light, displays additional colours or pictures.

Local publisher. A publisher whose premises are located in the area depicted on his picture postcards.

Maximum card. Postcard whose illustration corresponds to that of a postage stamp, usually affixed on the same side and cancelled with a first day of issue postmark.

Name. The identity given to a card by a collector. It may be based upon artist, publisher or theme.

Novelty. A postcard which deviates from the normal rectangular item made of standard board.

Official. A card produced by a Government Post Office. *See also* 'Postal stationery'.

Oversize. Also referred to as 'Continental' size, these are squarer and larger than the UPU full size cards. PHQ cards and German and Italian Period 5 official cards are typically 'oversize', being around 147 mm × 105 mm.

Photo-origin. The pictures found on postcards derive from two main sources—an artist's drawing (*see* 'Artist drawn') or a photograph. Those that originate from photographs are referred to here as 'photo-origin'. They may be printed—photographically (*real photo*), or by some 'normal' printing process involving the transfer of ink, (e.g. Tuck's 'Photochrome' series). Normally 'Real photo' cards have a clearer picture and better detail than other photo-origin cards and are therefore valued more highly. Photo-origin cards as a whole tend to be more valuable than artist drawn varieties, except where the drawings can be attributed to 'collectable' artists.

Postal stationery. Cards carrying pre-printed stamps issued by Government Post Offices. Sometimes designs are added later privately.

Postcard. A card produced with the intention of meeting the regulations concerning the appropriate Postcard Postal Rate.

Poster Ad. A card whose picture is a reproduction of a poster advertisement. The term is often loosely used to describe cards for which there is no firm connection with a known poster, but whose style suggests that an equivalent poster exists.

Printed stamp. The impressed or imprinted postage stamp on official (Post Office) postcards.

Private mailing card. Commercially produced American picture postcard for use with an adhesive stamp. Cards carry the words, 'Private mailing card' on the address side and were introduced on 1 July 1898.

Publisher. A term used to identify the issuing house. Strictly it may not identify the publisher in the dictionary sense of the word, but may also refer to the agent, importer, photographer or printer. The names used for Publishers in this catalogue are those in common usage, e.g. 'Tuck', rather than 'Raphael Tuck & Sons'.

Real photo. A card whose picture originated from a photograph and which has been printed by a photographic process, e.g. Tuck's 'Real photograph' series.

Under size. Applied to cards smaller than UPU 'Full size', but which are not 'Court size' (*qv*).

Undivided back. Cards without a dividing line on the back. The term is generally accepted as denoting an early card.

Vignette. A picture without ruled borders. Typically seen on Gruss Aus (*qv*) cards in twos or threes.

FREE POSTCARD OFFER!

Stanley Gibbons have commissioned a special series of 'Familar Figures of London' cards mirroring those which have appeared on all four editions of the Stanley Gibbons Postcard Catalogue. Number **3** in the series, **'The Flower Seller'** was given free with the 'Picture Postcard Monthly' and 'The British Postcard Collectors Magazine' as well as being distributed through Postcard Collectors Clubs.

Number 4, 'The Shoeblack' is available only to purchasers of this catalogue. In order to obtain your copy of this exclusive limited-edition card please clip off the coupon on the corner of this page and send it together with a stamp addressed envelope to:

Postcard Offer,
Stanley Gibbons Publications Limited
Parkside,
Ringwood, Hampshire BH24 3SH.

Remember the number of cards available is strictly limited and that they can only be obtained in exchange for the coupon.

Look out for card Number 5.

FREE POSTCARD COUPON

ABBREVIATIONS & SYMBOLS

The following abbreviations are used in this catalogue:

ad	advertisement
art.	artist drawn
Aust	Austrian
Austral	Australian
b & w	black and white
Belg	Belgian
Br	British
Bulg	Bulgarian
Can	Canadian
chromo	chromolithographically printed
chromo-litho	chromolithographically printed postcard
col.	coloured
Cont.	Continental
diff	different
Du	Dutch
Fr	French
GB	Great Britain
Ger	German
HTL	Hold-to-light
Hung	Hungarian
illus	illustrated/illustration
incl.	including
Int.	International
It	Italian
LH	left hand
Maxi	Maximum
nos.	numbers
o/s	oversize
ovp	overprint
PHQ	Postal Headquarters
PMC	Private Mailing Card
PS	Postal Stationery
PU	postally used
Pub.	Publisher
RH	right hand
rly.	railway
RP	real photo
Rum	Rumanian
Russ	Russian
UB	undivided back
UK	United Kingdom
UPU	Universal Postal Union
u/s	undersize
USA	American (United States)
WW1	World War 1
WW2	World War 2
†	Biographical entry in ARTISTS section

ADVERTISING

This collecting theme is one of the strongest in the hobby. However, collectors have become more selective in their buying and while once upon a time it was sufficient to describe a card as 'Poster-type' or 'Celebrated Poster' to ensure a high price, that is not now the case.

Poster-type designs remain amongst the more valued of this category, but other factors such as age, printing quality and the signature of a collectable artist, are frequently of equal or greater weight. The Tuck 'Celebrated Poster' series was listed in the fourth edition of this catalogue, pp. 248–249.

The range of advertising cards is endless and in order to provide a finite framework upon which to build a reference/valuation system, we have divided this section into six parts:

ALCOHOL/TOBACCO
ANIMAL FOODS/FOODS/MEDICINES
BOOKS/MAGAZINES/NEWSPAPERS
CHOCOLATE & NON-ALCOHOLIC DRINKS
COMMERCIAL/HOUSEHOLD/INDUSTRIAL
GENERAL POSTER TYPE ADVERTISING

An *Art Deco* influence in the design may add a premium value to an otherwise average advertising card.

Period 7 Ads are listed in the MODERN section.

ALCOHOL/TOBACCO
Dewars, James Buchanan, Thornes & Ogdens all have cards in the Tuck 'Celebrated Posters' series.

Ardite Vermouth
Poster type. Artist I. Stall ..   ..£8/**£11**/£12

Bacardi
Comic designs ..   ..   £1/**£2**/£3

Beer
Pullouts ..   ..   25p/**50p**/£1.50

Walker's Lager. Poster types for Warrington & Burton brewery ..   ..   £10/**£15**/£20

Beer & Baccy
Victoria State (1896) ..   ..   £20/**£25**/£30

Cavanders Army Mixture
Poster type. Period 3 ..   ..   £7/**£8**/£10

Chairman Cigarettes
Old English Pottery & Porcelain. 24 cards in series, also issued by other firms   ..   ..   £1/**£2**/£2.50

Champagne
Codorniu. Ten card composite set by artist Lorenzo Brunet. Per set ..   ..   £35/**£40**/£60
Henriot. Chromo vignettes   ..   ..   ..   £5/**£6**/£8

Kempinski. Chromo 'bon viveur' designs. At least 14 known
.. .. £6/**£9**/£10
Kupferberg Gold. Chromo 'bon viveur' and bottle designs
.. .. £3/**£6**/£7
Mercier. Chromo vignettes. Bottles and leisure activities
.. .. £4/**£7**/£10
Moet & Chandon. Mucha vignette .. .. .. £20/**£50**/£65
Ruinart Père et Fils. Overprint on a series of at least 6 cards
depicting revels at a masked ball. Pub. J. Goffin Fils.
Brussels.. .. .. £5/**£7**/£10

Chateau Loudenne
Lancet ad. Period 2 .. .. £3/**£4**/£5

Chianti
Italian wine bottle design .. .. £2/**£4**/£6

Cider
Schweppes poster type. Glamour. Period 4 .. £15/**£20**/£22
Symons. Devonshire .. .. £2/**£2.50**/£3

Cinzano
Dutch costume studies. UB .. .. £2/**£2.50**/£4
Pub. Rycker & Mendell. Chromos .. .. .. £2/**£3**/£4

Claymore Whisky
Pub. Tuck. Artist Harry Payne. Defenders of the Empire
(1924) .. .. £4/**£6**/£12

Cognac Bisquit
Pub. Bru Fils. Poster type .. .. £6/**£7**/£9

Dewars Whisky
Pub. Dewars. Artist Albert Hammond. Gems of Art series.
Period 2 .. .. 50p/**£1**/£1.50

Dimitrino Cigarettes
Artist A. Rossi. Chromos .. .. £5/**£6**/£10

Distillers Co.
Joseph Chamberlain silhouette .. ..£7/**£11**/£13

Dubonnet
Grand Prix 1900. Col. UB .. .. £4/**£5**/£6
Period 7. Rare card by artist Cassandre .. £10/**£20**/£40

Fernet Branca
Pub. Chappius Italy. Series of 10 chromolitho fashion studies.
Period 2 UB .. .. £40/**£45**/£50
Pub. Coen Milan. Chromo vignettes .. .. .. £3/**£4**/£7

Gallaghers Park Drive
Poster type. Period 3 .. .. £3/**£5**/£6

Gancia
Bottle vignette UB .. .. £3/**£4**/£5

Gitanes Cigarettes
Poster type. *Art Deco*. Artist René Vincent   £18/**£25**/£35

Godfrey Phillips
Inserts. Period 5. 127 × 89 mm
See fourth edition p. 3 for listing
Price range 25p/**50p**/75p
Franco-British Exhibition ..   ..   £2/**£4**/£5

Grapevine Cigarettes
Southend Imperial Lifeboat (1906)   ..   ..   ..   £2/**£3**/£4

Guinness
Brewery scenes. Period 4. Photographic   ..   £1/**£1.50**/£2
Period 6. Oversize   ..   ..   50p/**£1**/£1.50
Poster ads. Periods 2, 3   ..   ..   £1/**£2**/£4
Poster ads. Periods 4, 7. Oversize ('Alice', Strength, etc.)
     ..   ..   £1.50/**£2**/£3

Hofbrauhaus, Munich Beer House
Early Period 2. Gruss Aus type vignettes   ..   £1/**£2**/£2.50
Period 2. Pub. Karl Wittermuller. Comic types   £1/**£2**/£2.50
Period 4. Poster type   ..   ..   £2/**£4**/£6
Periods 6, 7 (incl. 'Beer Mat' postcards)   ..   25p/**50p**/75p

Job Cigarette Paper (see COLLECTIONS)
Poster type. Chromo-litho. Pub. Vercasson, Paris £15/**£40**/£75
Vignettes. Artists Leandre, Maxence ..   ..   ..   £5/**£8**/£10

Löwenbrau, Munich Beer
Col. poster type. Period 4 ..   ..   £6/**£9**/£12

Mitchell's 'Prize Crop' Cigarettes
Chromo-litho vignettes. Glasgow Exhibition 1901   ..   ..
     ..   ..   £12/**£15**/£18

Park Drive Cigarettes
Poster type, e.g. stagecoach   ..   ..   ..   £12/**£15**/£18

Players Navy Cut
Art with circular ad. Numbered series   ..   £10/**£12**/£14

'Principe di Piemonte' Cigarettes
Poster type. Artist A. Scorzon   ..   ..   £4/**£6**/£7

Sandorides 'Lucana' Cigarettes
Poster type   ..   ..   £12/**£16**/£20

Taillan Vermouth
Artist Mich. Poster type   ..   ..   £6/**£7**/£9

Vino Aroud
Comic situations   ..   ..   £1.50/**£2**/£3

White Horse Whisky
Pub. Alf. Cooke. Maggs coaching studies. Period 2   ..   ..
     ..   ..   25p/**50p**/£1

Wills
Poster types for Capstan, Gold Flake, Three Castles, and
Westward Ho! .. .. £15/**£26**/£30

ANIMAL FOODS/FOODS/MEDICINES

Banana Bread & Flour Co.
Bananine poster type .. .. .. £6/**£8**/£10

Beechams Pills
Blue card. 'Thanks' .. .. £3/**£4**/£6
Artist Tom Browne. Poster type .. .. .. £15/**£21**/£25
Others .. .. 50p/**75p**/£1.50

Birds Custard
Poster type. Ed. VII series .. .. £12/**£20**/£25
Other poster types .. .. £11/**£13**/£16

Buttapat Margarine
Poster type .. .. £10/**£13**/£15

Carnine Lefranc Health Food (1908)
Artist Weal. French Public Figures. (6 cards) .. £3/**£5**/£7

Carters Little Liver Pills
Poster type. Period 3 .. .. £7/**£9**/£10

Cerebos Salt
Poster type. Chromo-litho. Multi-vignettes .. £12/**£24**/£28

Champions Vinegar
Poster type. Chromo-litho .. .. .. £15/**£20**/£24

Chanteclair Embrocation
Poster type. Artist Mich .. .. £5/**£9**/£11

Chivers & Sons
English fruits .. .. 50p/**75p**/£1
Aerial views of Histon 25p/**50p**/75p

Crawfords Cream Crackers
Russo-Japanese war map (1905) .. .. .. £2/**£4**/£6
Poster type .. .. £3/**£5**/£7

Ellimans Embrocation
Artist Sturgess. Horse activities .. .. .. 75p/**£1**/£2

Flapper Sardines
Poster type. Period 4 .. .. £4/**£5**/£7

Force Cereal
Special offer cards. Early period 2 .. .. .. £3/**£6**/£9

Glaxo
Various subjects .. .. 75p/**£1**/£1.50

4

AD1

Harrison & Garthwaite Biscuits
VC winners. Action scenes with inset portraits. Set consists of
Burt, Dorrel, Holmes, Leefe Robinson, O'Leary and Pollock
.. .. £2.50/**£4**/£6

Hartley
Production scenes at Aintree. Interior and aerial 50p/**75p**/£1
Poster type. Marmalade .. .. £3/**£5**/£7

Huntley & Palmer Biscuits
Poster type. The Very Best Available .. .. £3/**£5**/£7
Poster type. *Art Deco*. Artist René Vincent £18/**£23**/£35

Jacobs Biscuits
Biscuit production scenes .. .. 50p/**75p**/£1
Cream crackers. Chromo-lithos .. ..£7/**£10**/£12

Jaffa Oranges
Poster type. Jaffa genie .. .. £14/**£22**/£25

Johnston's Corn Flour
Some Methods of Travelling series. Col. court size. Twenty-
four numbered cards.
1. Coracle 2. Chariot 3. Stage Coach 4. Sedan Chair 5. Pillion
6. Post-Chaise 7. Hobby Horse 8. Stage Coach 9. Sedan 10.
Carriage 11. Wheel Barrow 12. Carriage 21. Irish Jaunting
Car 22. Kago 23. Elephant
Per card .. .. £15/**£25**/£30

Lemco
Coronation series .. ..£8/**£10**/£15
Poster type. Artist Hassall. Set of 'Types of Lemco Cattle' (6
cards) .. .. £3/**£4**/£5

■AD 1 Pub. Tuck. Artist Dudley Hardy. Celebrated Posters No. 1502. Liebig's Extract. PU 1905 £30

Liebig Fray-Bentos ■AD 1
Meat processing scenes .. .. 75p/**£1**/£1.50
Oxo poster types, e.g. My Word! .. .. .. £10/**£15**/£18
Oxo Shackleton Expedition .. .. £3/**£5**/£7
Tuck's Celebrated Poster Artist D. Hardy .. £15/**£25**/£30

Lustucru Pâtes
Poster type. 1924 Centenary   ..   ..   £3/**£4**/£6

MacFarlane Lang & Co.
Poster type. 'Sultana Sandwich' series   ..   ..   £2/**£4**/£6

Mellins Food
Poster type   ..   ..   £2/**£4**/£5

Melox
Poster types. Animal and poultry food. Numbered sketches
   ..   ..   £2/**£3**/£4

Millenium Bread and Flour (1905)
Poster type. Series 2. Artist Cock   ..   ..   ..   £2/**£4**/£6
Poster type. Party invitation. Series 3   ..   ..   £3/**£5**/£7

Molassine Meal Animal Food
Various sketches   ..   ..   £1/**£1.50**/£2

Neaves Baby Food
Poster type   ..   ..   £10/**£12**/£18

New England Maple Syrup Co.
Poster type. 'Uncle John's Golden Tree', 'The Real Flavour
from the Maple Grove,' etc.   ..   ..£7/**£10**/£16

Pan Yan Pickle
Artist G. E. Studdy. Bonzo. Poster type   ..   ..   £3/**£4**/£7

Peark's Butter
Various   ..   ..   50p/**75p**/£1

Peek Frean
GB views 25p/**50p**/75p

Pitman Health Food Co.
Ideal food series   ..   ..   75p/**£1.50**/£3

Quaker Oats
Poster type. 'Smiles' Set of 10 (Postman, Grandpa, Sailor,
Cook, Tramp) ..   ..£8/**£10**/£12
Smiles, text on front ..   ..   £4/**£5**/£6

Ranks Flour
Poster type. Period 2 ..   ..   £4/**£6**/£7

St. Ivel
GB views 25p/**50p**/75p

Sainsbury's Margarine
Crelos overprint of Tuck's 'Early days of Sport'   75p/**£1**/£1.50

Scotts Emulsion
Ninety-two cards in series, one for each Department in
France, Corsica & Algeria. Period 2   ..   ..   £2/**£4**/£6

Shippams
Food production scenes .. .. 50p/**75p**/£1

Skipper Sardines
Poster type. Periods 2/3 .. .. £5/**£9**/£11

Spratts Dog Food
Dog studies .. .. 50p/**75p**/£1

Virol
Children of all Nations. Ideal Home Exhibition (1910) ..
.. .. £1/**£2**/£3

Walker, Harrison & Garthwaites
City Meat Dog Biscuit. Viscan. Dog studies. Poster type
.. .. £2/**£4**/£6
Phoenix Poultry Foods. Poultry studies. Poster type £2/**£4**/£6

BOOKS/MAGAZINES/NEWSPAPERS

Publications of all sorts frequently contained postcards; particularly so in Period 2 and again today. Sometimes the inserted card was intended to be an attractive giveaway that would encourage sales of the publication concerned. On other occasions insert cards advertised quite independent products. Almost all postcards associated with books, magazines and newspapers are insert giveaways, the major exception being the *Daily Mail* scenes (*see* MILITARY). Period 2 inserts are not highly valued and Period 7 varieties are not yet collected.

Answers
Poster type .. .. £1/**£2**/£3

Bazaar, Exchange & Mart
Bazaar, Exchange & Mart series, drawings each side .. ..
.. .. £2/**£3**/£4

Hutchinson
Period 1. Court size. Ads for novels .. .. £15/**£20**/£25

Inserts
Most insert views are not of good quality. There are some exceptions and it is these that will command the higher prices in the 'view' category. A list of inserts appeared on p. 8 of the fourth edition.

Price range .. .. 25p/**£1.50**/£5

Shureys Inserts
There are several collective varieties of which the following are the main ones.
1. Christian Novels. Dividing line on back is in thick dots only. 241 examples known.
2. Shureys. 5 line back in red/brown, magazines named. 207 examples known.
3. Shureys. 4 line back in red/brown, magazines named, but no mention of Great Prize Competition. 205 examples known.

Theatricals	..	..	..	..	..	25p/**75p**/£1.25
Tube stations	..	..	..	..	..	£1/**£2**/£3
Views	..	..	..	..	..	25p/**50p**/£1

Checklists of Shurey Theatrical, Tube Station and View cards (places A–G and H–L) were published in the third and fourth editions of this catalogue.

CHOCOLATE/COCOA/COFFEE/TEA/NON-ALCOHOLIC BEVERAGES

Cadbury's, Frys, Rowntrees, Mazawattee, Milkmaid, Idris, Schweppes, Bovril, Appolinaris, Edwards Soup are represented in the Tucks 'Celebrated Posters' series. Price range £15 to £75.

Arlatte Chicory
Pub. Tuck. Periods 1, 2. Flowers UB   ..   ..   ..   £3/**£4**/£5

Banania drink
Poster type   ..   ..   £15/**£17**/£20

Bensdorps
Dutch art ..   ..   £1/**£2**/£3
Dutch artist drawn views UB. Poster type, free sample offers
..   ..   £3/**£5**/£7
Dutch views. Brightly drawn. PMC backs. 12 cards in set
..   ..   £4/**£6**/£9
Pierrots UB   ..   ..   £1.50/**£2**/£3

Boon's Cocoa
European views 25p/**50p**/75p

Bovril
Art reproductions   ..   ..   75p/**£1**/£1.50
Pub. Moss. Famous posters in miniature   ..   £14/**£16**/£18

Broma Cocoa
Plantation sketches 25p/**50p**/75p

Cadbury
Bourneville village scenes ..   ..   50p/**75p**/£1
Cecil Aldin poster type. 'Famous Posters in Miniature'   ..
..   ..   £4/**£6**/£8

Camp Coffee
Breakfast scenes   ..   ..£7/**£10**/£12
Poster type. Artist Harry Payne   ..   ..   £25/**£30**/£40
Poster type. Others   ..   ..   £15/**£25**/£32
Write-Away type   ..   ..   £6/**£9**/£12

Advertising

Chocolat Lombart
Poster type. *Art Deco.* Artist René Vincent   £10/**£12**/£15
Scenes of boys, carts, railways, ships. Chromo-litho   ..   ..
..   ..£8/**£11**/£15

Coca Cola
Poster types. Periods 6, 7   ..   .. £2/**£3**/£5

De Beukelaer's Cocoa
Topographical sketches 25p/**50p**/75p

Epps Milenia Milk Chocolate
Poster type   ..   .. £12/**£18**/£23

S.G. Two-to-a-page Postcard Albums

Postcard Album (Order No 3521)
Attractively presented in a rich deep red PVC added binder
blocked in gold, this album contains 20 crystal clear double
pockets, each designed to hold four postcards to a maximum
size of 6½ × 4⅛ in. each. The pockets are held in a quick
release spring-arch fitting incorporating a special locking
device.

British Post Office Picture Card Album (Order No 3532) This
album is designed specifically to house the attractive series
of picture cards—popularly known by collectors as
PHQ's—Produced by the British Post Office. The compact,
fully padded, royal blue PVC two-ring binder contains two
single pockets to hold the first two cards, PHQ 1 and 2, and
13 double pockets to hold cards PHQ 3 onwards. Binder gold
blocked on spine. Space for additional pockets. Packs of
extra pockets are also available.

S.G. Four-to-a-page Postcard Albums
Golden Age Postcard Album (Order No. 3581)

The *Golden Age* has ten leaves each containing four crystal
clear top-loading pockets—perfect for the standard 'golden
age' size postcards, still in use after nearly a century. Extra
pages are available in packs of three (Order No. 3582)

Picture Postcard Album (Order No. 3584)

The *Picture Postcard Album* has the same overall format as
the *Golden Age Album*, but has larger pockets for PH1 and
other larger size cards. Extra pages are available in packs of
three (Order No. 3585)

For a copy of your brochure and price list write to:

Stanley Gibbons Publications Ltd
5 Parkside.
Christchurch Road,
RINGWOOD
Hants   BH24 3SH
Tel. Ringwood (042 54) 2363

Formosa Ooolong
Japanese types	..	..	..	..	..	£2/**£3**/£4
Japanese landscapes	..	..	..	..	..	£1/**£1.50**/£2

Fry's Chocolate or Cocoa
See the second and fourth editions of this catalogue (p. 11 p. 10 respectively) for details of these attractive cards.

Poster types	..	..	..	..	..	£20/**£35**/£45
Others	..	..	..	..	..	£1/**£2**/£6

George Payne Tea
GP Government Tea. Poster type	..	..	£12/**£14**/£16
Military vignettes	..	..	..	..	..	£2/**£3**/£4
Composite set of King at Windsor	..	..	..	.. **P/A**

Hornimans Tea
Poster type, e.g. Edward VII	..	..	..	..£5/**£11**/£15
Views	..	..	..	..	..	..	75p/**£1**/£1.50

Kathreiner's Kaffee
Artist Henri Meunier. Advertisement tastefully printed, front and back, onto the exquisite 'Girls of 1900' series, e.g. 'Aubépine', 'Iris', etc. .. .. **P/A**

Kohler Chocolate
This Lausanne manufacturer of chocolate and cocoa issued a series of 22 or more col. litho UB cards. Period 1/Early Period 2 .. .. £2/**£3**/£4

Liptons
American UB. Language of flowers	..	..	£10/**£15**/£20
Pub. C. W. Faulkner. Estate sketches	..	..	£1/**£2**/£3

Maggi
General views	..	..	..	..	..	25p/**50p**/75p
Pub. Maggi. Artist G. Fraipont. Our Churches series	..	..
..	..	..	..	..	..	..	£1/**£2**/£3

Menier Chocolate
Periods 2, 3. Views of Paris. Numbered. Probably over 100 cards .. .. £1/**£2**/£3

Moxie
Cola type drink. Period 4 .. .. 50p/**75p**/£1

Nestlés
Animals and birds. Series 575. 12 card set	..	75p/**£1**/£1.50
'Famous Posters in Miniature'. Series 4421	£10/**£20**/£30
Military vignettes. Poster type	..	..	..	£15/**£20**/£22
Pub. Williams. Patriotic Empire designs, incl. New Zealand, Australia, etc.	..	..	..	..	£2/**£3**/£3.50
Signed artists, e.g. Hassall. Poster types	..	£20/**£22**/£24

Ovaltine
Poster type (incl. Phyllis Cooper. Period 4. *Art Deco*) .. ..
.. .. £12/**£14**/£16

Paul Mairesse Chicory ■AD 2
Chicorée à la française. Period 2 .. .. .. £1/**£3**/£5

■AD 2 Pub. Anon. Paul Mairesse Chicory. Col. Period 2. UB £5

Ridgways Tea
Artist John Hayes. Pub. Norman Davy .. .. £2/**£3**/£5
Estate scenes .. .. £1/**£2**/£3

Rowntree
Rowntrees postcard series .. .. 75p/**£1**/£1.50
Various .. .. 50p/**75p**/£1

Salutaris Table Water
Poster type. Artist Hassall, o/s .. .. .. £10/**£14**/£16

Schweppes
Soda Water. Artist FS. Period 4 .. .. .. £17/**£20**/£24
Soda water. Others .. .. £3/**£4**/£7
Table water. Period 3 .. .. £3/**£5**/£7
Tonic water. Poster type. Period 4 .. .. .. £5/**£6**/£8

S.R.T.C. (Societa Romana Torrefazione Caffe) ■AD 3
Artist T. Corbella. Poster type. PU 1928 .. .. .. **£12**

■AD 3 S.R.T.C. Coffee. Artist T. Corbella. PU 1928 £12

Suchard Chocolate
There is a wide range of advertising cards from before 1890 until early Period 2. Valuation must take into the account the quality of the design as well as the subject matter and age.

Period 1. Multi-view	£3/**£4**/£8
Period 1. Souvenir—series	£10/**£20**/£24
1900 Paris Exhibition. Numbered chromo vignettes	
.. ..	£10/**£11**/£14
Period 2. UB. Chromo-litho	£5/**£8**/£10
Chromo-litho. PS back	£2/**£3**/£5
Vignettes. Children, etc.	£1/**£2**/£4

Symingtons
Foreign views	50p/**75p**/£1

Tower Tea
Poster type. Artist John Hassall	£12/**£16**/£18
Proverb series	
Hassall type	£5/**£7**/£8
Others	75p/**£1**/£1.50

Van Houten's Cocoa
European views	50p/**75p**/£1

COMMERCIAL/HOUSEHOLD/INDUSTRIAL
The total number of firms who either issued their own cards or overprinted their message on to already published cards is enormous. Here we list together, in alphabetical order, those companies, products and activities that currently attract collectors.

Allentown Adpostals
Between 1911 and 1913 the Allentown Adpostal Corporation (Pennsylvania) issued seven different advertising cards. They carried a mixture of advertisements (on both sides of Government postal cards) for a number of commercial organisations.

1 cent green printed stamp. 2 cards	£12/**£15**/£30
1 cent red printed stamp. 5 cards	£10/**£14**/£20

Bicycles
Humber Beeston. Self-addressed series (1907)	£7/**£10**/£12
Patcho Repair Kit. Art comics. Pub. Sharpe ..	£5/**£7**/£10
Rayleigh. Poster type	
Period 2	£7/**£9**/£10
Period 4	£3/**£6**/£8
Regent Cycles. Poster type. Vienna UB ..	£16/**£18**/£20
Royal Enfield UB	£2/**£4**/£6
Rudge Whitworth	
Cycling magazine inserts	75p/**£1**/£1.50
RP personalities. 'Lighting up Times' ..	£5/**£7**/£10
Sanpene. Artist Pascal Vion	£11/**£14**/£15
Singer. Poster type	£16/**£18**/£20
Others	£6/**£8**/£10

Boot Polish

Berry's Diamond. Poster type. Artist P. Lehmann   ..   ..

   ..   ..   £12/**£18**/£20

Kiwi. Emblem cut in chalk. Period 3   ..   ..   75p/**£1**/£1.50

Candles and Lamps

Bray Gas Burner Poster type	£2/**£4**/£5
Edison Lamps Poster type	£4/**£6**/£7
Philips Lamps	
'Arga' art	£3/**£4**/£7
Chromo. Dutch style	£2.50/**£4**/£10
Fr. designs	£1/**£2**/£4
Prices Candles	
Military studies	£2/**£2.50**/£3
Nursery Rhymes	£7/**£9**/£10
Primus It. Period 4	£2/**£4**/£6
Tantalum Lamps	£4/**£5**/£8
Veritas Mantles Poster type. Artist Hassall ..	£2/**£3**/£5

Carriers and Removers

Carter-Paterson Express Carriers Chromo-litho	£15/**£19**/£22
Others	
Photographic	75p/**£2**/£5
Artist drawn	50p/**£1**/£3

China and Pottery ■AD 4

Foley. Pub. E. Brain. Examples of Foley art china	£2/**£4**/£5
Goss. Pub. S. Oates. Goss china/Roman vases ..	£2/**£4**/£6
Goss. Nantgarw. Pub. R. & J. Lea	£1/**£2**/£3
Trent. Pub. Trent Bridge. Trent china/Roman vases	
	50p/**75p**/£1
Others	50p/**75p**/£1

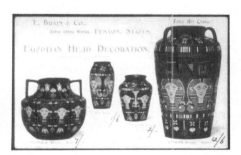

■AD 4 Pub. E. Brain & Co. Foley Egyptian Head China. £5

Coal

Clay Cross. Mining scenes	£2/**£3**/£4
Haydock. Art reproduction/views	50p/**75p**/£1
Others	50p/**75p**/£1

Dentifrice AD 5
Erasmic
 Col. poster type. Period 4 .. .. .. £2.50/**£4**/£5
Odol
 Series A112, b & w adverts, recommendations by famous
 stars—Camille Clifford, Zena Dare, Marie Studholme, etc.
  .. .. £1/**£1.50**/£3

■AD 5 Pub. Odol. Advert with actress Gladys Carrington.
PU 1908 £1.50

Engineering/General Products
Bell Telephone Co. Series of 12 'Uses' for the telephone ..
 .. .. £1.50/**£2**/£2.50
Brasso. Colouring cards .. .. 75p/**£1**/£1.50
Capewell Horse Nails Poster type. b & w .. .. £5/**£8**/£9

Continental Aeroplanstoff (Aircraft fabric) Poster type. Comic
 .. ..£6/**£10**/£12
Continental Ballonstoff (Balloon fabric) Poster type. Comic
 .. .. £12/**£20**/£23
Mustad Horse Nails. Poster type. Period 3 .. £10/**£12**/£13
North British Rubber Co. 'Chick' golf balls .. ..
 Rules of Golf, Artist Elcock .. .. £2/**£3**/£5
Pelaw Metal Polish. Poster type   .. .. £10/**£12**/£20

Friendly Societies ■AD 6
Grand United Order of Oddfellows .. .. .. £3/**£5**/£8
Hearts of Oak Benefit Society .. .. £3/**£5**/£8
Independent Order of Rechabites .. .. .. £3/**£5**/£8
Order of the Sons of Temperance .. .. .. £3/**£5**/£8
 Arms/Crest col. litho .. .. £3/**£5**/£8
 Bridges/Cathedrals, etc. .. .. 50p/**75p**/£1
Twentieth Century Equitable Friendly Society .. £3/**£5**/£8
Others .. .. 75p/**£3**/£8

■AD 6 Pub. Order of Sons of Temperance Friendly Soc. Period 2. £3

Hotels/Restaurants ■AD 7
Many cards showing hotels and restaurants are photographic in origin or printing. Therefore there is often a street scene or transport item associated with the picture, and this can greatly increase the value of the card (*see also* TOPOGRAPHICAL).

Foreign. Period 2 DB	25p/**50p**/75p
Foreign. 2 UB, not *Gruss Aus*	50p/£1/£1.50
London. Artist drawn. H. M. Bateman/Harold Oakley/T. Stephenson. Periods 2 to 4	£1/**£3**/£5
London. Artist drawn. Others	50p/**£1.50**/£2
London. Photographic origin	25p/**50p**/£1
Poster type	£1/**£3**/£5
Provincial	50p/**75p**/£1
US. Jack Dempsey Restaurant. Artist Montgomery Flagg. Period 4	75p/**£1**/£1.25

■AD 7 Pub. Anon. Artist Anon. Hotel Metropole, London. Period 2. chromo. £2

Industrial Scenes
Cammell Laird. Period 3 .. .. £1/**£1.50**/£3
Harland & Wolff. Pub. Valentine. Period 2 £1/**£1.50**/£3
Others .. .. 25p/**75p**/£1.50

Insurance Companies
Eagle. Head Office building , ... £1/**£2**/£3
Illustrated *Sunday Herald*. Period 4. Free Insurance scheme
    with Lloyds .. .. 50p/**75p**/£1
King Insurance Co. Royalty Sketches .. .. £1/**£2**/£3
    Kings of England. Probably 50 in series .. £1/**£2**/£3
Norwich Union. Pub. Scott Russell. Motor Fire Engine ..
    .. .. £6/**£8**/£10
Ocean Accident. Insurance postcard series .. £1/**£1.50**/£2
'Tit-bits' £1000 Insurance. Poster type .. .. £2/**£3**/£5
Others .. .. 75p/**£3**/£8

Kitchen Equipment
Produits du Lion Noir
Pub. Edition R.D.C., Seine. Artist Beatrice Mallet. Set of 6.
    Period 4 .. .. £1.50/**£3**/£4
Fonderie Nestor Martin
Pub. Goossens, J. G., Bruxelles. Artist Beatrice Mallet. Set of
    6. Period 4 .. .. £1.50/**£3**/£4

Motor Cars
Poster type designs .. .. £3/**£8**/£20
Period 2 .. .. £1.50/**£3**/£5
Period 3, 4 .. .. £2.50/**£5**/£10
Periods 5, 6 .. .. £1/**£1.50**/£2
Period 7 .. .. 25p/50p

Motor Shows
Period 2 .. .. £5/**£10**/£15
Period 4. Berlin (1937–9) .. .. £3/**£5**/£7.50
Period 6. Berlin .. .. £1.50/**£3**/£5
Others .. .. £1/**£2.50**/£4

Oils
Castrol
    Sir Malcolm Campbell in *Bluebird*. Artist Bryan de Grineau
    .. .. £5/**£6**/£8
    Photo-origin .. .. £1/**£1.50**/£2
Chantecler
    Poster type. Period 4 .. .. £4/**£10**/£15
Mex Motor Spirit (Bowring Petroleum Co.) Poster type ..
    .. .. £5/**£12**/£25
Mobiloil
    Period 4. Charles Lindbergh .. .. .. £7/**£9**/£10
Oilzum Motor Oil
    Poster type .. .. £8/**£12**/£14
Pratts Motor Spirit
    Artist drawn scenes showing use of Anglo-American oil
    products.. .. .. £3/**£5**/£7
Shell
    Benzine. HTL. Period 3 .. .. .. £17/**£20**/£25
    Period 4. Italian design .. .. .. £16/**£18**/£22

Poster type. Numbered, e.g. No. 41 'The Spirit of Great
Strength' .. .. **£12/£22**/£35
Poster type suffragette .. .. **£12/£22**/£35
Sternol Oil
Poster type. Comic. Artist Hassall .. .. **£12/£16**/£20
White Rose Kerosene
Hold to Light .. .. **£8/£10**/£15

Overprints

These are proprietary cards upon which an additional advertising message has been printed. They vary from one line additions, on either side of the card, to full out pictures. They should be valued on the basis of the original card, plus a premium (from 50p) for the advertising overprint according to its rarity or interest.

Phonographs

Edison
    USA. Poster type .. .. **£1/£2**/£4
    Others .. .. 75p/**£1.50**/£3

Schools

Many British schools were, and are, partly or fully supported by the fees paid by their pupils. Schools, therefore, had a need to advertise their facilities to the parents of potential pupils.

This was often done by picture postcards, particularly in Period 4.

Commercial schools, e.g. Pitmans .. .. .. **£1/£3**/£4
General views .. .. £1/**£1.50**/£2
Science laboratories with pupils .. .. **£2/£3**/£4

■AD 8 Pub. Pears' Soap (on back of 'Bubbles'). Period 2 75p

Shampoo/Soaps ■AD 8

Amami shampoo	50p/**75p**/£1
Colleen Shampoo. Poster type	£1.50/**£3**/£8
CWS soaps	75p/**£1**/£1.50
Fields Toilet Soap. Childhood series	£1/**£2**/£3
Gossages. 'The Right Sort'. Royalty and others :.	£4/**£6**/£8
Hudsons: Queen Victoria	£3/**£4**/£5
Vignette studies	£10/**£15**/£19
Knights' Family Soap. Poster type	.. £5/**£9**/£16
Lever Bros. Art views Port Sunlight	25p/**50p**/75p
Lux: Ger. Period 4. Poster type	.. £2/**£3**/£5
Pears: 'Bubbles'	25p/**50p**/75p
Poster types general	.. £5/**£7**/£10
Prices. Art nursery rhymes see above	
Wrights Coal Tar Soap. Wan-Tang-Fee. Chinaman series.	
Numbered	£1.50/**£2**/£3
'The Wright Sort' Poster type	£12/**£13**/£16
Others	.. £1/**£2**/£3

Shops and Stores

Throughout Europe interest has grown in recent years in pictures showing the way that things used to be. Shop fronts, showing goods displayed for sale, are a popular collecting category.

Stores. Artist drawn	.. £1/**£2**/£3
Photographic origin	.. £1/**£3**/£5
RP	..£8/**£12**/£20
Shop fronts. British or foreign. Close-ups ..	..£6/**£10**/£20
Shop interiors. Particularly collected in the USA	£3/**£8**/£12

Singer Sewing Machines

Aviation studies	.. £2/**£3**/£4
French. Periods 4/5	£1.50/**£2**/£4
Battleships	£1/**£1.50**/£2
Others	50p/**75p**/£1

Starch

Colmans. GB sketches	50p/**75p**/£1
Postmen of the Empire	.. £3/**£4**/£6
Remy	
Maps with vignette views	.. £1/**£2**/£3

Sutton Seeds

Flowers and vegetables	25p/**50p**/75p

Swan Fountain Pens

Artist Harrison (1906). Comic Historical types	50p/**75p**/£1.50

Thomas Cook

Periods 1, 2. UB Chromo-litho multi-vignettes	£20/**£25**/£30

(Madame) Tussauds

Pub. Tuck	.. £2/**£3**/£5

Typewriters

Oliver. Writing through the Ages	.. £1/**£2**/£3

Remington. Poster types	..	..	..	..	..	£3/**£5**/£7
Vignettes	..	..	..	..	£4/**£5**/£5.50
Royal. Edward VII caricature	..	..	..	.. £8/**£9**/£15
Underwood. Poster types. Period 3	..	..	.. £3/**£5**/£7

Tyres
Chaussures Raoul. Artist Caputi. Early motor cars .. ..

.. .. £10/**£15**/£17
Colonial. Poster type .. .. £7/**£8**/£10
Continental Pneumatique
    Periods 2, 3. Col. litho/*Gruss Aus* types .. .. £6/**£8**/£12
    Pub. Edler & Krische—Chromo art. Over 30 designs ..

  .. .. £1.50/**£2**/£3
Dunlop
    Periods 2, 3. Litho .. .. £5/**£7**/£8
    Pub. Doring & Huning. UB. Art .. .. £13/**£15**/£17
Engelbert. Poster type. Period 4 .. .. .. £5/**£9**/£11
Excelsior. Period 4 .. .. £3/**£4**/£5
Goodyear. Blimp. Pub. Tichnor USA. Period 6 .. £1/**£2**/£3
    Poster type .. .. £7/**£9**/£12
Grammont. Poster type .. .. £6/**£8**/£9
John Bull 1910 First International Cycle Show, Olympia

  .. .. £5/**£8**/£10
Palmer. Poster type. Period 2 .. .. .. £14/**£15**/£18
Others .. .. £1/**£7**/£15

Wood-Milne Rubber Heel ■AD 9
Artist Sager. Period 3 pin-up types .. .. .. £2/**£4**/£8
GB views. 40 numbered cards 25p/50p
Poster ads. Unnumbered .. .. £1/**£2**/£3

■AD 9 Pub. Fr. for Wellcome Heels (Wood-Milne). Artist Sager. Period 3 £8

COLLECTA POSTCARD ALBUMS

– incorporate a high capacity D-ring mechanism and contain 25 double-pocket leaves suitable for all modern 'Continental' cards including PHQs and Maximum Cards as well as the popular 'Golden Age' style. A single pocket leaf is also included for super-size cards or an index. All leaves are manufactured from tough polythene and contain black card inserts (leaf size 9 × 7in).

Two binder styles are offered: an attractive full-colour jacket, protected by a clear welded PVC cover (Item PA) and a plain leather-effect PVC binder with gold blocking on the front (Item PAP). The latter album is available in a choice of black, blue, red and green.

Extra leaves and binders are available for all Collecta albums – please write or telephone for our free brochure.

Collecta Albums
Stanley Gibbons Publications Ltd.,
Parkside, Christchurch Road
Ringwood, Hampshire BH29 3SH
Telephone: 042 54 2363

ANIMALS/BIRDS/FISH/INSECTS/ FLOWERS/FRUIT/VEGETABLES

BEARS

Novelty Bears
Embossed, 'Fab', leather, pull-out, 'strikers', etc.

Price range   ..   .. 75p/**£3**/£8

Performing Bears
Real photo. Period 2 ..   .. **£3**/**£5**/£8
Period 3–7 ..   .. 75p/**£1.50**/£3

Portraits of Bears (often with children)
RPs ..   .. 75p/**£2**/£4
Others   ..   .. 25p/**75p**/£1.50

'Roosevelt' or 'Teddy' Bears—see CHILDREN/TOYS

BIRDS ■AN 1

Artists
These include: Austin, Winifred; Daws, F.T.; Green, Roland; Müller, Augustus; Scrivener, Maud; Wardle, Arthur; West, A. L.; Others.

Price range   ..   .. 50p/**£1.50**/£4

■AN 1 Pub. Anon. Artist A. Müller. PU 1904 £1.50

Publishers
These include series by Hildesheimer; Vivian Mansell; Tuck (early chromos and many 'Oilette series); Others

Price range   ..   .. 25p/**75p**/£3

Animals/birds, etc.

British Museum of Natural History
Several series of British Game Birds, British Resident birds,
Summer Visitors, Artist Grunewald. Period 4   25p/**50p**/75p
*Add a premium of £1 per series if the original descriptive
leaflets still exist.*
    Period 7 ..   ..   **25p**

**Canary and Cage Bird Life Series and Capern's Bird
Foods Series**
See ADVERTISING

Doves/Love Birds
*Often found on highly embossed cards, usually of Continental
origin, in the GREETINGS category. Publishers include:
Stewart & Woolf, Tuck, Wildt & Kray.*
    Periods 2 to 4 ..   ..   50p/**£1**/£2

Parrots
A highly collectable category.
Artist Lawson Wood. Parrots. Period 4   ..   £1/**£1.50**/£2
Photographic or lesser known artist drawn   25p/**50p**/75p
Pub. Tuck. 'Pretty Polly' series. Period 2   ..   50p/**75p**/£1
    Educational series ..   ..   75p/**£1**/£1.50
Other miscellaneous, anonymous artist drawn, photographic
    studies, etc.   ..   ..   25p/**50p**/£1.50

Real Feathers: *see* NOVELTY

Swans
*Often featured in photographic view cards to add interest to
a static scene, and much collected. Publishers include Frith,
Valentine, Wildt & Kray and many local publishers. Periods
2 to 4. Value varies according to whether the swans are in the
foreground or in the distance.*
    Price range 25p/**50p**/75p

CATS ■AN 2
*This continues to be a popular category. A full listing of some
of the most sought after cat artists was given in the second
edition. They are: Barnes, G. L.; Boulanger, Maurice; Butcher,
Arthur; Carter, Reg; Cobbe, B; Ellam, W. H.; Kennedy, A. E.;
Knight, M; Lydon, A. F.; Maguire, Helena; Roberts, Violet;
Schropler, L; Thiele, Arthur; Travers Pope, Dorothy; Wain,
Louis.*

Price range (highest valuation for Wain)   ..   ..   £1/**£4**/£6
Louis Wain (early and late period)   ..   ..   ..£7/**£12**/£16

Black Cats
*A common and popular theme in Periods 2 to 4. Many series
were published by Inter-Art, and often re-printed with greetings overprints or French captions in WW1. Most catland
artists produced some postcards of this genre, in particular
Boulanger, Roberts, Thiele and Wain, whose cards command
a premium of up to £5. Values according to artist and period.*

Pub. Dennis, E. T. W. Periods 2, 3   ..   ..   £1.50/**£2**/£3
Pub. Inter-Art Comic Periods 2, 3   ..   ..   £1.50/**£2**/£3

■AN 2 Pub. Faulkner. Artist Anon. Series 267. Chromo. UB
£3

Comic Cats
Cats in humorous situations were featured by many of the well known postcard artists, such as Tom Browne, G. F. Christie, Donald McGill and Lawson Wood. Unfortunately many of the best cards of this type produced by the popular publishers were drawn by artists who will perhaps forever remain anonymous. Typical of the anonymous humour of this genre of card are those produced by the Scottish publishers Millar & Lang who reproduced their famous series 'When Father Says Turn' depicting cats.

Price range   ..   ..   £1.50/**£3.50**/£6

Felix the Cat—*see* ENTERTAINMENT: CINEMA

Photographic Studies (Periods 2–4)
The best known photographers include: Frees, Harry Whittier (Pub. Rotograph & Rotary); Landor (Pubs. Hildesheimer, Tuck, Wrench); Taber Bas Relief Co.

Price range   ..   ..   £1/**£2**/£4

Publishers
Faulkner, Hildesheimer, Stewart & Woolf, Tuck, Wrench and others all produced countless 'cat' cards, incl. some fine, early chromo-litho cards, often embossed. Periods 1, 2 ..   ..   ..
Price range   ..   ..   £1.50/**£3.50**/£6

Davidson Bros., Ettlinger, Inter-Art, Rotary, Tuck, Wildt & Kray and others produced many amusing, sentimental cards, many photographic, often on greetings cards. Periods 2 to 7
Price range   ..   ..   £1/**£2**/£3

DOGS ■AN 3

Artists

Aldin, Cecil†
Intelligent, characterful dogs, hunting scenes. Tuck and other publishers.
Period 2 .. .. £1/**£2**/£4

Daws, F. T.
Spratts 'Champion Dog' series. Period 2 .. 75p/**£1.25**/£1.75
Series for Birn Bros. High gloss finish. Periods 2 to 4 .. ..
.. .. 25p/**50p**/75p

Drummond, Norah
Researcher Linda Cowell has identified the following Tuck Oilette sets of dogs by this highly competent artist of country scenes and animals; 3046, 3184 Favourite Dogs, 3219, 3366, 8669, 9105 Sporting Dogs, 3294, 9273 With Dog and Gun, 9381 The Friend of Man, 9560 Scotch Collies, 9639 Pet Dogs

Price range .. .. 50p/**£1**/£1.50

■AN 3 Pub. R.P.S. Artist
George Studdy. No. 1026 £4

Muller, Augustus
Worked in Munich. Specialised in Dachsunds.
Pub. Hildesheimer. Periods 1, 2 .. .. .. 50p/**£1**/£1.50

Pope, Dorothy Travers
Fine chromo-litho series, e.g. Misch & Co. Series 806. 'Our Dogs'. Period 2 .. .. £1/**£2**/£3

Stokes, Vernon
Superb, early chromo-litho series on fine board (incl. Bulldog, Husky). Series 11825. Pub. Anon. Periods 1, 2 .. £1/**£2**/£4

Studdy, George†
The famous Bonzo dog. Publishers include Valentine's and 'RPS' Series. Period 4 .. .. £1/**£1.50**/£2

Wardle, Arthur
'Dog' series J1. 'Sporting Dogs & Birds', series J2. Pub. James
Henderson. Period 2 ..   .. 75p/**£1**/£2

Watson, Maud West
Tuck. Oilette, e.g. Sketches of Dogs, No. 9681. Period 2   ..
..   .. 75p/**£1**/£1.50

Comic Dogs
Dogs in humorous situations were featured by many fine
artists, like Tom Browne, Hassall, etc.: *see* ARTISTS.

Famous Dogs
See also MILITARY and Working Dogs below
Beddgelert's Grave RP
Edith Cavell's dog, *Jack* (now stuffed, in the Imperial War
Museum)
Edward VII's dog, *Ceasar*
Napoleon's dog on Elba (now stuffed, in *Les Invalides*)
Snowball, gassed in WW1

Price range 25p/**50p**/75p

Publishers
Eyre & Spottiswoode, Hildesheimer, Wrench, etc., produced
many early b & w series of photographic and art productions
of dogs and other animals by artists like Stanley Berkeley
and photographers like Reid. Periods 1, 2 ..   25p/**50p**/£1

Tuck produced countless series of Oilette and photographic
studies of varying worth. Periods 2 to 4   ..   50p/**75p**/£1

There are also many Periods 2 to 4 series and single cards of
photographic studies of animals in a sentimental vein, often
with actresses and pretty girls, often on greetings cards, by
Ettlinger, Rotary, Valentine, etc. 25p/**50p**/75p

Working Dogs
Swiss St. Bernards. Period 2   ..   ..   ..   50p/**75p**/£1.50

Dog Carts
Belgian milk carts   ..   .. £1.50/**£3.50**/£5
Belgian military carts   ..   .. £2.50/**£4**/£6
Belgian other carts   ..   .. £1.50/**£3.50**/£5
French milk carts   ..   .. £4/**£7.50**/£12
French other carts   ..   ..   £6/**£8**/£12
Dutch, German, Russian, Swiss carts ..   ..   .. £2/**£4**/£6

Military Dogs
Red Cross/Transport Dogs in WW1   ..   ..   £1/**£1.50**/£3

FISH
Angling Cards
Photographic studies, many local publishers. Periods 2 to 4
..   .. 25p/**£1**/£1.50
Tuck Oilette. Various series. Period 2   ..   50p/**75p**/£1

Poisson d'Avril:
Pub. Hawaii & South Seas Curio Co., Honolulu Chromo-litho
tropical fish. Large, colourful series .. 75p/£1/£1.50
Pub. Hawaii Jas. Steiner series Probably over 30 in series
.. .. 75p/£1/£1.50

Stranded Whales and Other Fish Curiosities
Many local photographers and publishers. Periods 2 to 4
.. .. 50p/**75p**/£1
Tuck Oilette/Connoisseur series, e.g. 'British Fresh Water
Fish', 'British Fish'. Period 2 .. .. .. 50p/£1/£1.50

FLOWERS/FRUIT/VEGETABLES ■AN 4
*A very attractive collecting theme, in which fine artist-drawn
and photographic examples can be found. The best known
artist of this genre is C. Klein (see Artists). Flowers abound on
greetings cards (see GREETINGS) and on novelty cards (see
NOVELTY).*

Artists
Billing, M; Gieste, A; Hedley (later Taylor) Nora; Hilde-
brandt, Fritz; Klein, Catherina; Lohmann, F; Walker,
Winifred; Others

Price range (highest valuation for Klein Chromos/Novelty)
.. .. 50p/**£1.50**/£5

Florists' Shops
Ads/displays .. .. £2/**£4**/£6

Horticultural shows
Periods 2 – 7 .. .. 50p/**£1.50**/£3

■AN 4 Pub. Imbert, Grasse.
Flowers grown by Antibes
nursery. Gold Medallists,
Cannes 1911, Nice 1912 £2

'Language of' (*see* GLAMOUR)
Flowers .. .. 50p/**75p**/£1.50
Fruit.. .. .. 75p/£1/£2.50
Vegetables .. .. 50p/£1/£3

Novelty

Appliquéd dried flowers	£1/**£2**/£3
Embossed designs	75p/**£1**/£2.50
Scented flowers	£2/**£3**/£4
Others	50p/**£2**/£6

Photographic (*see* SOCIAL HISTORY)
This section includes some beautiful coloured still-lives and pictures of growing, harvesting, etc.

Price range	25p/**£1**/£4

FROGS

Adverts. Much collected in the USA, especially for throat pastilles (e.g. 'Frog in Your Throat Co.')	£1/**£2**/£4
Alice in Wonderland frogs—*see* 'LITERARY'	
Frog Bands	50p/**75p**/£1
Pub. Meissner & Buch. Series 170 and 283	50p/**75p**/£1
Others	25p/**50p**/£1

HORSES ■AN 5
The most collectable cards in this sub-section are undoubtedly race horses and allied cards.

Ancient White Horses
An interesting category—early British White Horses carved in chalk on hillsides.
Publishers Wilkinson & Co., Trowbridge and many other local publishers.

Price range	50p/**75p**/£1

Artists' Impressions of Horses

Periods 2 to 5. Various publishers	50p/**75p**/£2

■AN 5 Pub. 'B & W.', Hastings. Artist W. H. Borrow. Meet at Battle Abbey £1.50

Animals/birds, etc.

Horse Studies
Pub. B.K.W. Artist Ludwic Koch. Series. Period 2   £1/**£2**/£4
Pub. 'P.F.' Artist Kocj (signed 'G.K.'). Embossed heads   ..
.. .. £1/**£2**/£4
Pub. Tuck. Norah Drummond. Oilette series (some with Harry
  Payne) .. .. 75p/**£1.50**/£3
Others .. .. 75p/**£1.50**/£2

Harry Payne Horses
Pub. Tuck early chromoliths. Periods 1 and 2   £5/**£10**/£15
Pub. Tuck Oilette, e.g. 'Horse Studies', 'Man's Best Friend'.
  Period 2 .. .. £1/**£2**/£4

Horse Fairs
In Britain and Eire (e.g. Buttevant) Periods 2 to 4 .. ..
.. .. £1/**£2.50**/£4

Hunting Scenes

Artists' Impressions
Many Tuck Oilette series, e.g. 'A Hunting We Will Go'. E. T.
W. Dennis 'Dainty' series. Other Periods 2 to 4   75p/**£1.50**/£3

Invitations to Meets
All Periods. Price according to Period .. 75p/**£1.50**/£3

Photographic Studies
Specified hunts, e.g. Compiègne (LL), Surrey Union. Period 2
.. .. 75p/**£1**/£2

Military Horses

Boer War
Artists Caton Woodville, Harry Payne. Periods 1, 2 .. ..
.. .. £3/**£5**/£10
Photographic. Periods 1, 2 .. .. £1/**£2**/£4

WW1
Artist Matania, Frederick .. .. 75p/**£1**/£2
Cavalry horses, Officers' horses, pulling gun limbers, military
  transport .. .. 50p/**75p**/£1.50

General Military
Pub. Gale & Polden type, etc. Period 2 .. 75p/**£1**/£1.50

Named Race Horses
Pub. Tuck. Derby Winners. UB. Periods 1, 2 .. £2/**£3**/£4
Pub. Walker & Co. 'Celebrated Racers' series. Period 2 ..
.. .. £1.50/**£2.50**/£3.50
Pub. Wrench series. Period 2 .. .. .. 75p/**£1**/£1.50

Point to Point Races
Periods 2 to 4. Artist drawn .. .. .. 50p/**75p**/£1
  Real photographic .. .. 50p/**£1**/£3

Races and Race Courses (British)
Photographic studies. Publishers Frith, Valentines and Wrench and many local publishers. Value varies according to clarity and detail. Periods 2 to 4. Artists' Impressions .. .. 75p/**£2**/£4

Races and Race Courses (Foreign)
Chantilly, Le Havre, Ostende, etc. Period 2   50p/**75p**/£1

Royalty at the Races
Photographic. Various Publishers. Periods 2 to 4   £1/**£2**/£3

Spanish Riding School, Vienna
Period 4. Photographer H. Schuhmann   ..   75p/**£1**/£1.50

Working Horses
Ploughing, Drawing Cabs, Fire Engines, etc. Various Publishers. Value increases according to rarity of occupation/vehicle and whether the picture is close-up or distant. Periods 2 to 5   ..   ..   75p/**£1.50**/£2

INSECTS
Many early Continental chromo-litho cards, often embossed, featured beetles, ladybirds, etc. Periods 1, 2   75p/**£1.50**/£2

Butterflies

British Museum of Natural History
'British Butterflies'. Probably 100 cards. Printed by Waterlow/Henry Stone & Sons. Period 4   ..   ..   ..   25p/**50p**/75p

Tuck Oilette
'Butterflies', 'British Butterflies & Moths'. Period 2   ..   ..   75p/**£1.50**/£2

Tuck 'Butterflies on the Wing'   ..   ..   £3/**£4**/£5

Fleas
Fleas were the subject of countless humorous cards of Periods 2 to 4, by artists like 'FS', Donald McGill, and many unnamed artists. Value varies according to artist.

Artist drawn   ..   ..   25p/**75p**/£1.50

Performing Fleas/Circuses
Period 2   ..   ..   £1/**£3**/£5

PIGS
Pigs were regarded as good luck symbols on the Continent and often appeared on greetings cards.
Early chromo-litho, artist drawn pigs. Periods 1, 2   ..   ..   75p/**£1.50**/£3
British humorous cards of pigs. Periods 2 to 5   25p/**75p**/£1.25
Modern French cards with 'dubious' captions. Period 7   ..   ..   25p/50p

MISCELLANEOUS

Animals on Greetings Cards
Greetings cards are, perhaps, the most prolific source for animal card collectors (bunnies and chicks on easter cards, robins on christmas cards, kittens, puppies, horses, etc. on birthday cards, fish on April Fool cards): see GREETINGS.

Circus and Performing Animals

Dogs, Elephants, Fleas, etc.
Barnum & Bailey and other named Circuses: *see* ENTERTAINMENT: Circus

Domestic/Farmyard Animals
Pub. Tuck. Educational series No. 4. Embossed. Late Period
2 .. .. £3/**£4**/£5

Mickey Mouse, Donald Duck: *see* ENTERTAINMENT Cinema

Monkeys on Barrel Organs
British and Continental. Period 2 .. .. £1.50/**£3**/£5

Nursery Animals
Many artist drawn cards, often published by the Medici Society in the 1920s–1950s, feature animals. They include:

Folkard, Charles; Tempest, Margaret, Thompson, G. H.

Price range .. .. 50p/**£1.50**/£3

Other Animals
Cows, Donkeys, Mice, Monkeys, Oxen, Rabbits, Squirrels, Stags, etc. often appear on cards. Some fine early Continental chromo-litho cards (often imported by C. W. Faulkner) some embossed, are well worth collecting. Later photographic designs are of little interest or worth. Value increases with age, quality of reproduction.

Price range .. .. 25p/**50p**/£1

Wild Animals
Pub. Tuck's Oilette series, e.g. 'Wild Animals'. Period 2
.. .. 50p/**75p**/£1.50
Pub. Wrench and other b & w photographic series of lions, polar bears, etc. Period 2 .. .. 25p/50p

Artist Rankin, George
Studies of lions, tigers, etc. Tuck's Oilette series, e.g. 'Wild Animal' series. Period 2 .. .. 50p/**75p**/£1.50

Artist Scrivener, Maud
Tuck's Oilette series, e.g. 'In the Jungle'. Period 2 .. ..
.. .. 50p/**75p**/£1.50

Animals/birds, etc.

Zoo Animals
Many 'Zoological' cards exist in long series.

Berlin Zoo
Col. chromo-litho set 1900 ..   ..   £1/**£3**/£4

Cologne Zoo
Various issues. Period 2   ..   ..   50p/**£1**/£1.50

London Zoo
'From the Gardens of the Zoological Society Regents Park',
b & w photographic studies by W. S. Berridge, Henry Irving,
etc. Period 2   ..   ..   25p/**50p**/75p

Zoo Buildings and Keepers

Dresden Zoo
Col. chromo-litho series. Vignettes. 1896   ..   ..   £2/**£4**/£6
Other types through to Period 7   ..   ..   25p/**50p**/£1

Other Zoos
*Photographic studies of zoos and their keepers were produced
by popular publishers of most of the famous zoos in Britain
and on the Continent. Value increases with age and rarity of
subject as well as clarity of photograph.*

Price range   ..   ..   25p/**£1**/£1.50

The prices given in this catalogue refer to the picture side of cards and unless otherwise stated take no account of the value of any stamps/cancellations or cachets. Most of the cards of the Golden Age period are found in used condition, normally bearing stamps of the minimum postcard rate and hence of little philatelic value. The prices for Modern cards should be taken to refer to unused cards with no damage. A single price is normally quoted for such cards, damaged copies will be worth considerably less than the quoted price.

For all non-Modern cards a minimum price of 25p is quoted, for Modern cards the usual retail price. For more details of the pricing system used, see page ix.

The postcard stocks of Stanley Gibbons Ltd are priced broadly on the valuations given in this catalogue. The prices quoted here have been compiled by Tonie & Valmai Holt and examined by R. Iles of J. A. L. Franks Ltd, to whom we extend our thanks.

S. G. Publications Ltd

ART

ART DECO

Art Deco (from *Art Decoratif*) derived from the more austere and abstract forms of *Art Nouveau* and was a reaction against its more florid aspects. The movement was characterised by the love of the symmetry in design that recalled the classic style. After an early emphasis on stylised garlands, roses and fruit, the style was more and more inspired by cubism and the geometric form. As with *Art Nouveau*, the style was applied to many branches of the arts, both useful and decorative—for example the 'streamlining' of racing cars, architecture, fashion, furniture and interior design.

Art Deco reached its apogee in 1925 with the Paris Exposition des Arts Decoratifs et Modernes, and died out in the mid-1930s.

To a lesser extent than with *Art Nouveau*, *Art Deco* influences can be seen in the borders and decorations of postcards in several general categories, such as Greetings cards and Adverts. Interesting examples of the *Art Deco* architectural style are to be found on postcards for example the Chrysler Building.

Art Deco styling adds about £4 to the value of cards collectable for other reasons. As the genre becomes more and more popular, the virtuoso exponents of the art command ever higher prices for signed examples of their work.

ADVERTISING/GENERAL/GLAMOUR ■ART 1, 2, AD 3, A 13, A 27, R 2

NAMED ARTISTS
Anichini, E.; Bakst, L.†; Barbier, P.; Bentivoglio; Bertelli, P.; Bianchi, V.; Birgo; Boccasile, G.; Bompard, S.; Bonnotte; Brunelleschi, U.†; Bruno, A.; Busi, A.; Calderara, C.†; Cappiello, L.; Carrere, R.; Chiostri, C. S. E.†; Corbella, T.†; Cramer, R.; Degani; Delorme, R.; Diveky, J.; Dudovich, M.†; Edel, L.; Garry, C.; Gesmar, C.; Giles, J.; Gobbi, D.; Gobbo, C.; Graf, M.; Grassi, V.; Grosze, M.; Guillaume, A.; Guitry, S.; Hardy; Hoffmann, J.†; Iribe, P.; Jung, M.; Koehler, M.†; Kokoschka, O.†; Larcombe, E.; Lendecke, O.; Likartz, M.; Loffler, B.†; Longley, C.; Lupa; Marty, A.; Mauzan, A. L.†; Mercer, J.†; Meschini, G.; Metlicovitz, L.; Nanni, G.†; Monier, M.; Montassier, H.; Montedoro, M.; Moser, K.†; Nanni, G.†; Nashnyekov; Pinochi; Sborgi; Scattina; Singer, S.; Sironi, M.; Solanges; Tofi; Vincent, R.; Willoughby, H.; Witt, M.
Price range (if unlisted elsewhere)   £3/**£10**/£40

UN-NAMED ARTISTS
Many unsigned, or undecipherable artist signed Art Deco postcards are now emerging. In particular there are some fine advertising designs of Period 4, many of them French or Italian.

Price range   ..   ..   £3/**£8**/£15

32

■ART 1 Pub. W. de Haan, Utrecht. Artist Rie Cramer 'In The Hague there was a Count'. Art Deco. Period 4 £10

■ART 2 Pub. Elite. Artist D. Gobbi. Art Deco design. PU 1932 £10

'NURSERY' ARTISTS

In some cases these artists went through an Art Deco phase in a more general artistic career. See CHILDREN *for a listing.*
Price range . . . . £2/**£5**/£10

ART NOUVEAU

Now perhaps reaching 'over-exposure', this has since the mid-1970s been the most prized style of design illustrated on the postcard. The style which emerged almost simultaneously in the mid-1880s in Glasgow and Brussels (where it was known as *le style belge*) is characterised by lyrical, flowing, complex, curvilinear designs, often with floral, ivy and clover leaf and peacock feather symbols. The art form spread to Germany and France where it got its name from S. Bing's Paris shop, founded in 1895, *L'Art Nouveau*. It is immortalised in Hector Guimard's entrances to the Paris *Métro* and in Glasgow in the form of stained glass and copper work—notably in the superb building that housed Millar & Lang the postcard publishers. Reaching its apogee in 1900–1902, the style faded out about 1910.

Art

Many of the sought after *Art Nouveau* postcards were originally designed for the poster, but the influence of the style is seen strongly in borders and decorations of advertising/photographic/view and many other types of postcards.

All cards in this category are Periods 1 and 2.

NAMED ARTISTS ■A 1, 9, 13, 23, 25, 26, L 4
Abeille, J.†; Abbéma, L.; Basch, A.†; Beardsley, A.; Beggarstaff Bros.; Bianchi, V.; Bilibine, I.†; Bompard, L.; Bonnet, G.; Boutet, H.†; Busi, A.; Capiello, L.†; Casas; Cauvy, L.; Chéret, J.†; Christiansen, H.†; Combaz, G.†; Conrad, G.; Dannenberg; Dedina, J.; Diez, J.; Faivre, A.; De Feure, G.†; 'Fidus'†; Fredillo; Géraud; Grasset, E.; Grün, J.; Guillaume, A.; Helleu, P.; Henrida, C.; Hoffmann, J.†; Hohenstein, A.; Iribe, P.; Jossot, H.†; Jozsa, C.†; Kandinsky, W.; Kienerk, G.†; Kieskow; Kirchner, R.†; Klimt, G.; Kosa; Kuhn-Regnier; Laskoff, F.; Léandre, C.; Lélée, L.†; Lessieux, L.; Macdonald, A. K.†; Martini, A.†; Mataloni, G.; Maurice, D.; Mazza, A.; Melina, C. L.; Metlicovitz, L.; Meunier, H.†; Mignot, V.†; Moser, K.†; Mucha, A.†; Noury, G.†; Patella, B.†; Péan, R.; Rau, L.; Riviere, J.; Sem, J.; Sonrel, E.; Steinlen, T.†; Tempestini; Toulouse-Lautrec, H. de; Utrillo, M.; Valloton, F.; Villa, A.; Villon, J.†; Wanke, A.

Price range   ..   ..£8/**£25**/£75

UN-NAMED ARTISTS ■ART 3, 4
Some extremely beautiful unsigned, or undecipherable artist signed *Art Nouveau* cards exist. They are highly prized and often fetch high prices. Publishers include: 'A & M, B.' (series of fine heads, printed in Saxony. UB); Davidson's 'Artistic Series' (printed in Saxony. UB); *Femmes Modernes* series and Tuck 'Art' Postcards (UB).

Price range   ..   ..£5/**£10**/£20

■ART 3 Pub. C. Lampe, Insbruck. Superb Art Nouveau design. Red, black and gilt. UB. Period 1 £10

█ART 4 Pub. Tuek. 'Elite' postcard. Series 3001. 'Silver' Art Nouveau card embossed with 'gold'. UB. PU 1904 £10

ART NOUVEAU BORDERS/DECORATION

B & w	.. ..	75p/**£1.50**/£3
Coloured	.. ..	£2/**£4**/£6
Russo-Japanese War	.. ..	£3/**£5**/£6

ART NOUVEAU BUILDINGS/FURNITURE

Paris Métro in *Paris Vécu* series	.. .. ..	£1/**£3**/£5
Others	.. ..	£1/**£1.50**/£3

ART NOUVEAU FANTASY

Large Letter	.. ..	£1/**£1.50**/£2
Others	.. ..	75p/**£1**/£3

ART REPRODUCTIONS

One of the most under-estimated categories, which can yield some of the very finest colour printing to be found on the postcard. The section includes reproductions of friezes, heraldic devices, mosaics, paintings, sculpture and tapestries.

FRIEZES

Pub. Gaddis & Sief, Luxor
Mortuary chapels of the Nobles, Thebes. Period 2 (premium of 25% for complete set of at least 30) .. 25p/**50p**/75p

Pub. Luca Gentile & Co., Naples
Pompeii scenes with red border. Period 2 .. 50p/**75p**/£1

CLAN TARTANS/COATS OF ARMS/HERALDIC DEVICES
■ART 5

The intricate designs and bold colours of heraldic devices and Scottish tartans were natural for transfer to the picture postcard as the rotary printing processes came into full production early in Period 2. Most Period 1 examples are of foreign designs often used on commemorative issues. A listing of the main British publishers appeared on p. 39 of the fourth edition of this catalogue. They include:

Brown & Rawcliffe (B & R); Byers, W. E.; Cambridge Picture Postcard Co.; Highland Clan; Jarrold; Johnston, W. & A. K.; Millar & Lang; Peel, Robert; Ritchie, William (W.R. & S.); Stoddard (Ja-Ja); Tuck; Valentine.

Period 1	**£4**/**£6**/**£8**
Periods 2 – 4	25p/**75p**/**£2**

Addition to edition four listing:
Pub. Tuck. Oilette Series 9886 (3 sets of 6)
Artist J. C. Shepard. 'House of Lords', 'Peers of the Realm', Arms, Crest, Motto, Description.

Price range .. .. 75p/**£1**/**£2**

■ART 5 Pub. Stoddart ('Ja-Ja') Heraldic Series. 'United Kingdom' Coat of Arms. Period 4. £2

MOSAICS

Pub. A. Reber, Palermo
Mosaic from the Palatine Chapel, gold & silver print. Cards form a type of 'composite'. Period 2 (a large premium would be attached to a complete picture) .. .. 50p/**75p**/**£1**

PAINTINGS

Pub. Fine Arts Publishing Co.
Royal Exchange paintings. Period 4. Two sets of 6 in original packets with explanatory leaflet.

Set with packet	£2/**£4**/£6
Set without packet	£1/**£3**/£4

Pub. Misch & Co.
World's Galleries series, bearing a Stengel number, as well as a Misch number. Brilliant colours on heavy board. From 1905 .. .. 50p/**75p**/£1

Pub. Misch & Stock/Other Misch & Co. series/Stengel. From the National Gallery

Rembrandt series	25p/**50p**/75p
Millet's masterpieces. Period 2	25p/**50p**/75p

Pub. Tuck
Many series throughout Periods 2 to 4 in a variety of presentations 25p/**50p**/75p

Other British publishers
Alpha, Boots, Cassell's, Ettlinger, Eyre & Spottiswoode 'Woodbury' series, C. W. Faulkner & Co., S. Hildesheimer, W. MacKenzie, Medici Society, Ernest Nister, Photochrom, Celesque 'Famous Picture' series, Rotary, Schwerdtfeger, Valentine, J. Welch, Wildt & Kray, Wrench.

Period 1	25p/**50p**/75p
Periods 2 to 4	25p/50p
Periods 5 to 7	**25p**

Foreign publishers

Period 1	25p/**50p**/75p
Periods 2 to 4	25p/50p

Carlo Bestetti, Rome, Toulouse-Lautrec reproductions.
Period 6 .. .. £2/**£3**/£5

Reproductions from Art Galleries

Birmingham, Lady Lever Art Gallery, Louvre, Manchester, National Gallery, Prado, etc.

Period 1	25p/50p
Periods 2–7	**25p**

SCULPTURES

Alpha/Paris Salon/Others

Period 1	25p/50p
Periods 2–7	**25p**

Pub. Anon. Artist Giris. Personalities like Farman and the Kaiser. Periods 2, 3 .. .. £1.50/**£3**/£6

Pub. D.M. Italy. Artist L. Rizzi. WW1 satire Tzar, Emperor of Austria, Poincaré, etc. .. .. .. £1.50/**£3**/£6

Pub. A. Noyer, Paris. Artist Mastroianni. Photographs of sculptured military scenes. Periods 2, 3 .. 50p/**75p**/£1

The Stanley Gibbons Postcard Department is at 399 Strand, London, WC2. Open Mon – Fri. 9.30 am – 5.30 pm; Sat. 10.00 am – 12.30 pm.

ARTISTS

This section gives general information about the work of the better-known postcard artists, together with some biographical background. It also refers to the sections where more details and specific valuations of the artists' work are to be found. Valuations in this section indicate the price range of the artists' general work.

ABEILLE, JACK ■A 1

One of the earliest French artists to design for the postcard (from about 1898) with delightful vignettes, often featuring lovely ladies (see SOCIAL HISTORY). He also designed for the Paris Exhibition of 1900 (see EXHIBITIONS) and went on producing postcards well into Period 3, when he produced some military designs.

Pre-1900 designs	£15/**£25**/£30
Paris Exhibition	£10/**£15**/£20
Period 2. Flower series/Head-dress styles through the ages/	
'Sins' series	..£6/**£10**/£18
Later designs	..£5/**£10**/£15

■A1 Pub. P.S.A.D. 640H. Artist Abeille 'Erika'. Paris Exhibition. 1900 £25

ALDIN, CECIL (d. 1935) ■A 2

Educated at Solihull Grammar School and then under Calderon in Kensington, he was a popular founder member of the London Sketch Club, of which he was President in 1905. He specialised in dogs, hunting scenes and other animal studies and was a Master of Foxhounds.

Lawrence & Jellicoe	£1/**£2**/£3
Savory, E. W. Ltd., Bristol	£1/**£2**/£3
Tuck 'Celebrated Poster' series No. 1500 (1 card), series No.	
1502 (2 cards), Cadbury's Cocoa, Colman's Blue, Colman's	
Starch	£15/**£17**/£25
Tuck. Other series	£1.50/**£2**/£4
Valentine & Sons. The five senses	£1.50/**£2**/£4

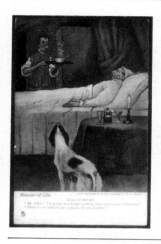

Humour of Life.

■A2 Pub. Tuck. 'Humour of Life'. No. 6440 Artist Cecil Adlin. PU 1905 £4

ALLEN, DAPHNE (b. 1899)
Daphne Allen achieved fame as a child artist. Much of her work was published in two books—A Child's Visions and The Birth of the Opal. Some of her drawings were reproduced as postcards for Glaxo adverts. Periods 2 and 3.

Price range   ..   ..   £2.50/**£4**/£5

ANDERSON, MARTIN (Cynicus) (1854–1932) ■A 3
A rare, original vein of unconventional humour and satire characterised this prolific artist's work. A Scot by birth and breeding, Anderson moved to London to establish himself as an artist. He set up his own company which produced hundreds of designs, some of them hand-tinted, which dealt with many facets of Edwardian life—bicycling, courtship, marriage, parenthood, the railway, Scottish life, and the seaside. See COMIC, NOVELTY.

Blum & Degen (1899). Three court-sized sets   ..   £1/**£3**/£6
Cynicus Pub. Co. (1902–1916).   ..   ..   ..   50p/**75p**/£2
Tuck (1914). Set of 'By and Bye' Darby & Joan types ..   ..
  ..   .. 75p/**£1**/£2

ANDERSON, V. C.
Period 2. American artist. Subjects include children and comic.
Publishers include: Charles Scribner's Sons, Reinthal & Newman, Wildt & Kray.

Price range   ..   ..   75p/**£1**/£1.50

■A3 Pub. Cynicus Pub. Co. Artist 'Cynicus' (Martin Anderson). Period 2 £2

ARDIZZONE, EDWARD (b. 1900)
Born in Haiphong, China, he came to England to be educated in 1905. He studied at the Westminster School of Art. He is best known as an official War Artist of WW2.

Price range   ..   ..   50p/**£1**/£1.50

ARMITAGE, WILLIAM (1856–1941)
Son of a Nottingham Quaker family, he worked in the family corn merchant business for some years before taking up painting becoming a proficient landscape artist and animal painter. His famous WW1 patriotic design of the lion and its mane is the only Armstrong postcard so far identified. Other information would be welcomed by the compilers.

Period 3. Pub. Boots. WW1 design 25p/**50p**/75p

ASTI, ANGELO (1847–1903) ■ C 3
Italian artist who mostly worked in France. He was born in Paris and died in Mantua. His work was exhibited in the Paris Salon between 1890 and 1901. He was mostly known for his bosomy beauties (see GLAMOUR*) but his most famous design was for the Collection Job (see* COLLECTIONS*).*

Collection Job
1903	£20/**£25**/£30
1905/07/11/14	£10/**£15**/£20

Pub. Braun (Salons de Paris)   ..   ..   £1/**£2**/£3
Pub. H. J. Smith of Brighton 1902   ..   ..   £1/**£1.50**/£2
Pub. Tuck. Several series of girls' heads, many designs
   reversed ..   ..   £1/**£1.50**/£2

ATTWELL, MABEL LUCIE (1879–1964) ■A 4.
The Queen of the 'cute' child type of illustration, her postcard career spanned at least four decades. Wife of Harold Earnshaw (qv). Her first postcards appeared before WW1 and she continued drawing through the Great War (with many patriotic and morale-raising designs). Her most prolific output was

between the two wars. During WW2 her kiddies donned uniforms and gas masks and queued for their rations. In Period 6 they commented gently on current fashions and mores. See CHILDREN. *Her main publishers were Tuck and Valentine.*

Periods 2, 3	£1/**£1.50**/£3
Period 4	25p/**50p**/75p
Period 5	75p/**£1**/£1.50
Period 6	25p/**50p**/75p

WE HAVE NO COUPONS
FOR ANYTHING NEW
BUT WOT'S A LITTLE PATCH O? TWO,
TO LOYAL PALS LIKE ME AND YOU?

■A4 Pub. Valentine. Artist Mabel Lucie Attwell. No. 508. War-time slogan on reverse. Period 5 £1.50

AVELINE, F.
Portrayer of elegant ladies, often in period dress.

Pub. James Henderson & Sons. Periods 3, 4. Head studies/In
Hoops & Furbelows, etc. Others .. .. .. 75p/**£1**/£2

BANTOCK
Stylised Art Deco designs. Period 4.

'Bantock' series .. .. £1/**£2**/£3

BAIRNSFATHER, BRUCE (1887–1959) ■A 5
*Best known for his 'Fragments from France' series of postcards
(see* MILITARY). *Bairnsfather, who trained at the John Hassall
Art School, also did comic strips on postcards between the
wars (see* COMIC) *and some fine theatre advertising postcards.*

Period 3.
British Red Cross Society. Surrey Branch fund raiser .. ..
.. .. £3/**£5**/£8
The Follies. Four Div. .. .. £2/**£4**/£6
Pub. Beagles/Lilywhite Photographic portraits .. £3/**£5**/£10
Pub. *The Bystander* 'Fragments from France' Nine series of 6
cards (*see* the Second Edition for complete list)
Per card .. .. £1/**£1.50**/£2
Pub. 'Red Letter' Midget Message miniature versions of 'Frag-
ments from France' series .. .. .. £1.25/**£2.50**/£3

Pub. Tuck. Oilette No. 3189. 'Better 'Ole' series .. £1/**£2**/£3
Theatre advertising (poster types). Pub. David Allen. C. E.
Cochran's 'The Better 'Ole' .. .. .. £10/**£15**/£30
Theatre advertising (poster types). Pub. Waddington. 'Flying
Colours' .. .. £10/**£15**/£30
Theatre advertising. Pub. Anon. 'Old Bill M.P.' £8/**£10**/£15

Period 4
British Legion fund raiser .. .. £1.50/**£3**/£5
Pub. Tuck. Comic strips of Old Bill and Bert from *The Passing
Show* .. .. £1/**£2**/£4

Period 5
Pub. Valentine. 'Old Bill Again' from *The Bystander*
.. .. £1/**£2.50**/£4

■A5 Pub. Lilywhite.
Captain Bruce Bairnsfather.
No. S2. Period 3 £10

BAKST, LEON NIKOLAEVICH (1866–1924)
*Bakst grew up in St. Petersburg, attended the Imperial
Academy of Arts and became a member of the Society of Painters in Water Colours and a theatrical designer. In 1906 he
exhibited in the Russian section of the Salon d'Automne in
Paris and in 1908 designed scenery and costumes for Diaghilev's fabulous Ballet Russe. The seeds of Art Deco were born.
He later became both producer and designer for theatrical and
balletic productions in Paris and London.*

Set of 12 characters from *La Fée des Poupées* c. 1903. Per set
.. .. £50/**£80**/£120
Carnaval de Schouman. Per card .. .. £10/**£20**/£30
Other designs. Per card .. ..£5/**£15**/£40

BARHAM, SYBIL
*Sybil Barham was one of the artists commissioned by C. W.
Faulkner to design their charming 'nursery' postcards (see*

CHILDREN). *Series include a particularly charming 'Peter Pan'*
set. Periods 2, 3, 4.

Price range   ..   .. 75p/**£2**/£4

BARRIBAL, W. ■A 6
Known as 'Barri', he was best known for his glamorous
girls—all based on his wife, Babs. He was a very successful
commercial artist and drew advertisements for many products,
designed playing cards and contributed to numerous magaz-
ines. His postcard output spanned both World Wars. See
CHILDREN *and* GLAMOUR.

Advertising and Theatre poster cards   ..   £16/**£18**/£20
Glamour and Others ..   ..   £2/**£4**/£6

Barribal Advertising and Theatre Poster Cards were listed in
the third edition (p. 39), also some of his General Designs.

A British "Destroyer" 1   Une Sirene.

■A6 Pub. Inter-Art. Artist
W. Barribal. 'Artistique'
Series No. 1588. Period 3 £4

BASCH, ARPAD
A Hungarian by birth, he was one of the most spectacular Art
Nouveau artists producing in Paris around the turn of the
century. He worked with Bonnard, mainly for the many illus-
trated reviews then being published.

Set of 6 'International Girls' (1900)   ..   ..   £40/**£60**/£75
Town Portrait series ..   ..   £20/**£25**/£35
WW1 Military Scenes, b & w. Pub. Hungary   £2.50/**£5**/£10
Others   ..   ..   £15/**£20**/£30

43

BATEMAN, H. M.
British cartoonist of the first rank, an admirer of Caran D'Ache (qv) and Aubrey Beardsley, his work appeared all too rarely on the postcard. A contributor to a host of magazines and journals, including Punch, *he specialised in the social 'gaffe'.*

Price range .. .. £1/**£2**/£3

BATES, MARJORIE CHRISTINE (1883–1962) ■A 7
Born in Derbyshire, she studied at the Nottingham School of Art and later in Paris. In a working style similar to that of 'Jotter' (Hayward Young) she travelled the British Isles, sketching, mostly in her distinctive style of pencil and crayon. During Periods 4, 5 her work was published by the British Art Co. (trademark initials 'B.A.C.' later changed to 'F.A.C.'). Bates also illustrated books and her work was reproduced as prints and trade cards.

■A7 Pub. B.A.C. Artist Marjorie C. Bates. Weavers' Houses, Cantebury. Period 4 £1.25

Pub. British Art Co. (B.A.C., later F.A.C.)
Period 4 Series of distinctive but delicate pastel/pencil sketches of rural and town scenes: Cambridge; Canterbury; Chester; Edinburgh; London; Oxford; Salisbury; Scarborough; Shrewsbury; Stratford-on-Avon; Whitby; Windsor and Worcestershire.

Period 4. Series of Characters from Shakespeare. So far identified are: 1. Lady Macbeth; 2. Romeo & Juliet; 3. Hamlet; 4. Rosalind (*As You Like It*); 5. Clown (*Twelfth Night*); 6. Malvolio (*Twelfth Night*); 7. Falstaff & the Merry Wives of Windsor; 8. Portia (*Merchant of Venice*); 9. Titania & Bottom (*Midsummer Night's Dream*); 10. Katharina (*The Taming of the Shrew*). 11. Clown (*Twelfth Night*), 12. Malvolio (*Twelfth Night*).

Pub. Bolland & Sons
Bolland's Restaurant.

Pub. Lewitt. (Larger than standard size).
The Flying Horse Hotel, Nottingham
Nottingham Castle
Nottingham Castle & 'Trip to Jerusalem' Inn
The Old Gateway, Nottingham Castle.

Pub. P. R. Series
Period 4. Princess Royal Hotel Whitby, and other adverts for
Princess Royal Hotels.

Pub. Phillipson & Golder of Chester
Period 4 Chester designs.

Others

Price range (highest price for Shakespeare set and the ad.)
..   ..   50p/**75p**/£2

BEECROFT, HERBERT
Australian artist, whose work is also seen in the UK. He drew
portraits and views.

Pub. NSW Bookstall Co. 'Art Series' Australian Characters.
Set of 6 female portraits ..   ..   £3.50/**£4.50**/£6
Australian Coast (6 cards) ..   ..   £2/**£2.50**/£3
Sydney Views (6 cards)   ..   ..   £3/**£3.50**/£4

BEIRNE, F. O.
Superb early UB *chromo-litho military vignettes reminiscent of*
Harry Payne.

Pub. Anon.   ..   ..   £6/**£7**/£8

BELCHER, GEORGE
Royal Academician who specialised in analytical charcoal
character studies of cockney life. He contributed to Punch, The
Tatler *and many books, working from live, authentic models.*
Sadly few of his designs were reproduced on the postcard. See
also COMIC.

Pub. Tuck 'Celebrated Posters', Ogden's Guinea Gold. No.
1501   ..   ..   £12/**£15**/£22
Pub. Tuck. Period 2. Two humorous sets   ..   ..   £3/**£5**/£6

BERTIGLIA, A.
Italian artist whose work spanned Periods 2 to 5. Subjects
include children, glamour and military subjects for WW1 and
WW2.

Price range   ..   ..   £2/**£3**/£6

BILIBINE, IVAN (1876–1942) ■A 8

A much-travelled Russian, who, trained as a lawyer, Bilibine soon started to draw and became highly successful as a theatrical designer. He worked for Diaghilev and the Theatre des Champs-Elysees. His postcard work, captured the everyday working life and spirit of his countrymen. His local scenes and characters are often surrounded by attractive decorative borders. He also drew some designs for the Red Cross. Periods 2, 3.

Price range   ..   ..£5/**£10**/£15

■A8 Pub. Golike & Bilibor - Red Cross. Artist Ivan Bilibine. 1902 £15

BIRD, CYRIL KENNETH (1887–1965)

Postcards signed Fougasse. Studied at the Percy Bradshaw Art School. During WW1 he was wounded in the spine at Gallipoli, leaving him bed-ridden for a while. Fighting back to fitness he became a contributor to Punch, eventually becoming art editor. His nom de plume comes from a small explosive mine! He is best remembered for his WW2 propaganda posters, many of which were reproduced as postcards.

Price range   ..   ..   £1/**£1.25**/£2

BISHOP

American artist who drew appealing children, comic, glamour and greetings cards. One of his best known sets is the 'What do you know about that?' series, with a picture and a verse. Another attractive set is the colourful red, green and yellow Valentine set for A. H. & Co.

Pub. A. H. Co. Valentine set   ..   ..   ..   50p/**75p**/£1.50
Pub. Anon.
     'What do you know about that?' set   ..   50p/**75p**/£1.25
     Other miscellaneous designs   ..   ..   ..   25p/**75p**/£1

BOETIUS, J. O.
Comic artist whose postcard work was reproduced by the prolific British publisher, S. Hildesheimer in their important '5000 series' (see Edition 3 for a full listing). He often signed his designs with his initials, 'J.O.B.' only. Period 2.

Price range   ..   .. 50p/**75p**/£1

BOILEAU, PHILIP (1864–1917) ▮A 9
Born in Quebec to a French diplomat and an American society beauty, Philip studied art and music in Milan. Eventually he settled in the USA where his second wife—Emily Gilbert became his model and inspiration. Success came with his drawings of the 'American Girl'—the transatlantic rival to the 'Gibson Girl', which appeared in newspapers, on posters, prints and calendars as well as on postcards. See GLAMOUR.

Advertising work. Contrary Mary Book, Flood & Conklin, Metropolitan Life Ins. Co., Nat. Suit and Cloak Co. Period 2
.. .. **£2/£3.50/£6**

For a listing of cards published by Reinthal & Newman, see Second Edition, pp. 39–40.

Other Pubs. (incl. National Art Co., Wildt & Kray)
Original designs and re-issues of Reinthal titles.

Price range   ..   .. £2/**£3**/£5

▮A9   Pub.   Tuck.   Artist   Philip Boileau. Period 2. £6

BOMPARD, LUIGI (1873–1953)
Italian Artist, best known for his Period 2 glamour designs. He also drew some attractive adverts for various commemorative events. Periods 2/3.

Price range   ..   ..   £2/**£4**/£8

BONZAGNI, AROLDO (1887–1918)
Italian artist who drew both glamorous girls en déshabillé *and fund-raising designs. These included anti-Austrian caricatures. Periods 2 to 4.*

Price range   ..   ..   £3/**£6**/£10

BOUTET, HENRI (1851–1921)
An important French postcard artist of Period 1/early Period 2. The 1979 Neudin Argus *lists nearly three hundred cards. His inspiration was in Paris night life, the* midinettes *and artists' models. His 'Corsets' series created a moral furore in England in 1901. Main publishers include Motot, A. D., La Librairie Charles, L'Atelier d'Art, and in England, Southwood. He contributed card No. 8 of the 'Collection des Cent' (see* COLLECTIONS*) and apart from his glamorous art designs, produced some cards with a military theme.*

Price range (highest value for the 'Cent' card)   £7.50/**£25**/£70

BRADSHAW, PERCY V.
Bradshaw always had the desire to draw. At age 18 he became a freelance artist gradually getting work with a number of magazines. He also started writing and eventually started the correspondence art school that made him famous. During his long productive years, many of his clever and humorous drawings were reproduced as postcards. Over one hundred and fifty designs have been recognised, some signed only with his initials, 'P.V.B.'

Pub. Misch & Co. (Early Period 2)
Series No. 947 Excentricity   ..   ..   ..   £2/**£4**/£5
948 Smiles   ..   ..   £2/**£4**/£5
Others   ..   ..   £1.50/**£2**/£4

Pub. Moss & Co. (Early Period 2)
Series No. 4415 Musical Terms up to Date ..   ..   £2/**£4**/£6
Others   ..   ..   £1.50/**£3**/£5

Pub. Tuck
22 known series—for details of which *see* Second Edition, p. 41.
Price range   ..   ..   £2/**£4**/£6

Pub. Wrench
Nos. 18043–18048 Shakespeare Illustrated by 'Toasts'   ..
   ..   ..   £3/**£4**/£6

Others

Various   ..   ..   £1/**£2**/£4

BRETT, MOLLY
Subjects include animals and fairies.

Pub. Faulkner, C. W.   ..   ..   75p/**£1**/£1.50
Pub. Medici Society   ..   ..   75p/**£1**/£1.50

BROWNE, TOM (1870–1910) ■A 10
Born and educated in Nottingham where he attended the local art school. Later in London his comic style developed. He created 'Weary Willie and Tired Tim', joined the Langham Sketching Club and was published in Punch. *A co-founder with his friend, Dudley Hardy, of the rip-roaring London Sketch Club (of which he was President in 1907), his work was first exhibited at the Royal Academy in 1897. His acute but sympathetic observation made him the recorder* par excellence *of the Edwardian working classes at play and at home. On the serious side, his Dutch themes, the result of cycling tours in Holland, are sensitively executed. Two visits to the USA produced some amusing American postcard comments. To date his known postcard output is more than 1300 designs. See* COMIC.

Details of Tom B's main series were given on pp. 51–52 of the fourth edition of this catalogue. Publishers include: Baird, Alexander; Davidson Bros.; Hartmann; Landeker & Brown; Pasco; Tuck; Valentine; Wrench; Others.

Comic/general designs   ..   ..   £1.50/**£3**/£6
Commercial designs   ..   ..   £7.50/**£15**/£25

■A10 Pub. 'Pasco Series'. Artist Tom Browne. *Weekly Telegraph* Cartoon. Period 2 £6

BRUNDAGE, FRANCES (1854–1937)
Born in New Jersey, USA, she started illustrating books for Tuck in their New York offices, progressing to postcard designs for them and for Sam Gabriel. She travelled to England, working for Tuck there. Nearly three hundred signed designs have been identified. She specialised in CHILDREN *and* GREETINGS *(qv).*

Pub. Gabriel, Sam (from 1910)
Nineteen sets of 10 cards have been identified, including Halloween and Thanksgiving   ..   ..   ..   £2/**£3**/£5

Pub. Tuck (from 1900)
About 25 sets, some unsigned, including 'coons', Dutch children, greetings ..   ..   £2/**£4**/£8

Others   ..   ..   £2/**£3**/£5

BRUNELLESCHI, UMBERTO (1886–1949)
Italian artist whose finest work was a series of imaginative girls as birds, butterflies, etc. published c. 1920 in the Art Deco style. He also did strong patriotic and military designs and some commercial work, incl. illustrations for the French fashion magazine, Journal des Dames et des Modes *and the* Guirlande des Mois.

Price range   ..   ..   £30/**£50**/£60

BUCHANAN, FRED
Comic artist, Periods 2 to 4.

Pub. Tuck
Taking the Waters, etc.   ..   ..   75p/**£1.50**/£2.50

Pub. Woolstone Bros.
Comic series   ..   ..   50p/**75p**/£1

Others 25p/**50p**/75p

BULL, RENE
Period 2 comic artist, whose humour often had a political flavour. Publishers include Davidson Bros., C. W. Faulkner,

---

Three Band Pricing System
Left Hand Band: The lowest price you will probably be asked to pay for this card.
Middle Band: What you will normally be asked to pay for this card: its average, reasonable price.
Right Hand Band: The highest price you will probably be asked to pay for this card.
For a full explanation of the system see page ix.

Landeker & Brown (Ellanbee)—Humorous & Fiscal series, Chas. Voisey—Humours of Billiards, and others.

Price range .. .. £2/**£3**/£4

BUXTON, DUDLEY
Period 2 comic artist. Publishers include Inter-Art 'Comique' series, A. V. N. Jones and others.

Price range .. .. 50p/**75p**/£1.50

CALDECOTT, RANDOLPH (1846–1886)
Born the son of a Cheshire accountant who forced him to stifle his love of art in order to train in a 'sound profession', Caldecott became a bank clerk. Later he studied in the evenings at the Manchester Art School and had drawings published in a local paper. Befriended and encouraged by Thomas Armstrong of the South Kensington Museum, he became a regular contributor to London Society, The Graphic *and* Punch *and an illustrator of children's books—drawings from which were reproduced in postcard form by Frederick Warne & Co. in 1929/30.*

Pub. Frederick Warne & Co. Period 4
Eight sets of six cards on Nursery Rhyme themes—*see* listing in Second Edition, p. 44.

Price range .. .. 50p/**75p**/£1

CALDERARA, C.
Italian artist of fashion and glamour with a distinct Art Deco flavour, often featuring motor cars in the design. See also GLAMOUR.

Price range .. .. £2/**£4**/£6

CAMARA, LEAL de (1877–1948)
Spanish artist, most of whose best postcard work was done in Paris. Most famous for his limited edition political caricatures (see also POLITICAL*). He also contributed many illustrations which were reproduced as postcards for the satirical magazine* L'Assiette au Beurre. *Bicycles and motor cars were favourite subjects (Period 2).*

Bicycle themes .. ..£8/**£10**/£15
Motor car themes .. .. £10/**£15**/£20
Others .. .. £7/**£9**/£12

CAMPBELL, B.
Australian artist who portrayed the enduringly popular Australian subjects of country and cattle stations.

Pub. NSW Bookstall Co.
  Series of 6 cards .. .. £3/**£3.50**/£5

CANTLE, J. M.
Australian artist who specialized in bird studies.

Pub. NSW Bookstall Co. 'Art Series'
   New Zealand and Tasmanian scenes (6 cards)   £1.50/**£2**/£3
Pub. Samuel Wood
   Bird Studies (6 cards) ..   ..   £1/**£1.50**/£2
Pub. Anon.
   38 identified bird paintings ..   ..   £3/**£4**/£6

CAPIELLO, LEONETTO (1875–1942)
Versatile Italian artist whose work spanned Periods 2, 3 and 4 with a variety of styles and themes. During Period 2 he did exhibition and advert designs in the Art Nouveau style. Possessing a lively sense of caricature, he contributed to the French publications Le Rire *and* L'Assiette au Beurre, *and to the* Album Mariani *collection in 1910. During WW1 he produced patriotic designs and during Period 4 he drew adverts for drink and toothpaste companies etc.*

Period 2
   Art Nouveau adverts   ..   ..   £15/**£20**/£25
   Mariani design   ..   ..   £7.50/**£10**/£15
Period 3
   Patriotic designs ..   ..   £5/**£7.50**/£10
Period 4
   Adverts ..   ..   £10/**£15**/£20
   Propaganda ..   ..   £7.50/**£10**/£15

CARAN D'ACHE
See Poiré, Emmanuel.

CARR, GENE (1881–1959)
American artist who captured the spirit of childhood in his series of games, like 'Baseball', 'Hide and Seek', 'Marbles', etc. He also drew Greetings designs for the postcard. A natural cartoonist with no art training. Carr found success whilst still in his teens, and worked for many famous newspapers and magazines—e.g. New York Herald *and* Saturday Evening Post. *Periods 2, 3, 4.*

Pub. Rotograph and others.
Price range   ..   ..   75p/**£1.50**/£3

CARTER, REGINALD ARTHUR LEE (1886–1950) ■A 11
Carter was born, and lived most of his life, in Southwold, Suffolk. A member of the North British Academy, he contributed to magazines like The Sketch *and* The Tatler. *His versatile and prolific output of postcards spanned Periods 2 to 4 and was produced by a variety of publishers, including himself ('The Sorrows of Southwold' printed by the Southwold Press).* See ANIMALS.

Details of Carter's postcard work were published in the fourth edition of this catalogue, p. 55. Publishers include: B. P. &

Co.; Dennis; Ettlinger; Mack; Millar & Lang; Salmon; Southwold Press; Stiebel; Valentine; Verdier; Wildt & Kray; Others

Price range   ..   .. 75p/**£1**/£2

TOM PALMER – "HI! HERE'S A YOUNG TOFF WANTS TO KNOW IF SIXPENCE INCLUDES A BIT OF SOAP"

■All Pub. Southwold Press. Artist Reg. Carter. 'Sorrows of Southwold' Series No. 2. PU 1924 £1.50

CARTER, SYDNEY (1874–1945)
Born in Enfield, Middlesex, he moved shortly to Epping Forest, where his lifelong love of trees started. At 15 he went to Walthamstow Art School, was exhibited at the Royal Academy at the age of 20 and went on to the Royal College of Art. He won several art scholarships and was exhibited at the Paris Salon and the British Institute of Watercolours and Oils. After WW1 he emigrated to South Africa. About 170 postcard designs have been identified.

Pub. Birn Bros. (1904)
London views, set of 6   ..   .. 50p/**75p**/£1.50

Pub. Hildesheimer
See also LITERARY.
At least twenty series, including 'How Men Propose' (twelve cards), 'Months of the Year' (twelve cards), Hans Andersen Fairy Tales, sketches from Scott, Shakespeare, Thackeray. (50% premium for complete sets of twelve) ..   .. 50p/**£1**/£2

Pub. Smith, W. H. and Ashton, Wm.
Ancient British Halls, set of 6   ..   ..   .. 50p/**75p**/£1.50

Pub. Tuck
The Homes of Literary Men, set of 6   ..   .. 50p/**75p**/£1.50

CASCELLA, BASILIO (1860–1950)
Italian artist who drew a range of topics—adverts, commemorative, glamour, peasant types, etc. The early studies show a strong Art Nouveau influence.

Price range   ..   .. £3/**£6**/£10

CASSIERS, HENRI (b. 1858) ■A 12

*Fine Belgian artist who designed for the postcard from its
earliest pictorial days. His distinctive but delicate style found
expression in Dutch scenes with figures, landscapes and town
scenes. His series for the shipping line 'Red Star' are beautiful
examples of how well the art of the poster translates to the
smaller medium.*

Pub. Dietrich of Brussels from 1900

Bruxelles et Anvers Pittoresque	..	..	..	£3/**£4**/£5
Glasgow Exhibition (*see* EXHIBITIONS)		..	..	£2/**£3**/£5
La Hollande Pittoresque	..	..	..	£2/**£3**/£5
Le Littoral Belge	..	..	..	£2/**£3**/£5
London views	..	..	..	£2/**£3**/£5
18th-century Characters	..	..	..	£2/**£3**/£5
En Zélande	..	..	..	£2/**£3**/£5

Pub. W. de Haan, Utrecht

Costumes hollondais (12 cards)	..	..	..	£2/**£3**/£5
Various Dutch views ..	..	..	..	£2/**£3**/£5

Pub. Moss, Henry & Co. (1903–1905)

Several series	..	..	..	£2/**£3**/£5

Pub. Huardel, P. G. & Co. from 1900

Paris views	..	..	..	£2/**£3**/£5

Pub. Southwood, F. C. (1901)

Several series	..	..	..	£1/**£2**/£4

Red Star Liner Advertisements

Thirty cards have been identified	..	..	..£5/**£10**/£15

■A12 Pub. W. de Haan. Artist Henri Cassiers. 'Amsterdam'.
UB. Early Period 2 £5

CATON WOODVILLE, RICHARD (1856–1927)■ M 1

*Born of a German mother and partly educated in Germany,
Caton Woodville served under Kitchener in Egypt. He covered
the Boer War as a military artist and continued his military
work during WW1. See also* MILITARY.

Early Period 2

Pub. Collectors' Pub. Co. (1901). Five sets of Boer War cards

.. .. £1.50/**£3**/£5

Pub. Hartmann, Fred. (1901). Famous British Battles ..

.. .. £1/**£2**/£4

Pub. 'Imperial Army Series' (1904) Military types £1/**£2**/£4

Pub. Picture Postcard Co. Boer War designs £1.50/**£3**/£5

Pub. Watkins & McCombie. The Gentleman in Khaki ..

.. .. £1/**£2**/£3

Period 3

Designs for St. Dunstans .. .. £1/**£1.50**/£2

Others (tanks, etc.) .. .. 75p/**£1**/£1.50

CHÉRET, JULES (1836–1932) ■A 13

French Art Nouveau artist who contributed to many of the important early French series, like the 'Job', Editions Cino, Les Affiches Célèbres, La Collection des Cent *and* Les Cartes Postales Mariani. *He designed over 1000 theatrical posters.*

Price range .. .. £30/**£50**/£75

Period 7 reproductions **25p**

■A13 Pub. Dalkeith. Artist Jules Chéret. Classic Poster. Card No. P26. Period 7 25p

CHIOSTRI, CARLO (1863–1939), SOFIA & ELINA ■A 14

Born in Florence, Chiostri became well-known for his illustrations of childrens' books. Subjects of his postcards include comic themes, flower and fruit still-lives. Carlo Chiostri always signed his full name. Cards signed only 'Chiostri' are by his daughter, Sofia (1896–1945) who worked with her sister Elina.

Price range .. .. £4/**£7.50**/£15

■A14 Pub. Ballerini & Fratini. Artist Chiostri (Sofia). Rare Art Deco Series No. 350. Period 4 £20

CHRISTIANSEN, HANS
Art Nouveau artist who contributed to many of the important early French and German series, e.g. 'Les Maîtres de la Carte Postale' (1898–1900) and 'Jugend' (1899).

Price range   ..   ..   £25/**£50**/£70

CHRISTIE, GEORGE FYFFE ■A 15
Scottish artist who often signed with his initials 'G.F.C.' and who worked for many Scottish as well as London companies. His work on the postcard spanned Periods 2 to 5. See COMIC.

Publishers of his work include: Lyon, Wm; McKenzie, W. & Co.; Misch & Co., Photochrom; Ritchie; Others

Price range   ..   ..   50p/**£1**/£2

CHRISTY, F. EARL (1883–1961)
This American artist (no relation to Howard Christy) was trained at the Pennsylvania Academy of Fine Arts. His specialised version of the American Girl was the 'College Girl' or 'Belle'. He drew for magazines and posters, and the many postcard versions of his designs were produced by a variety of publishers. See GLAMOUR.

Price range   ..   ..   £2.50/**£3**/£12

CHRISTY, HOWARD CHANDLER (1873–1952)
American exponent of a brand of the American Girl known as the 'Christy Girl'. He studied at the National Academy of Design and the Art Students League and became a successful commercial artist, working as a war illustrator in Cuba and for Scribner's Magazine, Harpers, Colliers *and* Cosmopolitan.

During WW1 he did many patriotic designs. See also
GLAMOUR.

Price range   ..   ..   £1/**£2**/£3

"THE END OF A PERFECT DAY"
POPULAR SONG

■A15 Pub. W. McKenzie &
Co. Artist G. F. Christie.
Period 2 £2

CLAPSADDLE, ELLEN (1865–1934)
One of America's most popular artists, specialising in
CHILDREN *and* GREETINGS *(qv)—she is credited with 3000
designs. Most of her work was published by the International
Art Co. Subjects include Christmas, 'Coons', Easter,
Hallowe'en, Patriotics (4 July, Decoration Day, etc.), St.
Patrick's Day, Valentines, and some rare and sought after
Suffragette designs. Although somewhat stilted and stereo-
typed, her designs are appealing, and greatly collected in the
USA. Periods 2, 3, 4.*

Pub. International Art Co.
   General children, greetings, holidays   ..   ..   £2/**£3**/£4
   Novelty series 1236 (mechanical)   ..   ..   .. £3/**£6**/£10
Pub. Wolf
   2 Suffragette designs on Valentine cards   ..£5/**£10**/£15

CLARK, J. CLAYTON (Kyd)
Famous for his representations of characters from Dickens. See
LITERARY. Publishers include:

Pub. Faulkner, C. W. Characters from Dickens. Series 497/
8/9; **Pub. Hildesheimer** 'Heads—And the Tales They Tell'
(1903); **Pub. Pictorial Stationery Co.; Pub. Tuck** Characters from Dickens; **Pub. Welch, J. & Sons (1905)** Studies
from Life by Charles Dickens; **Pub. Wrench** About 50
Dickens characters; Others

Price range   ..   ..   £1/**£2**/£4

CLOKE, RENE

*Still actively working as an illustrator, Rene Cloke had no
formal art training other than at school. She had always
wanted to draw, and soon found success in greetings cards
designs and then as a book illustrator, specialising in fairies
and small animals. In the late 1930s the first designs were
reproduced as postcards, since when 18 sets have been
published, up to 1956.*
Publishers include:
*C. W. Faulkner; Medici Society (Periods 6, 7); J. Salmon;
Valentine (Periods 4, 5, 6). Others*

Price range   .. ..   50p/**£1.25**/£2

COMBAZ, GISBERT (1869–1941)

*Forced to study law by his father, this versatile Belgian then
went on to the Brussels Academy, where he eventually became
Professor of Decorative Composition. It was as a poster artist
that he gained his reputation as one of the most original
exponents of Art Nouveau. His 1898–1900 series of 12 of 'The
Elements', 'The Proverbs', 'The Sins' are particularly sought
after. Pub. Dietrich of Brussels.*

Price range   .. ..   £20/**£40**/£60

COMICUS
See Parlett, Harry.

■A16 Pub. Tuck. Artist
Harold Copping. Oilette No.
3406. 'Dickens' Characters'.
Period 2 £3

COPPING, HAROLD (1863–1932) ■A 16

*Artist who drew the famous picture 'The Hope of the World'.
In his postcard work he specialised in classical and religious
themes, also sentimental designs during Period 3. Pub.*

Degen & Co. 'England, Home and Beauty'. Tuck series include 'Dickens' characters', and 'Hamlet' 1901 (12 cards).

Price range   ..   ..   £2/**£3**/£5

CORBELLA, TITO (b. 1885) ■AD 3

Versatile Italian artist, who is best known in the glamour field. Like Barribal, Boileau and Kirchner he used his wife as his model. He also drew powerful propaganda designs. See also GLAMOUR.

Advertising designs ..   ..   £6/**£8**/£12
Glamour designs   ..   ..   £1.50/**£2.50**/£4
Edith Cavell set. Period 3 (*see also* POLITICAL) (up to 50%
   premium for complete set)   ..   ..   £5/**£7**/£8

COWHAM, HILDA

An artist who specialised in drawing children and cats, her work is becoming increasingly popular. From 1913 to 1922 she produced 24 different designs for Inter-Art and several series for Valentine's.

Price range   ..   ..   75p/**£1**/£1.50

■A17   Pub.   Charles   Skilton & Fry. Artist David Cuppledith.   Lincolnshire   Poacher   Series.   No.   10. Period 7 25p

CUPPLEDITCH, DAVID (b. 1946) ■A17

Author of books on the London Sketch Club, Phil May, and Lincolnshire area picture postcards, Cuppleditch was born in Louth, Lincs. He studied at the Ruskin School of Drawing and

59

Fine Arts, Oxford and in 1974 became Secretary of the London Sketch Club. In 1981 he had an important retrospective exhibition at the Usher Gallery, Lincoln. In 1983 he designed 3 postcards, in 1984, 13 designs and in 1985 32 designs, for Charles Skilton & Fry.

Lincolnshire Landscapes. Series Nos. 1–5
Lincolnshire Poacher. Humorous. Series of 10
Lincolnshire Seaside Humour. Series of 10.
Lincolnshire Views, Nos. 0321–0391
Per card **25p**

Giant Postcards (15 × 21cm)
Lincolnshire Poacher (no. 0402G)
Lincoln from Reepham (No. 0376G)
Per card **30p**

DAMBLANS, EUGENE (b. 1865)
Born in Montevideo of French parents, Damblans was a pupil of M. G. Buland. A life member of the Salon of French Art, he specialised in etchings and water colours, gaining several silver medals for his work. Damblans drew peasant 'types' (e.g. Bretonne *and* Vieille Béarnaise*) and was the artist of the fine series of postcards* La Poste en . . . (qv).

Price range   ..   ..   £3/**£5**/£7.50

DANIELL, EVANGELINE MARY (1880–1902)
Although only about half a dozen postcard designs have been identified because of her tragically early death, this superb Art Nouveau *artist is amongst the most highly regarded exponents of the style. She is as highly esteemed on the Continent as in Britain, and even Queen Victoria chose one of her designs for the Royal New Year card in 1901.*

Pub. Tuck. Modern Art series 2524/5 ..   ..   £30/**£40**/£50

DAVEY, GEORGE
Period 2 comic artist whose humour often contained political overtones. See also POLITICAL. *Publishers include:*
Mandel, J. & Co.; Misch & Stock; Valentine; Others

Price range   ..   ..   75p/**£1.50**/£2

DAVEY, L. H.
Australian artist who specialised in Northern Tasmanian scenes.

Pubs: Osboldstone & Co./W. T. Pater
  Bush homes (6 cards)   ..   ..   £2.50/**£3**/£4
  Scenery (12 cards) ..   ..   £2.25/**£3**/£3.50

DEDINA, JEAN (b. 1870)

Born in Strak, Czechoslovakia, Dedina was a pupil of Zenisek at the Prague Academy of Beaux Arts. He also studied under Bresnard in Paris where his work was exhibited in 1895. He also painted murals for the Comédie Francaise *and contributed illustrations and philosophical articles to the paper* Fliegende Blätter. *His elegant beauties were reproduced in postcard form by J. Otty, Prague, and include a delightful 'Months of the Year' set. Early Period 2.*

Price range .. .. £2.50/**£5**/£8

DE FEURE, GEORGES (1868–1928)

Highly sought after French artist of the Art Nouveau *genre who contributed to the rare* Cocorico *series (qv). A pupil of Chéret, he also produced theatrical designs and adverts. Periods 1/2.*

Cocorico .. .. £100/**£150**/£350
Others .. .. £40/**£60**/£80

DENIZARD
See Orens.

DEXTER, MARJORIE MAY (b. *c.* 1900)

Born in Wellingborough, she attended the Northampton School of Arts & Crafts. Most of her designs were for folded greetings cards and she also illustrated books. The small number of postcards so far identified by this attractive children's artist were for Salmon and Valentine's during Periods 4, 5.

Pub. Salmon. Nos. 3765, 3766, 3769, others.
Pub. Valentine's. Hand-painted effect, others.
Price range 25p/**50p**/75p

■A18 Pub. Tuck. Artist 'Dinah'. Period 4 with message from Prime Minister on reverse £2

DINAH ■A 18
*Prolific, but unfortunately totally anonymous, artist of Periods
5 and 6. During the wartime her postcards published by Tuck
showed her typical 'cute Kids' in wartime situations and many
bore a patriotic slogan on the reverse (often from the Prime
Minister). Biographic information would be appreciated.*

A listing of Dinah cards is given below as a Supplement to
this section.

General designs..	..	..	..	..	..	50p/**75p**/£1.50
Second World War themes ..		..	..	..		75p/**£1.50**/£2

DUDE
See Larsen, L. H.

DUDOVICH MARCELLO (1878–1962)
*Italian artist whose postcard work spanned from 1900 to 1950.
His subject matter raged from commemorative (e.g. exhibitions,
festivals) to adverts for theatrical productions, products like
Vermouth, Tyres, Fernet-Branca, etc. to patriotic propaganda
during WW1, to glamour in Period 4.*

Price range .. ..£4/**£20**/£30

DUNCAN, COWAN
Specialist in comic heads and Scottish themes in Period 4.

Pub. Millar & Lang, Series 2616/7 and others   75p/**£1**/£1.50

DUNCAN, JAMES ALLAN (Hamish)
*Comic artist, usually on Scottish themes, who drew under the
name 'Hamish' or 'Hamish Duncan'. He used his real name
for his more serious work. Publishers include:*

Davidson Bros.; Monson Bros., Glasgow; Tuck; Others
Price range .. .. 25p/**75p**/£1.25

DWIGGINS, CLARE VICTOR (Dwig) (1873–1958)
*Born in Wilmington, Ohio, Dwiggins became a self-taught,
self-appointed professor of freehand drawing, who contributed
to various newspapers and journals. His first postcard was
designed in 1903 for Tuck and he went on to design well over
350 identified cards, some unsigned, for a variety of publishers.
He often used his wife as his model. Even his girlie cards bear
an unmistakeable touch of humour. See also* COMIC. *Publishers
include: Anderson, W. P.; Blue, A.; Cardinell, Vincent;
Gabriel, Sam; Gross, Eric; Kaplan, R.; Newspaper Cartoon
Series (Period 4); Rose, Charles; Tuck.*

Price range .. .. £2/**£4**/£6

EARNSHAW, HAROLD (d. 1937)
Member of the London Sketch Club and Chelsea Arts Club, he

married Mabel Lucie Attwell (qv) *and they had two sons and a daughter. During WW1 he lost his right arm but he learnt to draw with his left and went on to contribute to* Punch, *illustrate books for Blackie, etc. His postcard work is mostly of a comic nature. Publishers include Gottschalk, Dreyfus & Davis and George Pulman & Sons.*

Price range 25p/**50p**/75p

EDMONDS, MABELLE B.
Australian artist with a versatile range of subjects in both colour and black and white—from children to glamour (in a style reminiscent of Dana Gibson) to 'Large Letter' designs, by a variety of publishers, who include Harding & Billings and NSW Bookstall Co. ('Art Series').
Price range   ..   ..   £2.50/**£5**/£7

■A19 Pub. Hildesheimer. Artist 'Ellam' No. 5243. PU 1904 £1.50

ELLAM, WILLIAM HENRY ■A 19
Versatile and competent Period 2 artist, whose work includes a variety of general and humorous subjects.

Pub. Excelsior Fine Art Pub. Co.
Famous personages in their cars (e.g. Joseph Chamberlain in his Dixi, Duke of Connaught in his Daimler)   ..   £1/**£2**/£4

Pub. Faulkner, C. W.
Several series of Teddy Bears   ..   ..   ..   £1/**£1.50**/£3

Pub. Hildesheimer
Various designs, incl. 'Hard Workers', 'Japanese'   ..   ..
   ..   ..   75p/**£1.50**/£2

Pub. Stewart & Woolf
Seaside themes ..   ..   75p/**£1.50**/£3

Pub. Tuck
Breakfast in Bed, Gentle Art of Angling and other series
.. .. £1/**£2**/£3
'Japanese' series .. .. £1.50/**£2**/£3

ENDACOTT, LILLIE
Wife of Sidney Endacott (see below).

15 cards for the publisher, Worth .. .. £1/**£1.50**/£2

ENDACOTT, SIDNEY (1873–1918)
*Born in Devon, Endacott worked for several years in the USA
and after establishing a reputation as a wood carver, he
returned to Devon and worked at painting for Worth's Gallery
in Exeter, as well as continuing to sculpt. He married Lillie
Haydon and when his health began to fail, he taught her to
paint in his style (see above). More biographical details, and
a full check list of Endacott's postcard work, supplied by Joan
Humphreys, were published in the Second Edition (pp. 51–53).*

Pub. Frith's of Reigate .. .. £1/**£1.50**/£1.75
Pub. Worth & Co.
  'Devon Worthies' Series .. .. £1.50/**£2**/£3
  Others .. .. £1/**£1.75**/£2
Pub. Unknown .. .. £1/**£1.50**/£1.75

ENGLISH, ARCHIBALD ('A.E.')
*Prolific comic artist of Periods 2 and 3 whose work was usually
signed with his initials only. Publishers include: Mitchell &
Watkins, William Ritchie & Sons, Thridgould & Co.*

Price range .. .. 50p/**75p**/£1

FELLER, FRANK
An illustrator for journals like Boys Own Paper, *Feller produced some of the most thrilling action scenes reproduced in the
postcard. Several series were published in the Tuck 'Oilette'
range and those that have been identified were listed in the
fourth edition of this catalogue p. 64.*

Price range .. .. £1/**£1.50**/£2
Pub. Tuck. Boer War Empire series No. 840. Roberts & Kitchener. UB. .. .. £7/**£9**/£12

FERNAND, FERNEL
French artist, best known for his racing car series (see ROAD
TRANSPORT*) with black background and manic-looking
drivers. A regular contributor to the satirical magazine,* Le
Rire, *from 1898 to 1908, and to the 'Collection des Cent' (qv)*

Courses Automobile (10 cards)
Various sporting series
Others

Price range for the above (highest valuation for the 'Cent' cards) .. .. £4/**£6**/£50

FIDUS
See Höppener, Hugo.

FISHER, HARRISON (1877–1934) ■A 20
American artist born to an artistic family who, from an early age, had success as a commercial artist. He worked for the San Francisco Call & Examiner, *and on moving to New York, for* Puck, Scribner's, Cosmopolitan, Life, The Saturday Evening Post *and* McLure's. *He drew the archetypal American Girl and many of his magazine covers and illustrations were reproduced on the postcard.* See GLAMOUR.

Price range .. .. £2/**£4**/£6

■A20 Pub. Reinthal & Newman. Artist Harrison Fisher. Water colour series No. 381. Period 2 £4

FLAGG, JAMES MONTGOMERY (1877–1960)
Best known for his poster of Uncle Sam in WW1, 'I Want You for the US Army', Flagg was born in New York. He was a member of the Arts Students League and studied in England and France. He sold work from the age of 12 and was particularly successful with his female studies. See GLAMOUR.

Price range .. .. £1/**£2**/£3

FLOWER, CHARLES E. (1871–1951) ■EX 1
Watercolour artist who exhibited at the Royal Academy. Most of his postcard work was for Tuck in their Oilette series. Best known for his London series, he also drew cards from other parts of the UK, Germany, North and South America. Between 600 and 700 designs have so far been identified.

General								75p/**£1**/£2
Advertising designs								£1/**£2**/£4

FOLKARD, CHARLES (1878–1963)
Creator of the 'Teddy Tail' strip in the Daily Mail, *Folkard was one of the best loved 'Nursery Artists' of Period 4. See also* CHILDREN.

Pub. Black, A. C.

Series of Mother Goose Nursery Rhymes			£2/**£3**/£4
Songs from *Alice in Wonderland* (Period 4)			£2/**£3**/£4
Period 7 reprint			**50p**

FOUGASSE
See Bird, Cyril Kenneth.

FULLER, EDMUND G.
Competent general artist, often with a touch of humour, whose best postcard work was in early Period 2.

Pub. Moss, Henry & Co. (before 1905)
Horse Racing
Hunting

Pub. Stewart & Woolf
London Types
Others

Price range for all Fuller cards				£1/**£1.50**/£2

FULLEYLOVE, JOHN R. I. (1847–1908)
Born in Leicester, he was apprenticed to an architect. Travelling widely throughout Britain, Europe and the Near East, he drew town scenes and landscapes. As well as drawing for the postcard, he also illustrated books. Publishers include Regal Art Co., Robert Peel, Tuck (many 'Oilette' series)

Price range						50p/**75p**/£1

FULLWOOD, A. H.
Australian artist whose postcards were all published by Raphael Tuck in their 'Wide-Wide-World' series. The originals were probably first published in The Illustrated Atlas of Australasie, *an instalment publication, later published in book form between 1886 and 1888. The series vary in rarity and, hence, in value.*

Pub. Tuck. 'Wide-Wide-World' series

Australian series					£3.50/**£5**/£7
New Zealand series					£2/**£2.50**/£3

Pub. Tuck 'Oilette' Oxford Views Series No. 7561 . . . .
. . . . 50p/**75p**/£1.50

GIBBS, MAY
Australian illustrator of 'Gumnut babies', scenes and W. Australian events.

Pub. Osboldstone & Co.
Periods 4/5 designs ..   ..   £6/**£9**/£12
Pub. Anon
'Gumnut Series' (12 cards)   ..   ..£9/**£12**/£15
W. Australia mining disaster/local scenes in b & w ..   ..
..   ..   £3.50/**£5**/£6

GIBSON, CHARLES DANA ■G 2
American artist now mostly remembered for his fashionable, glamorous creation, 'The Gibson Girl' (thought to be modelled on the artiste Camille Clifford, and on his wife, Irene Langhorne, sister of the future Lady Astor). During WW1 he was President of the Society of Illustrators and directed propaganda designs for the US war effort. After the war he became owner and editor of Life *magazine.*

Most of his postcard work is gentle, acutely observed situation humour of the mores and pastimes of the Edwardian middle classes—especially their courtship rituals. At least seventy-two designs have been identified. See GLAMOUR.

Price range   ..   ..   £1/**£1.50**/£2

GILBERT, CHARLES ALLAN (b. 1873)
Born in Hartford, Connecticut, USA he studied in New York and Paris. He illustrated Women of Fiction *and* A Message from Mars *and, on the postcard, typical 'American Girls' (see* GLAMOUR).

Price range   ..   ..   75p/**£1**/£2

GILL, ARTHUR
Much under-rated artist with a light comic touch. Period 2.

Pub. Tuck. Seaside Sketches. Humorous series 6077   £1/**£2**/£3
Pub. Tuck. Others   ..   ..   £1/**£2**/£3

GILSON, T. ■COM 2
Little is known about this amusing postcard artist whose 'Kute Kids' type of comic cards helped to lighten the years 1914–1918. He drew postcard designs for J. Salmon between 1922 and 1928 but the bulk of his output was for E. J. Hey & Co., who added the trade name 'Ludgate'. Cards were also published by 'Alphalsa', Marcuse Day, 'N.P.G./R.P.A.', and J. Salmon. Some postcards bear the legend 'This is a genuine 'Gilson' Post Card', implying that his style (like so many other successful artists) was being copied, and indeed some very 'Gilson-like', but unsigned postcards exist. It has been suggested that cards signed 'Ludgate' are also by Gilson, although no proof has been found. Most of his postcards portray children, often in adult situations, sometimes 'coons', sometimes Chinese, frequently Scottish. Through their small eyes, many of the hardships and dangers of WW1 were portrayed.

Price range
Pre-WW1 Glamour ..	..	..	..	..	£1/**£1.50**/£2
Pre-WW1 Children ..	..	..	..	..	50p/**75p**/£1.50
Period 3 designs	..	..	..	..	25p/**75p**/£1.50
Period 4 designs	..	..	..	..	50p/**75p**/£1.50

A checklist of Gilson cards was published in the second edition (pp. 59–60).

GODILLOT
See Orens.

GOTHARD, FREDERICK (Spatz) (1882–1971)
Fred Gothard was born in Holmfirth, a town best known for its Bamforth connexions. He started drawing postcards whilst working as a bank clerk and used the pseudonym 'SPATZ' to protect his identity from his employers. Later he used his initials 'F.G.'. Period 2 comic designs examine all aspects of contemporary life, Period 3 designs have a military theme. His cards were published by Thomas Hind (a local Huddersfield printer), E. Mack, Salmon, Tollit & Harvey and Tuck.

Price range .. .. 25p/**50p**/£1

GUNN, ARCHIE (b. 1863)
Born in Taunton, Somerset, he found fame in the USA for his portrayals of 'The American Girl' (see GLAMOUR) *and for his patriotic designs during WW1.*

Price range .. .. £1/**£1.50**/£2

GWENNET, GUNN
He produced some highly coloured, comic designs for Philco, e.g. Series 4001—'Some British Workmen', 4002—'London Antiquities Up-to-Date', 4009—'Abbreviations'. Also floral design for Johnston's Patent Corn Flour, chromo vignette UB.

Price range (highest price for the Johnston ad.) .. £5/**£8**/£12

HAMISH
See Duncan, James Allen.

HAMPEL, WALTER (sometimes seen as HAMPL)
Austrian artist, much of whose fine work was published by Philipp & Kramer soon after the turn of the century. Series include 'Carnaval', 'Variété'.

Price range .. .. £15/**£25**/£35

68

HANSEN
See Nolde, Emil.

HANSI
See Waltz, J. J.

HARBOUR, JENNIE
Delicate artist of lovely ladies, etc., often in Period dress. Her main output was for Tuck (Oilette de Luxe). Some designs show an Art Deco flavour.

Price range .. .. **£2/£4/£6**

HARDY, DUDLEY (1867–1922) ■A 21
Born in Sheffield, son of the marine painter, T. B. Hardy, he was sent at the age of 15 to Düsseldorf to study under Crola and Lowenstein, but irked by the constricting tuition he rebelled and was dismissed but was later re-admitted to the Academy. He exhibited in the Royal Academy in 1885 and at the Paris Salon in 1888. His humorous work (which accounts for most of his 125 postcard designs) was also published in Punch. *He designed theatrical posters as well. See* ADVERTISING *and* COMIC.

Advertising work
Tuck 'Celebrated Posters' No. 1502 Liebig
The Pearl Girl
Egyptian Mail Steamship Co.
Royal Naval Tournament
Others

Price range .. .. **£10/£15/£25**

Other work
Price range .. .. **£1/£3/£6**

■A21 Pub. J. J. Allen. Artist Dudley Hardy. Advertisement (details on reverse) for 'Special Exhibition of Oriental Carpets and Rugs. Tuesday 19 November 1907' £12

HARDY, FLORENCE
She produced delightful studies of children, often in a Dutch setting, and attractive scenes with figures in period dress. Her main output was for C. W. Faulkner in Period 2.

Price range .. .. £1/**£2**/£4

HARE, J. KNOWLES (b. 1882)
Born in Montclair, New Jersey, USA, he designed covers for the Saturday Evening Post *and* American Magazine. *His postcard work was in the 'American Girl' genre* (see GLAMOUR). *Periods 2 to 4.*

Price range .. .. 75p/**£1**/£2.50

HASSALL, JOHN (1868–1948)
Hassall came from Walmer, Kent, and was educated at Newton Abbot College and Neuenheim College, Heidelberg. His association with the theatrical publisher David Allen led to the prolific commercial output that gave him the title 'The Poster King'. His postcard work is also vast—over 300 designs have been positively identified. A natural clown, Hassall was a leading light in the artistic and entertainment activities of the London Sketch Club. See ADVERTISING *and* COMIC.
Details of his postcards were published in the third edition of this catalogue, p 63.

Advertising work .. ..£7/**£18**/£25
Comic & General work .. .. £1/**£3**/£5

HAYES, FREDERICK WILLIAM (1848–1918)
Born in Cheshire, he trained as an architect in Ipswich and studied painting in Liverpool and London. A man of many talents, he was a musician, song writer and author as well as painting well enough to be exhibited at the Royal Academy. His postcard work was of the scenic 'Oilette' variety for Meissner & Buch, Tuck and others. Period 2.

Price range 25p/**50p**/75p

HEARTFIELD, JOHN (1891–1968)
Heartfield's real name was Helmut Herzfelde. He took his English sounding pseudonym as a protest against German xenophobia during WW1. In 1917 he founded the publishing house of Malik Verlag with his brother, Wieland. Heartfield perfected the technique of photomontage, of which he is often credited with being 'the father'. During the 1920s and 1930s Heartfield produced aggressive and satirical photomontage designs, many with virulent anti-National Socialist, anti-Capitalist, anti-Militarist themes. In 1933 he fled Berlin and continued his anti-Nazi agitation from Prague and later London. He returned to Germany in 1950.

Period 4 postcards .. ..£5/**£10**/£15

HEATH-ROBINSON, WILLIAM (1872–1944)
Born to an artistic family, he left school at 15 to go to the Royal Academy and from an early age showed great artistic ability and enjoyed commercial success. He is now best remembered for his pictures of almost surrealist inventions that made him a household name.

Advertising work .. ..£3/**£10**/£15
Comic and General work .. .. 75p/**£2**/£4

'HERGÉ'
See Remi, Georges.

HOFFMAN, JOSEF (1870–1956)
Austrian artist, much of whose early work was published by Philipp and Kramer He also contributed to the 'Wiener Werkstätte' (see COLLECTIONS*) and the 'Ver Sacrum' series.*

Price range .. .. £20/**£35**/£60

HÖPPENER, HUGO (Fidus) (1868–1948)
German artist who created a distinctive genre of Art Nouveau *symbolic and fantasy designs, many in black and white, often erotic. A number of his postcards are reproduced from his work for the magazines* Jugend *and* Pan. *Periods 1 and 2.*

Black and white designs .. .. £3/**£5**/£8
Coloured designs .. .. £5/**£8**/£12
Portrait (phot.) of artist/his studio .. .. .. £3/**£6**/£10

HORRELL, CHARLES
Artist of sentimental glamour, mostly known for his WW1 designs for James Henderson. His wholesome pretty girls often pose with their pets.

Price range .. .. 75p/**£1**/£2.50

HORSFALL, MARY
Portrayer of delicate female beauties in glowing colours, also children and the occasional women's suffrage theme. Publishers include Carlton Publishing Co., Wm. Ritchie and Tuck. Periods 2, 3.

Price range .. .. £1/**£1.50**/£2

The Stanley Gibbons Postcard Department is at 399 Strand, London, WC2. Open Mon – Fri. 9.30 am – 5.30 pm; Sat. 10.00 am – 12.30 pm.

HOWARD, FRED, S.
His postcard work includes Irish subjects in a comic vein and horse racing. Publishers include Misch and Pictorial Stationery Co. (Peacock). Period 2.

Price range .. .. 50p/**75p**/£1

HUBER, G.
Continental comic artist, with a most distinctive style. He specialised in caricatures of rotund, earthy, peasant types, often in courting scenes. Different language versions appear of many of his designs—English, French and German—with continental style backs. Most cards date from 1906–7. A list of the cards so far identified was printed in the Second Edition, p. 61.

Price range .. .. 50p/**£1**/£1.50

HUTCHINGS, J.
One of the most popular portrayers of Australian life in the bush. His 'Oilette type' views tend to glamorise and romanticise the rugged life of the Pioneer. The 36 identified titles are well sought after, although some are slightly 'fuzzy'.

Pub. NSW Bookstall Co. 'Art series'
   Australian series .. .. £3/**£3.50**/£4

IBBETSON, ERNEST ■M 2
Best known for his Military work (see MILITARY*) for Gale & Polden, he also drew general subjects for Faulkner, showing a light and humorous touch. His work spans Periods 2-5.*

Price range .. .. £1/**£3**/£5

ILLINGWORTH, LESLIE
Popular cartoonist with a distinctive and pleasing style who, during WW2, succeeded in capturing the Axis leaders' features and mannerisms in unmistakeable fashion. He worked for the Daily Mail, *his cartoons doing much for morale to a populace beset by bombs, blackout and rationing. Illingworth was amongst the cartoonists whose work was chosen by the British wartime propaganda machine to be reprinted as postcards and distributed through the British Embassy in Lisbon, Portugal.*

Period 5. Propaganda .. .. 75p/**£1.25**/£1.50

INNES, JOHN (1864–1941)
Sought after Canadian artist of 'Western' subjects, published by W. G. MacFarlane. Over 50 designs have been identified.

Price range .. .. £1/**£1.50**/£3

JACOBS, HELEN (1888–1970)
Sister of author W. W. Jacobs. Subjects of her postcard work

include elves and fairies and most of her output was published by C. W. Faulkner. See CHILDREN.

Price range .. .. £2/**£3**/£4

JAMES, IVY MILLICENT (1879–1965)

Born in Weston-super-Mare, she studied at the Western School of Art and had additional art tuition in London. Both Ivy and her sister Maud drew greetings cards and calendars for Delgado, Faulkner, Hills, Tuck and Valentine's from 1901 to 1904 but only Faulkner published her postcard work, (1907–19). 19 sets have been identified. The designs are mostly of appealing children in the style of Florence Hardy and Ethel Parkinson, many in the popular 'Dutch' style.

Periods 2, 3, early period 4. Sets of 6 .. .. .. £1/**£2**/£3
Perforated Painting Books of 12 cards. Per card 75p/**£1**/£1.50

JOSSOT, HENRI (b. 1866)

One of the group of sought-after early French postcard artists who contributed to many of the great series like the Collection des Cent, Maîtres de la Carte Postale (see COLLECTIONS). *He also drew advertisements and political designs including Dreyfus.*

Price range .. .. £50/**£70**/£100

JOTTER

See Young, Walter Hayward.

JOZSA, KARL (b. 1872)

Sought after artist of the Vienna Secessionist School. His famous series include 'Heart Ladies', Sirens and Circes', 'Smoke Rings' and 'World of Fairy Tales'

Price range .. .. £15/**£25**/£40

KEM

Cartoonist who produced 3000 political cartoons during WW2. They were printed in magazines in London (e.g. Cartoon Comment*), in China, Greece, Morocco and in Portugal, where many of them were reproduced as postcards and distributed through the British Embassy in Lisbon.*

Period 5. Propaganda .. .. 50p/**£1**/£1.25

KIENERK, GEORGIO (1869–1948)

Powerful Italian artist, best known for his portrayals of Dante's Divine Comedy *and his 'Cocorico' designs.*

Period 1 (incl. Cocorico) .. .. £75/**£100**/£150
Period 2 .. ..£5/**£15**/£30

KIMBALL, ALONZO MYRON (1874–1923)
Born in Green Bay, Wisconsin, USA, he studied in New York and Paris (under Lefebre and Whistler). He was a member of the Society of Illustrators and is best known on the postcard for his 'American Girls' (see GLAMOUR).

Price range   ..   ..   £1/**£1.50**/£2

KING, HAMILTON (b. 1871)
Born in Lewiston, Maine, USA, he studied in Paris and was a member of the Society of Illustrators. He is best known in the postcard world for his female studies.

Price range   ..   ..   £2/**£3**/£4

KING, JESSIE MARION (1876–1949)
One of the most prized of the children's artists, who produced beautiful nursery rhyme illustrations in the Art Nouveau *style, but with strong hints of the* Art Deco *style to come. Publishers include Millar & Lang.*

Price range   ..   ..   £20/**£40**/£50

KINSELLA, EDWARD PATRICK
Irish artist, usually known as Pat, he specialised in sporting children and theatre posters.

Pub. David Allen, Theatre posters   ..   ..   £5/**£10**/£12
Pub. Langsdorff, Sporting Children   ..   ..   £1.50/**£3**/£5

KIRCHNER, RAPHAEL (1876–1917)
Born in Vienna, Kirchner moved to Paris in 1905 following his enormous early success in the postcard field. He also became well known in the fields of magazine illustration, portrait painting and theatrical design. Probably the best known Art Nouveau/Glamour *artist, designed some 630 cards—some of which became the subject of poems, sketches in stage revues, etc. They were avidly collected by young officers during WW1 and pinned up in the trenches. His girls were all based on his wife, Nina. After her husband's tragic early death she took to drugs and died in a mental hospital.*
   Kirchner's work divides into three sections:

Period 1
The rare pre-1900 designs (many published by Philipp & Kramer) including the 'Leda' series of 10   ..   £25/**£40**/£50

Early Period 2 (1900–1903)
Beautiful chromo-litho UB's with a strong *Art Nouveau* flavour.

Price range   ..   ..   £15/**£25**/£50

Later Period 2 and Period 3

These later designs move away from the *Art Nouveau* style and into the 'Glamour' category. *See* GLAMOUR.

Designs include The *Maude* series, the *Riquette* series, the *Montmartre* series, *Les Zeppelins à Paris*, *Peinte par elle-même*, *Lolotte*, etc.

Price range   ..   ..£8/**£12**/£15

Many unsigned designs were printed by M. Munk, Pascalis Moss, 'B.K.W' and others, which are generally accepted as Kirchners.

Price range   ..   ..£5/**£10**/£15

KLEE, PAUL (1879–1940)

Born in Munchenbuchsee bei Bern, Switzerland, Klee studied art in Munich. He travelled extensively in Italy and Tunisia and served in the Great War from 1916–1918. In 1920 he joined the Bauhaus group of Walter Gropius in Weimar, becoming an instructor. In 1931 he moved to the Dusseldorf Academy, but was dismissed in 1933 by the Nazis. He died in Locarno.

Bauhaus Postcards Nos. 4 and 5 (only 25 examples of each are thought to have been printed)   ..   £500/**£1000**/£2500

KLEIN, CATHERINA (b. 1861)

Born in Prussia, she attended the Berlin Academy of Art and also studied in Dresden and Munich. Specialising in flower studies and still-life (fruits, etc.) her superbly coloured postcard work was published by Birn Bros.; Douglass Post Card Co., Philadelphia and Berlin; Max Ettlinger; C. W. Faulkner; G.O.M.; Hildesheimer; International Art Pub. Co. New York and Berlin; 'K. F.' Paris; Meissner and Buch; Miller & Lang; Stenli of Zurich; Stiebel (Alpha); Stecher Litho Co., New York; Theo Stroefer, Nuremberg; Tuck and Wildt & Kray. Many of her designs were 'pirated'.

Price range   ..   ..   50p/**£1.50**/£5

Novelty

Tuck No. 4078 painting book 'In Garden Ways', with 16 perforated postcards and hard cover. Others.

Per complete booklet ..   .. £5/**£8**/£10

KOEHLER, MELA ■A 22

Elegant designs for the Wiener Werkstätte *(see* COLLECTIONS*) for which she designed about 90 cards and other fashion and glamour designs with an* Art Deco *flavour.*

Wiener Werkstätte	..	..	..	..	..	£40/**£50**/£70
Others	..	..	..	..	..	..	£10/**£15**/£20

■A22 Pub. Brüder Kohn. Vienna (B.K.W.) Artist Mela Koehler. 'Tango' No. 843–4. Message written 1919 £20

KOKOSCHKA, OSKAR (1886–1980)
The son of a goldsmith, the young Oskar wanted to become a chemist. He studied at the School of Arts and Crafts in Vienna, intending to become a teacher. Impressed by painters as contrasting as Klimt and Van Gogh, he drifted into art. In 1907 he worked with the Wiener Werkstätte (see COLLECTIONS) *drawing 13 designs for a series of postcards. These are amongst the most highly prized—and priced—of all postcards. After this initial success, he become a portrait painter, but his distorted, tormented style found little acclaim. Gradually he won renown as an Expressionist, and member of the Vienna Secession. He gained recognition for his original and powerful style between the wars, but it was condemned as 'decadent' by the National Socialist regime, who destroyed 400 of his works during the late 1930s.*

Price range . . . . £100/**£300**/£750

KYD
See Clark, J. Clayton.

LARSEN, L. H. (Dude)
American artist whose droll sense of humour shone through his 'Western' pictures, reproduced as postcards in the late 1930s and early 1940s. A product of the 1930s Depression, the 'Dude' moved from the ranching business in Utah to seek his fortune as an artist. He found success in Washington—his cards portray a variety of ranching activities, cowboys, Indians, horses, steers, and landscapes. His wife, Dot, also drew the occasional (difficult to find nowadays) postcard design. Periods 4, 5.

Price range . . . . 75p/**£1.50**/£2

LEETE, ALFRED (b. 1882)
Most famous for his WW1 recruiting poster, 'Your King and Country Need You', he contributed to The Passing Show *and other magazines and was President of the London Sketch Club in 1925. His postcard work includes several comic designs.*

Price range   ..   ..   £1/**£1.50**/£2

LELEE, LEOPOLD (b. 1872)
French artist of the Art Nouveau *school who studied at the School of Decorative Arts in Paris but who settled in Arles in Provence, which had a local influence on his work. Some of his work contained elements of surrealism.*

Girls' Eyes (10)	£10/**£15**/£30
Mid-day and Midnight	£10/**£15**/£30
Others	..£5/**£10**/£15

LINDSAY, NORMAN
Australia's most sought after, best loved and most easily recognised artist. A versatile painter, he was equally at home with pen and ink, oil and etchings.

Bulletin Series
Australian types (10 cards)	£30/**£40**/£50
Other sets	£25/**£30**/£50

NSW Bookstall Co. 'Art Series'
Australian Native Series (6 cards)	£20/**£25**/£30

LOIR, LUIGI
French artist who did many fine UB *chromo-litho scenes and town types, notably Paris. His work was published in Britian by P. G. Huardel 1900–1904.*

Price range   ..   ..   £1/**£3**/£5

LUDOVICI, ANTHONY
An accomplished general and comic artist, he is best known for his satirical political caricatures of Joseph Chamberlain, Roseberry, etc. See Comic, Political.

Pub. Davidson Bros. (Period 2)
See the fourth edition of this catalogue p. 77 for a list of series nos.

Price range   ..   ..   £2/**£3**/£4

Pub. Valentine's
'Write Away' series, signed 'AL'	£2/**£3**/£4
Others	£1/**£2**/£3

Others   ..   ..   £1/**£1.50**/£2

LYNEN, AMEDEE (b. 1852)

A proficient Belgian typographer and stone mason, who became better known for his poster, newspaper and book illustrations. His acute observations of everyday life inspired his great series of over 200 postcards known as De-ci, de-là, à Bruxelles et en Brabant *(Here and there in Brussels and Brabant). Period 2.*

Price range   .. ..   **£4/£6**/£8.50

MACDONALD, A. K. ■A 23

An elegant artist, about whom little seems known.

Various Publishers (Early Period 2)
Coloured *Art Nouveau* designs .. .. ..   £10/**£25**/£30

Pub. Henderson, James (1909)
Gibson-like pen and ink designs   .. .. ..   £1/**£2**/£3

Pub. Valentine (1908–1910)
Designs for Franco-British and Japanese-British exhibitions
(more for signed examples)   .. ..£5/**£10**/£15

■A23 Pub. Hildesheimer. Artist A. K. Macdonald. UB. Early Period 2 £25

MAILICK, A.

Versatile German artist whose work includes charming views/ Faith, Hope, Charity, etc. and other greetings, WW1 sentiment and propaganda.

Early Period 2 and Period 3   .. ..   £1/**£2**/£3

MARTINI, ALBERTO (1876–1954)

Italian artist who drew some powerful propaganda surrealist

*designs during WW1, also adverts and pretty girls, e.g.
'Venetia Antiqua'—medieval maidens (1903).*

Price range .. ..£5/**£15**/£30

MARTY, ANDRÉ

*French artist of the Art Deco school, he trained at the Paris
Ecole des Beaux Arts. He had a witty and highly original
approach and was well known for his fashion illustrations in
magazines such as the Gazette du Bon Ton, Modes et Manières
d'Aujourd'hui etc. Period 4.*

range .. ..£5/**£10**/£15

MATALONI, GIOVANNI

*Italian artist whose attractive Art Nouveau designs were used
in Period 2 to publicise political events (for the Italian Socialist
Party, etc.) products, hotels, exhibitions and operas, e.g.
Puccini's Madame Butterfly and Mascagni's Iris. Mataloni
also illustrated the Divine Comedy published by Alterocca-
Terni. During Period 3 he drew wartime propaganda .*

Periods 1 and 2 designs .. .. £7.50/**£15**/£20
Period 3 WW1 .. .. £1.50/**£3**/£5

MATANIA, FORTUNINO (1881–1963)

*A child prodigy born in Naples, he first exhibited at the Naples
Academy in 1892. His news pictures for L'Illustrazione led to
an invitation to come to London to cover the coronation of
Edward VII for The Graphic. Later he worked for The Sphere
covering every royal event until the coronation of Elizabeth II.
During WW1 he was appointed an official war artist and drew
his most famous postcard design 'Goodbye Old Man' (see
MILITARY).*

Pub. *The Sphere.* Reproductions of his illustrations for the
  magazine. Periods 2 to 4
Others, including advertising cards, WW1 themes (incl.
  Italian military scenes/War Bond issues)

Price range .. .. 75p/**£1**/£1.50

MAURICE, REG.

*A popular comic artist, much of whose work appeared during
Period 3 (as military humour) and in Period 4 (general
humour). Most cards published by Regent Pub. Co.*

Chaplin Humour .. ..75p/**£1.50**/£2.50
General or WW1 Humour .. ..75p/**£1.50**/£2.50

MAUZAN, ACHILLE (1886–1940) ■A 24

This under-estimated Italian artist is mostly collected for his blander, 'glamour' designs. In fact he was a most versatile and original artist. His work includes wartime propaganda and patriotism during WW1, advertisements, both in France and Italy, for a variety of famous products in Period 4. His best work has a distinct Art Deco *flavour, amongst which is a most attractive 'Months of the Year' series.*

Period 3		
Glamour		£1/**£3**/£5
Propaganda/Patriotism		£1.50/**£5**/£7.50
Period 4		
Adverts		£3/**£7**/£10
Glamour		£2/**£5**/£8
Others		£1/**£3**/£5

■A24 Pub. Uff. Rev. Stampa, Milan. Artist A. Mauzan. 'Months of the Year. September,' No. 94. PU 1917 £8

MAY, PHIL (1864–1903)

Born near Leeds, Phil May soon gravitated to London. He had a well-developed sense of humour that led him easily into the company of Whistler, Wilde and, inevitably, the other founder members of the London Sketch Club. He lived for 3 years in Australia and worked on the Sydney Bulletin. *Back in London he worked for* Punch, The Graphic *and joined the Chelsea Arts Club. His tragically early death curtailed a prolific output of brilliantly observed sketches of London Life and other types. Ninety postcard designs have been identified to date. See* Comic.

Advertising work

Dewar's Whisky	£15/**£20**/£25
Tuck's Celebrated Posters 1506. Appolinaris	£15/**£20**/£25

Comic and General work

Publishers include Davidson Bros.; Landerer & Brown; Tuck,
Valentine and Wrench. (See the fourth edition p. 80 for
details)

Price range   ..   ..   **£1/£3/£6**

McCUTCHEON, JOHN T. (1870–1949)

*Described as 'The Dean of American Cartoonists . . .' in his
obituary in the* New York Times. *McCutcheon captured the
carefree innocence of boyhood in many of his designs—always
with a gentle touch of humour. His 'Boy in . . .' (Spring-Time,
Summer-Time, Fall-Time, Winter-Time) series is particularly
fine. His first postcards appeared in 1903 and production
continued until after WW2. McCutcheon worked as a war artist
and correspondent in many campaigns—from 1896 to 1945,
notching up many reporting 'firsts'. Periods 2–5.*

Price range   ..   ..   **£1.50/£3/£5**

McGILL, DONALD (1875–1962) ▮SH 2

*Donald McGill started designing postcards in 1904 for a sick
nephew. He continued pouring out designs for most of the rest
of his long life and is, without doubt, Britain's most prolific
postcard artist. McGill himself claimed 10,000 designs and
experts believe this cannot be too inaccurate a figure (nearly
9000 have been positively identified). Chiefly known for his
rumbustious, often vulgar, seaside comics, McGill also drew
pungent social and political comments during both World
Wars, as well as military humour and patriotic designs.
McGill's output is usually classified into 4 periods and, generally speaking, the earlier the card, the higher the value.*

Early Period (1904–1906)

About 650 designs. Publishers include Eyre & Spottiswoode,
Hudson Bros. and Pictorial P.C. Co.   ..   ..   **£1/£2/£3**

Second Period (1907–1914)

About 1750 designs. Publishers include Joseph Asher,
Thridgould & Co., Woolstone Bros. and others   **75p/£1/£1.50**

Inter-Art Period (1914–1935)

About 3500 designs. The most prolific period of all, which
included some designs for Woolstone Bros. and for Thridgould & Co.   ..   ..   **50p/75p/£1**

Modern Period (1935–1952)

About 2500 designs. Asher now formed a new company under
the name of D. Constance Ltd. which produced the 'New
Donald McGill Comics'—greatly inferior printing on poor
quality board. Nevertheless the WW2 designs have some
interest—*see* MILITARY. At the beginning of this period McGill
also drew for Birn Bros. and McCrum (Inter-Art)

..   ..   **25p/50p/75p**

MENPES, MORTIMER (1860–1938) ■EX 2

Water-colorist who is best remembered for his Boer War sketches of Churchill, Conan Doyle, Kipling, Rhodes, Roberts, etc. and scenes at Ladysmith, Modder River, etc. His postcard work includes a delightful series of 'The World's Children' published by Wrench and souvenir postcards for the Japan-British Exhibition of 1910. (See EXHIBITIONS).

Price range   ..   ..   50p/**75p**/£2

MERCER, JOYCE (1896–1965)

One of the 'Nursery Artists' (see CHILDREN) *whose subjects include children, fairy stories and nursery rhymes, with an Art Deco flavour. Most of her work was published by C. W. Faulkner.*

Price range   ..   ..   £2/**£4**/£6

METLICOVITZ, LEOPOLDO (1864–1944)

Italian artist whose work spanned the periods of Art Nouveau and Art Deco. His versatile designs covered the themes of Adverts, Glamour, Landscapes and Propaganda. Metlicovitz is perhaps best known for his opera studies, published by G. Ricordi of Milan. Periods 1–4.

Price range   ..   ..   £3/**£7.50**/£15

MEUNIER, HENRI (1873–1922)

Born in Ixelles in Belgium, Meunier was a highly competent engraver, painter, book illustrator as well as a postcard designer. Many of his beautiful Art Nouveau designs were published by the fine publishing house of Dietrich in Brussels. Meunier also contributed to the famous Editions Cinos series and the Collection Job (qv). His glorious series of 12 Girls, 1900, is particularly sought after, as are the series Girls, Flowers, Signs of the Zodiac and Le Chic de Paris.

Price range   ..   ..   £30/**£50**/£65

MIGNOT, VICTOR (1872–1944) ■A 25

Belgian Art Nouveau artist, best known for his beautiful series of Sports (Bicycling, Horse Racing, Ice Skating, Mountaineering, etc.) Pub. Dietrich.

Price range   ..   ..   £5/**£12**/£15

MILLIÈRE, MAURICE (b. 1871)

Born in Le Havre, Millière studied under Bonnat at L'Ecole des Beaux Arts. He contributed to La Vie Parisienne and was exhibited in Paris, London and New York. His postcard work is mainly known for 'glamour' subjects during WW1, although there are fine examples of his work during Period 2. See MILITARY.

Early Period 2
M. Munk Vienna series .. .. £3/**£5**/£10

Period 3
La Vie dans La Campe Indienne à Rouen .. .. £2/**£3**/£5
Petites Femmes de Paris .. .. £2/**£3**/£5
Others .. .. £2/**£3**/£5

■A25 Pub. Dietrich, Brussels. Artist V. Mignot. UB. Early Period 2. PU 1903 £12

MORELAND, ARTHUR

One of Britain's most under-estimated comic artists, who was also capable of making political comments (see POLITICAL). *Over 160 designs have been identified from early Period 2. The 'Humours of History' series were originally published in* The Morning Leader *and also appeared in book form. Publishers include: Faulkner, C. W.; Eyre & Spottiswoode (Woodbury Series).*

Price range .. .. £1/**£3**/£5

■A26 Pub. F. A. Ackermann, Munich. Artist Koloman Moser. 'Good Morning'. UB. PU 1902 £30

MOSER, KOLOMAN (1868–1918) ■A 26

Austrian artist, co-founder of the Secessionist Movement in Vienna and a member of the Wiener Werkstätte *(though none of his postcards appeared in that collection). His best postcard work was published by Philipp & Kramer and is in a restrained* Art Nouveau *style. He also contributed to the great German series* Meggendorfer Blätter.

Price range   ..   ..   £15/**£30**/£50

MUCHA, ALPHONSE (1860–1939)

Czech artist who came to Paris at the age of 26 in 1887. His first success,which assured his future career, was with a poster of Sarah Bernhardt in 1894. His poster work was published by M. Champenois of Paris, who reproduced the designs on postcards. The most reproduced of all the Art Nouveau *artists, Mucha contributed to many of the important early French series* (see COLLECTIONS). *Mucha returned to his native Czechoslovakia for the last years of his life and died in Prague. His work falls into five categories:*

Period 1
The glorious pre-1900 era. Sarah Bernhardt Posters (1898): Dame aux Camélias, Gismonda, Lorenzaccio, La Samaritaine; Cocorico (1899) ..   ..   £60/**£75**/£150

Early Period 2
Collection des Cent (2 designs); *Champenois* series, incl. The Four Seasons, The Months of the Year, Precious Stones; Moet et Chandon (10 designs)   ..   ..   ..   £50/**£70**/£100

Later Period 2
Postcard reproductions of 1897, 1898 *Job* Calendars in 1911; Album Mariani; Others   ..   ..   ..   £25/**£40**/£60

Nearly 110 cards have been identified for these three 'French' periods.

Late Period 2/Periods 3, 4 (The Czechoslovakian Period)
Mucha's output from about 1909 was mostly produced in Prague, often with Czech themes, moving away from the stylised *Art Nouveau* influence of the French period. Nearly 60 designs have been identified for this period   £20/**£30**/£40

The *Champenois* designs were republished in Britain by Huardel, Pascalis Moss, Henry Moss, H. J. Smith and F. C. Southwood from 1900 to about 1905. Dietrich of Belgium also published many early Period 2 designs   ..   £15/**£30**/£45

Period 4
Advertisements for the YWCA ..   ..   ..   £15/**£20**/£30

MUTTER, K.

German landscape artist. Publishers include Schmidt, Staub & Co., with many fine UB *chromo-litho.*

Price range .. .. £1/**£2**/£3

NANNI, GIOVANNI (1888–1969) ■A 27

Italian artist best known for his elegant, fashionable girls, notably a superb series of behatted heads, Periods 3, 4. He also drew patriotic, propagandist designs in the 1920s and 1930s and commercial work for products like Pirelli. During this period his work was strongly influenced by the Art Deco *style and included some beautiful film posters (see* CINEMA *and* GLAMOUR*).*

Price range (higher price for *Art Deco* posters) .. £5/**£7**/£18

■A27 Pub. Alberani. Artist G. Nanni. 'Carmen'. Period 4 £18

NASH, ADRIENNE, A.

Subjects include children, patriotic and suffragettes etc. in Periods 2 and 3.

Pub. Henderson

Children's Birthdays (7 cards)	50p/**75p**/£1.50
Others	50p/**75p**/£2.50

Pub. Inter-Art
25 series between 1913–1918 (*see also* PUBLISHERS, Inter-Art)
.. .. 50p/**75p**/£2.50

NIXON, KATHLEEN (b. 1895)

Children's artist (see CHILDREN*). To date 18 postcards only have been recognised, published by C. W. Faulkner, including animals and* Alice in Wonderland *series.*

Price range .. .. £1/**£2**/£3

NOLDE, EMIL (1867–1956)

Christened Emil Hansen, he changed his name to Nolde after his birthplace. Brought up on his father's farm, he became a wood carver and in 1890 moved to Berlin as a furniture designer. In 1894 he drew the personifications of the Swiss mountains which, reproduced on postcards, were such a financial success that he became an independent painter. His frenetic, excited, brightly coloured style emerged as he exper- imented with Impressionism. He became a member of the Dresden group, Die Brucke (the Bridge) from about 1905. His religiously inspired paintings were extremely controversial. In 1918, established as an expressionist, he joined the November- gruppe. His work was regarded as 'degenerate' by the National Socialist regime and over 1000 examples of it were destroyed during the 1930s.

Fantasy mountain designs. Pub. F. Killinger. Period 2   ..
   ..   .. **£5/£8/£12**

NOURY, GASTON (b. 1866)

French artist, born at Elboeuf, he was one of the great Art Nouveau artists. A poster designer and book illustrator, his postcards show great imagination, with designs that often border on 'fantasy'. Noury contributed to the famous Editions Cinos (q.v.) collection. Some of his designs were in black and white, while others were highly coloured. Periods 1 and 2.

Price range (lowest for b & w, highest for the *Cinos*)   ..   ..
   ..   ..   **£10/£30/£70**

NYSTROM, JENNY (1854–1946)

Born in 1854 in Kalmar, Sweden, Jenny attended Art school, and in 1871 illustrated 'Little Vig's Fairy Tales on Christmas Eve' in the Gothenborg newspaper. In 1873 she became a member of the Academy of Independent Artists and in 1882 moved to Paris. In 1886 she moved back to Stockholm and married in 1887. In the 1890s she started to design postcards to support her ailing husband, Dr. Daniel Stoopendaal. Their son Curt was also a postcard artist (see ANIMALS*). She special- ised in folklore, fairy tales, greetings cards and 'glamour' and often used her father's face to illustrate her gnomes. Some of her work was distinctly Art Deco in flavour and her greetings cards were sometimes produced in 'miniature' form. Periods 2–5.*

Price range   ..   ..   **£2/£4/£6**

O'NEILL, ROSE (1874–1944)

American artist, renowned as the inventor of the 'Kewpie' (corruption of Cupid) doll in 1909. She also wrote rhyming stories and verse (some of which appear on her cards). Over 200 postcards have been identified, mostly published by the Gibson Art Co. Periods 2, 3, 4.

Advertising designs for Victory Cream (Rare)	£15/**£25**/£35
Novelty designs ('Klever Kards'—mechanical)	£5/**£10**/£15
Pub. Gibson Art Co.	
General Kewpie designs	£2/**£5**/£8
Santas and other sought after themes	£3/**£5**/£8
Women's Suffrage	
Campbell Art Co. 1915	£10/**£12**/£15
National Woman Suffrage Pub. Co. 1915	£10/**£12**/£15

ORENS (Denizard *or* Godillot)

French satirical caricaturist, many of whose designs were produced in small limited editions (of 75 to 250 only). He also drew under the names 'Denizard' and 'Godillot', and contributed to the Collection des Cent. See POLITICAL.

Price range (highest valuation for the *Cent* cards)   £5/**£10**/£40

OST, ALFRED (1884–1945) ■A 28

One of Belgium's most popular postcard artists, he studied at the School of Fine Arts at Anvers, specialising in animal studies. Ost's work, which encompassed styles from traditional Flemish baroque to modernism, made strong social comment. More than 300 designs have been identified, many of them in black and white.

■A28 Pub. J. Goffin Fils, Brussels. Artist A. Ost. *Au Bal Masque de la Monnaie* (At the masked Ball at the Theatre Royal de la Monnaie). On the reverse, an advert for Ruinart Pere et Fils, Champagne, Reims. Period 4 £20

OUTCAULT, RICHARD F. (b. 1863)

Born in Lancaster, Ohio, USA, his creation in 1896 in 'The New York World' of the 'Yellow Kid' comic strip was a sensation. He followed its success with 'Buster Brown' in The New York Herald *in 1902. Newspapers vied for his services and many of his comical drawings appeared on postcards (see* CHILDREN *and* COMIC).

Price range   ..   ..   £1/**£2**/£4

OUTHWAITE, IDA RENTOUL (1889–1961)
Australian artist of the nursery genre (see CHILDREN).

Pub. A. & C. Black
Postcard reproductions of the illustrations she drew for their
books. Period 4 .. .. £1.50/**£3**/£4

Pub. Anon. Australia.
2 series of b&w cards under her maiden name, 'Rentoul',
signed 'I.S.R.' .. .. £5/**£7**/£8

OWEN, WILL (d. 1957)
*Member of the London Sketch Club, most famous for his 'Aah,
Bisto' advertisement, he contributed to* Punch, *illustrated
books, drew posters and also published books.*

Advertising work (e.g. for Pub. David Allen) .. £4/**£8**/£12
General/comic work (e.g. for Davidson Bros. Meissner & Buch,
  Tuck L, Wrench) .. .. £1/**£2**/£4

PARKINSON, ETHEL
*Several series of charming wintry scenes and children, mainly
published by C. W. Faulkner.*

Price range .. .. £2/**£3**/£4

PARLETT, HARRY (Comicus)
*Many of Parlett's comic cards are signed by his pseudonym,
'Comicus', and others bear only his initials, 'H.P.'*
Publishers include:
*Gottschalk, Dreyfus & Davis (Star series); H. B. Series;
Midland Pictorial Postcard Co.; Others*

Price range .. .. 50p/**75p**/£1.50

PARTRIDGE, SIR BERNARD (1861–1945)
*Encouraged by his traditionally artistic family to pursue that
tradition, Partridge expressed his independence by going into
the theatre—working for a while with such illustrious names
as Henry Irving and Forbes-Robertson. Later he became a
cartoonist, joining the staff of* Punch *in 1909. He worked for
that magazine until his death. Wrench reproduced some of his
early* Punch *cartoons as postcards.*

Pub. Wrench. 'Pictures from Punch' .. .. .. £2/**£3**/£4
Others .. .. £1/**£2**/£3

PATELLA, B.
French Art Nouveau *artist, often confused with Raphael Kirchner. His most famous series are the* Femmes Voilées.

Price range   ..   ..£5/**£10**/£15

PAYNE, ARTHUR CHARLES (1856–1933)
Brother of the more famous Harry (q.v.) with whom he occasionally did joint work. Arthur painted the background and architectural detail while Harry did the foreground figures. Although Arthur also drew many military designs, his postcard work mainly comprised cathedrals, views and river scenes. Publishers include: De Little, Fenwick & Co.; Hildesheimer; Ruddock; Tuck.

'Oilette type' designs ..   ..   50p/**75p**/£1.50
Early chromo designs   ..   ..   £3/**£4**/£6

PAYNE, G. M.
A highly competent, somewhat under-estimated artist of comic and general subjects during Period 2. Subjects include Bathing, 'Before our Time', sporting, etc. He did many series for Gale & Polden and other publishers. Period 3.

Price range   ..   ..   50p/**75p**/£1.50

PAYNE, HARRY (1858–1927) ■M 6
Though his drawings now seem somewhat stereotyped and wooden, Harry Payne is undoubtedly the most famous of all the military postcard artists. He had only a sketchy art training at evening school, but his splendid, colourful pictures, with an attention to detail of uniform and horses' trappings, had an early success. He and his brother Arthur (q.v.) with whom he had a long artistic collaboration, were fascinated as boys by all things military. He was engaged by Tuck (for whom he had been designing 'scraps' and books for several years), to design postcards for them and produced some of their earliest picture postcards. The association was to last until 1918. Then Gale & Polden commissioned 67 designs, of which 22 are estimated to have been published, including his last postcard. It is estimated he prepared about 700 postcard designs. See MILITARY.

Pub. Davis, A. M. & Co.
Period 3 War Bond poster ..   ..   £3/**£6**/£8

Pub. Gale & Polden (1918/1919)
Twenty-two known military designs ..   ..   ..   £3/**£6**/£8

Pub. Hildesheimer
At least 2 Rural series   ..   ..   £2/**£4**/£6

Pub. Stewart & Woolf
At least 4 series of military designs ..   ..   ..   £3/**£6**/£8

Pub. Tuck

Chromo-litho UBS. *Period 1/early Period 2*
British Army series Nos. 100–124; Empire series (Baden-Powell, CIV's, Wiping Something off the Slate, etc.); Animal Life series; Types of the British Army .. £10/**£15**/£25
Military Oilettes. Periods 2/3
About 40 sets and many single designs on Ceremonial, Regimental, Uniforms, etc. .. .. £3/**£6**/£8
Badges and their Wearers (30 identified) .. ..£7/**£12**/£15
Boy Scouts/Red Cross/US Army .. .. £4/**£6**/£10
Defenders of the Empire. Period 3 .. .. .. £3/**£5**/£8
Defenders of the Empire with whisky advert (1924) .. ..
.. .. £4/**£8**/£12
King George V series 9877 .. .. £3/**£6**/£8
Period 3 Patriotics incl. 'Wake up England' .. £2/**£4**/£6
Rural Oilettes
About 40 series, including 'County' series, Country Life, Man's Best Friend, Seasonal .. .. £2/**£4**/£6
Wild West, USA (1907)
Two series and single designs .. .. £3/**£6**/£8
Others (highest for adverts) .. .. £3/**£7**/£20

PERLBERG, F.
Prolific, globe-trotting German artist of attractive landscapes, views, historic sites and 'types'. Little is known of the man. Full listings of Perlberg series were given in the third and fourth edition of this catalogue (pp. 82–4 and 91 respectively).

Pub. C. A. & Co.
Series covering Egypt, the Levant, the Mediterranean and Palestine.

Price range .. .. 75p/**£1.50**/£3

Pub. Rommler, Jonas, Dresden
Nos. R101–154. Arab/Egyptian subjects.

Price range .. .. 75p/**£1.50**/£3

PHILLIMORE, REGINALD (1855–1941)
Born the son of a Nottingham doctor, Reginald graduated from Oxford University in the early 1870s and went on to teach at a private school in Lancashire. Over the next twenty years he enjoyed sketching in the Manchester area and his interest in history grew. When the picture postcard, became popular in the 1890s, he saw a way of combining his two interests commercially. In 1894 Phillimore went into the business of designing, printing and publishing postcards, many of them being hand tinted by his assistant, Mary Pearson. Phillimore postcards are characterised by their fascinating historical and architectural detail, often combining several designs on a single card. Typical, too, are the small pictures which continue the story on the reverse. Peak production was from 1900 to 1910. Nearly 700 different designs have so far been identified.

---

*A full listing of Phillimore cards was given in the second
edition of this catalogue, pp. 75–81.*

Price range   ..   ..   £1/**£2**/£3

PINKAWA, ANTON
Art Nouveau *artist, particularly highly regarded for his delicate* Seasons *Series. Early Period 2.*

Price range   ..   ..£5/**£10**/£15

PIRKIS, ALBERT GEORGE
*Amusing and skilful artist, best known for his series showing
accident-prone cyclists and motorists for Hildesheimer, many
of them 'Write-Aways'. He also did views and London scenes.*

Price range   ..   ..   £1/**£2**/£3

POIRE, EMMANUEL (Caran d'Ache) (1859–1909)
*French artist of Russian extraction ('Caran D'Ache' is a gallic-
ised version of the Russian for pencil) he contributed to some
of the great early French series* (see COLLECTIONS) *and is most
famous for his military designs.*

Price range (highest valuation for the 'Cent' cards)   ..   ..
..   ..   £10/**£25**/£100

POULBOT, FRANCISQUE (1879–1946)
*French artist who came to the public eye in WW1 with his
pitiful but spirited urchins ('gosses') orphaned and made
homeless by the horror of war. C. B. Cochran introduced a
Poulbot sketch into his Bairnsfather 'Better 'Ole' play. Poulbot
also drew advertisements and political cards, notably of the
famous 'Landru' trial. See* POLITICS.

Adverts. Period 4	£1/**£1.50**/£4
Specials (Landru, Novelty, *Lusitania*, etc.)	£3/**£6**/£12
Various 'Good Causes' Periods 3/4	£1/**£1.50**/£3
WW1 'Gosses'	75p/**£1.25**/£2

'PYP'
*Comic artist of Period 2, many of whose designs were published
by Davidson Bros., e.g.* UB *Illustrated Songs, credited as 'Originals by PYP'.*

Price range   ..   ..   75p/**£1.50**/£3

QUINTON, ALFRED ROBERT (1853–1934) ■T 1
*Born in Peckham and educated at Hornsey School and
Heatherley Arts School, he excelled in oils, exhibiting at the
Royal Academy, the Royal Society of British Artists, etc. He
travelled extensively through the British Isles on his bicycle,
sketching, and illustrated several books with his watercolours.*

His most productive association was with J. Salmon, the post-card publishers of Sevenoaks, and he worked for the firm from 1911 until his death.
Publishers include:
Faulkner, C. W.; McKenzie, W. & Co.; Salmon, J; Tuck.

Price range .. .. 75p/**£1.50**/£3

RAEMAEKERS, LOUIS (1869–1956)
Dutch artist whose bitter, anti-German cartoons, published as 'Drawings of a Neutral' did much for the Allied Propaganda machine in WW1. They were published for the Amsterdam paper De Telegraaf *and reprinted in booklet form in aid of British and French wounded and published by Geo. Pulman & Sons.*

Price range .. .. £1/**£2**/£2.50

RAVEN-HILL, LEONARD (1876–1942)
Raven-Hill studied art in London and Paris, where his work was exhibited in the Salon *in 1886. Finding success as an illustrator, he worked for a variety of magazines, notably* Punch. *He commented in his cartoons on politics, social life and wars. Perhaps his best known postcards are in the fine WW1 'Out for Victory' series, and in the reproduction of some of his early* Punch *cartoons by Wrench.*

Pub. Wrench. (1901)
'Pictures from Punch' .. .. £1.50/**£2**/£3

Pub. Anon
'Out for Victory' WW1 series
501 Tommy
502 Man at the Front
503 The Airman
504 The Poilu
505 Johnnie Tuck; 'For Peace at Any Price'
506 Little Willie; 'Who Said Verdun?'
507 The Bomber
511 The Destroyer Captain
512 The Farm Girl
513 The Allotment Holder
514 The Munition Girl
515 The British Working Man
Other comic/political designs

Price range .. .. 50p/**£1**/£2

RÉMI, GEORGES ('Hergé') (1907–1983) ■L 3
Creator of the universally popular children's book character 'Tintin', Rémi was born near Brussels. He was a keen scouter in his youth, and early cards often reflect the scouting theme and the American Indian theme he was fascinated by. In the late 1920s he developed his distinctive strip cartoon style and 'Tintin' went on to star in 23 books, which were translated into 30 languages. The colourful covers of these books have

appeared recently in postcard form, but postcards of Tintin's adventures and other 'Hergé' designs appeared from c. 1928.

Period 4	..	..	..	..	..	..	..	£2/**£4**/£8
Periods 5, 6		..	..	..	..	..	..	50p/**£1.50**/£3
Period 7	..	..	..	..	..	..	..	**25p**

REMINGTON, FREDERIC (1861–1909)
Perhaps the most sought after of all the American 'Western' artists, Remington became a cowboy after studying art at Yale. 2700 of his paintings have been identified, and those reproduced as postcards are highly prized. The majority were printed in magazines like Collier's, *and* Harper's *and in books on the American West. Period 2.*

Price range .. .. £2.50/**£5**/£7.50

REYNOLDS, FRANK (b. 1876)
Art editor of Punch *for 10 years, he also worked for* The Sketch *and was a member of the London Sketch Club of which he was President in 1909 and 1922. His 'Characters from Dickens' were reproduced as postcards by A. V. N. Jones & Co.*

Price range .. .. £1/**£1.50**/£2

RICHARDSON, AGNES (1884–1951) ■GR 4
Popular artist, whose postcard work spanned Periods 2 to 4. Subjects include children and patriotic designs. Publishers include: Birn Bros; Davidson Bros; Faulkner, C. W.; Geographia Ltd.; Hauff, Charles; Inter-Art.; Millar & Lang; Photochrom; Regent Pub. Co.; Tuck; Valentine's; Vivian Mansell.

Price range .. .. £1/**£2**/£3

ROBIDA, A.
French artist who did many charming landscapes and town scenes in early Period 2 and who contributed to many of the important French series e.g. Collection des Cent, The Gala Henri Monnier, *Album Mariani* (see COLLECTIONS).

Price range (highest valuation for the 'Monnier') £2/**£5**/£50+

ROBINSON, ROBERT (1886–1952)
American artist in the genre of Norman Rockwell, who drew covers for Saturday Evening Post *and illustrations for* Colliers, Harpers, *etc. His postcards depict ordinary Americans and ordinary American life for Edmund Gross. Period 4.*

Price range .. .. £1/**£2.50**/£4

RUBINO, ANTONIO (1880–1964)
Italian artist who drew some fine Period 3 caricatures, also advertisements.

Price range .. .. £3/**£5**/£8

RUSSELL, CHARLES M. (1865–1926)

American artist of lively and dramatic Western scenes—cowboys and indians, buffalos and bears, etc.—often with a humorous touch. His authentic atmosphere comes from his years of working as a rancher in Montana. Russell used this experience in his paintings and achieved great success. His work was published in Harper's, *in portfolio form and as book illustrations. At the height of his fame, the Prince of Wales bought one of his pictures. Periods 2, 3, 4.*

Pub. Charles E. Morris	£1/**£2**/£4
Pub. W. T. Ridgley Press	
Calendar Co. designs	£2/**£4**/£6
Others	£1/**£2**/£4

SAGER, XAVIER ■AD 9

Most prolific of all French postcard artists (Neudin has ident-ified 3000 designs), Sager is best known for his risqué glamour designs. He also produced commercial work and during WW1 his designs had a distinct propaganda message. Sager drew under several pseudonyms, including 'Leger' and 'Salt Lake'. All his work shows a light and humorous touch.

Early Period 2 from 1900	£3/**£6**/£10
Mid period 2	£2/**£4**/£5
Period 3 (*see also* MILITARY)	£2/**£4**/£6
Period 4	£2/**£4**/£5
Ads for 'Wellcome' heels/chocolate	£3/**£5**/£8
Pseudonyms/Kirchner copies	£6/**£8**/£10

SAUBER, ROBERT (1865–1936) ■ Back cover

One of the founder members of the London Sketch Club in 1898, Sauber spent much of his working life in Northampton. He is chiefly known for his 'London Types' series.

Pub. Pictorial Stationery Co. (from 1901)

Set of 12 'Familiar Figures of London' (*see* SOCIAL HISTORY). At least four different printings have been identified, some with white borders and some without. The borderless cards are UB.

Per card	£4/**£5**/£6
Complete set	£50/**£65**/£80

Pub. Tuck

Works of literary figures (1900)	£4/**£5**/£6
Tuck Celebrated Posters No. 1502 Tatcho ..	£15/**£20**/£25

SCHIELE, EGON (1890–1918) ■A 29

Recognising his talent while at secondary school, his teachers, against his family's wishes, sent him to study at the Vienna Academy in 1906. The following year he set up his own studio and developed his harsh, disturbing, expressionist style. The erotic element in some of his drawings led to his detention for indecency. Schiele became part of the Vienna Secessionist Group and also worked with the 'Sema' group and for the Wiener Werkstätte, *designing some fine postcards in a gentler style. In 1916 he contributed a special issue of the political Berlin review* Aktion. *His brilliant career was tragically cut short in 1918 when both he and his wife died in the great influenza epidemic.*

Aktion/Wiener Werkstätte	£75/**£250**/£500
Others	£10/**£20**/£40

■A29 Pub. Max Jaffe, Vienna. Artist Egon Schiele. 'Portrait of Arthur Roessler'. 1914 £40

SCHMUCKER, SAMUEL, L.
Schmucker was perhaps America's most accomplished post-card artist, working mostly for the fine publishing company of Winsch, for whom he created the 'Winsch Girl', and for the Detroit Pub. Co. He often signed cards with his initials—S.L.S.—only. Schmucker's designs were imaginative, and his glamour pictures often pure Art Nouveau *in concept. Period 2.*

Pub. Detroit Pub. Co. Art Series (some signed SLS)
Butterfly Girls, Childhood Days, Drinks, Gnomes, International Girls, Mermaids, Smokes .. .. £5/**£9**/£30
Pub. John Winsch
1911 onwards: Greetings, incl. Christmas, Easter, Hallowe'en, New Year, St. Patrick's Day, Thanksgiving, Valentine, etc.
.. .. £2.50/**£7.50**/£15

SCHÖNPFLUG, FRITZ (1873–1951)
Born in Vienna, son of a prosperous solicitor, Schönpflug was a 'natural', untaught artist, with a sharply observant eye. He recorded with benign accuracy the life and leisure pursuits of fashionable Austrian society and the Austrian army—from personal experience gained during his military service. He had a distinctly humorous touch. His output was prolific, well over 500 designs are estimated and the majority of his postcards were published by Brüder Köhn.

Pub. Köhn, Brüder (Periods 2 to 4)
Many sets of 6 .. .. £2/**£3**/£5

Pub. Munk, M. (Period 2)
Glamour and caricatures .. .. £2.50/**£4**/£6

Period 5
Designs with Nazi interest, e.g. *Tag der Wehrmacht fur das
K.W.H.W.* (Winter Relief Campaign. Army Day)   £3/**£5**/£10

SEVERN, WALTER (1830–1904)
*Born in Rome, he was educated at Westminster. After a short
spell as a civil servant he became a landscape artist and
designer, founding the Dudley Art Gallery. Pub. Tuck
('Oilette') and others.*

Price range 25p/**50p**/75p

SHEPHEARD, GEORGE EDWARD
*Talented caricaturist, many of whose designs were reproduced
on, or drawn for, the postcard. He is perhaps most famous for
his caricature of Rudyard Kipling. Some Faulkner sets are
'remainders'.*
Publishers include:
*Avenue Pub. Co. (1906); Faulkner, C. W.; Photochrom Co.
(Period 3); Tuck.*

Price range   .. .. 25p/**75p**/£1.50

SHINN. COBB X. (1887–1951)
*Cobb Shinn was a WW1 'Doughboy' and served in France with
the Camouflage Division. During the War he drew cartoons of
his fellow soldiers and on his return to civilian life he started
drawing a daily newspaper strip cartoon and soon achieved
national fame. His postcard output is large, and varies in
quality. Sometimes Shinn signed his full name, sometimes his
initials only, and the pseudonym 'Tom Yad' is also attributed
to him. Periods 2, 3, 4.*
Publishers include:
Commercial Colortype Co.; E. B. Scofield; T. P. & Co.

Price range   .. .. 50p/**£1.50**/£2.50

SMITH, JESSIE WILLCOX (1863–1935)
*Born in Philadelphia, Jessie trained as a teacher before she
discovered her drawing ability. After studying at the Pennsylvania Academy of Fine Arts, she went on to become one of
America's most successful women artists of Periods 2, 3. Children are her favourite subjects and her work often shows a
strong, and beautiful Art Deco influence. Much of her postcard
work was published by Reinthal & Newman.*

Price range   .. .. £3/**£8**/£15

SOWERBY, MILLICENT (1878–1967)

Millicent was born to a well-to-do Tyneside family who supported and encouraged her artistic ambitions. Her natural love of children led her to express her art in illustrating for and about the younger generation. She became the first illustrator of Alice in Wonderland *after the copyright on Tenniel's pictures expired. Her postcard work started in 1905 for C. W. Faulkner and was an instant success. Her career reached its apogée in the 1920s and 1930s when it had a charming* Art Deco *flavour. The bulk of her colourful postcards, featuring children, fairies, flowers and nursery tales were published by Humphrey Milford. During the Great War she drew a few patriotic designs, and afterwards many of her most popular designs were repeatedly reprinted.*

Price range   ..   ..   £1.50/**£3**/£5

SPATZ

See Gothard, Fred.

SPURGIN, FRED (also 'F.S.') (1882–1968)

Of Latvian origin, born Izydor Spungin, Fred Spurgin came to Britain with his parents at the turn of the century and became a naturalised British subject in 1925. Success came soon, with postcard designs, magazine and book illustrations and advertisements (notably for Rothmans—he married Lilly Rothman). One of the postcard's most versatile artists, he drew humour (from the vulgar seaside type to the political), glamour and many patriotic designs during WW1. His output was enormous, over 2000 designs have been identified, through Periods 2 to 4. In his twilight years he did many 'hack' designs for folded greetings cards. He used many pseudonyms, 'F.S.', collected by many, being the most famous.

Publishers include:
Anon (many printed in Germany); Art & Humour/Inter-Art; Bamforth; Blum & Degen; Ettlinger; Gale & Polden; Garner, H.; J.W.A. & Co.; London View Card Co.; Paternoster; Regent Pub. Co.; Tuck; Vertigen; Wildt & Kray

Price range   ..   ..   50p**£1**/£2

Theatre advertisements
Princess Charming; Take your Girl Friend to See the Girl Friend   ..   ..   £3/**£5**/£10

Best known Series
'Khaki' (12 cards) per set   ..   ..   £15/**£20**/£30
'Leap Year' (12 cards) per set   ..   ..   ..   £15/**£20**/£30

SPY

See Ward, Sir Leslie.

STANNARD, HENRY JOHN SYLVESTER (1870–1951)

Born in London, the son of the sporting painter, Henry Stannard, he studied at South Kensington and painted rustic and garden studies. In 1922 he held a joint exhibition with his daughter Theresa in the Brook Street Galleries. Publishers of his postcard work include Boots and Tuck ('Oilettes')

Price range   ..   ..   50p/**75p**/£1

STARR-WOOD, H. ('S.W.')

A self-taught artist, his first exhibition was in 1903. He was a member of the London Sketch Club, where he played an active role in the clowning escapades. He produced few postcards, mainly for Valentine, during Period 2.

Price range   ..   ..   £1/**£1.50**/£2

STEINLEN, ALEXANDRE THEOPHILE (1859–1923)

A Swiss artist who became one of the brilliant group working in Paris around the turn of the century. He was a contributor to many of the important early French series (see COLLECTIONS) *and to magazines and poster designs. Many of his designs show the* Art Nouveau *influence and were published by M. F. Champenois. Neudin 1980 identifies 50 postcard designs.*

Price range   ..   ..   £25/**£50**/£100+

STUDDY, GEORGE (1878–1948) ■AN 3

Born in Devonshire, educated at Newton and Dulwich and Heatherley Art School, Studdy contributed to The Sketch, Titbits *and other publications and became a member of the Savage, Chelsea Arts and London Sketch clubs. His most famous creation was 'Bonzo', a cheeky, cuddly puppy with a distinct personality. Bonzo emerged in the 1920s and like 'Old Bill' appeared on all manner of toys, pottery items, car mascots, etc.*

Advertising work

Excelsior Reisen. Ger.	.. £3/**£8**/£15
Pascall Butter Almonds	£7.50/**£15**/£20
Sandeman, Stanley. Cotton Belting Co. ..	.. £3/**£8**/£15
Wolseley 10 Motor	£7.50/**£15**/£20

Pub. Deans

Various designs ..   ..   £2/**£3**/£4

Pub. Inter-Art

12 different designs. Early Period 4   ..   ..   ..   £2/**£3**/£4

Pub. Photochrom

Celesque Series. Pre-Bonzo WW1 Patriotics   ..   £2/**£3**/£4

Pub. 'R.P.S.'

Period 4. Nos. 1002–1072, possibly more   ..   ..   £2/**£3**/£4

Pub. Valentine

Period 4. The Bonzo Series	..	..	..	.. £2/**£3**/£4
Period 5. Anti-Hitler designs	..	..	..	.. £3/**£4**/£5

Pub. Warne

Various designs..   ..   ..   £2/**£3**/£4

SZYK, ARTHUR

A Polish Jew who fled the Nazi régime and moved to London in 1937, Szyk gained acclaim for his illustrations for a book called The Haggadah *in 1940. His powerful designs and technical brilliance make Szyk (pronounced 'SHICK') one of the greatest WW2 propaganda artists. One of his designs, 'Death in an SS Uniform', was used by the Japanese as aerial dropped propaganda to frighten the defenders of Bataan. See* MILITARY.

Pub. Esquire Magazine. Period 5. Set of 6 oversize cards of anti-Axis leaders cartoons. Highly coloured. Rare. The set

..   .. £75/**£100**/£125

Others. Per card   ..   ..£5/**£10**/£15

TARRANT, MARGARET (1888–1959) ■A 30

Artist who specialised in children and flower designs during Periods 2 to 5. Publishers include C. W. Faulkner, Humphrey Milford, The Medici Society and Ward Lock. See CHILDREN.

Price range   ..   .. 50p/**75p**/£1.50

■A30 Pub. The Medici Society. Artist Margaret Tarrant. 'The Little Son'. No. 41/3669. PU 1941 £1.50

TAYLER, LAURIE

Australian comic artist with a light and sympathetic touch, whose work was also published in the UK during WW2

Pub. 'Anzac Series'

B & w comics ..	..	..	..	.. £1.50/**£2.50**/£3
Prince's Court Advertising cards		..	..	..£8/**£10**/£12

Pub. Tuck/Others

Various comic designs   ..   ..   .. £1.50/**£2.50**/£3.50

TEMPEST, MARGARET (b. 1892)

After studying at art school in Ipswich, Westminster and Chelsea, she became a founder member of the Chelsea Illustrators' Club. She was most famous for her illustrations of Alison Uttley's Little Grey Rabbit. *The Medici Society published postcards of some of her animal designs.*

Price range .. .. 50p/**75p**/£1

THACKERAY, LANCE (d. 1916) ■A 31

Born in Yorkshire, Thackeray was a founder member of the London Sketch Club in 1898. Thackeray was Tuck's leading comic artist, and the grand master of the 'Write-Away' genre. He worked for Tuck from 1900 to his death in 1916. He produced nearly 1000 postcard designs. A great traveller, Thackeray's Egyptian scenes and types are comparable to Tom Browne's Dutch work. Where Browne portrayed the working classes in a multiplicity of social situations, Thackeray's types were generally middle to upper class. A Thackeray trademark was the small sketch in the border of the design that was a continuation of the main joke. Most of his work was comic in nature, but a couple of advertising cards have been identified.

Pub. David Allen. Theatre Poster Adverts
The Earl and the Girl .. .. £5/**£8**/£10

Pub. Black, A. & C.
People of Egypt. Series 12/13 .. .. £2/**£3**/£4

Pub. Faulkner, C. W.
Series 181 .. .. £3/**£5**/£8

Pub. Hills
'For the Empire' horse pictures .. .. £2/**£3**/£4

Pub. Nestlé's
Advert for Swiss Milk .. .. £5/**£8**/£10

Pub. Tuck
Early chromographed series (over 30). Subjects include Cricket, Golf, Journals Illustrated, Motoring, Popular Plays, Greetings cards (re-issues—over 30). Write-Away designs, incl. Boer War .. .. £1.50/**£4**/£8

Oilette series. Subjects include Bridge, Golf, Egypt, Leap Year, Motoring, Roller Skating, Sea & Riverside, Varsity
.. .. £1.50/**£3**/£5

Proof Limited Editions. Series 955, 983, 984 .. £3/**£5**/£8

THIELE, ARTHUR

Much confusion surrounds this increasingly popular artist. It is now felt by several researchers that recently published biographical information about Thiele refers to another, earlier artist of the same name. Thiele's signed production spans the years 1899–1930s—clearly impossible for an artist thought to

■A31 Pub. Hildesheimer. Artist Lance Thackeray. UB. Early Period 2 £4

have died in 1919. There is also doubt as to his nationality. One school of thought is that he was Belgian, not German. Whatever his history, Thiele is an artist whose work becomes increasingly appreciated as even more and varied examples are discovered; prices for good Thiele cards are rising fast. Confusion arises in cataloguing his cards. As he was collected throughout Europe, Britain and the USA, many series were reproduced by several publishers in a variety of qualities; and few of his many series are named. As research is still continuing and no definitive check list has appeared we list here only the most important series or famous sets. Publishers include: Bürger, Bruno & Ottillie, Leipzig; Faulkner, C. W.; 'F.E.D.'; Gebrüder Dietrich, Leipzig; Klaus, Adolf & Co., Leipzig; Kunzli, Carl, Zurich; Stroefer; 'T.S.N.'; Tuck; Ziehar, Ottmar, Munich.

Animals
Cats—*see* ANIMALS.
Chicken/cockerels/hens	£2/£4/£5
Chimpanzees	£4/£6/£8
Dogs' heads	£4/£5/£7
Dogs—Others	£3/£4/£5
Monkeys (in school etc.)	£3/£5/£7

Dusky Belles/Braves .. .. £4/£6/£8

Motoring
'Horse Power Series'—Rare .. .. .. £6/£8/£10
Others .. .. £3/£5/£7

Period 1
Gruss aus Moorbad (Mudbath) Chromo-litho vignettes 1899
.. .. £6/£8/£10
Others .. .. £4/£6/£8

Period 4
Poorer quality designs, e.g. bathing scenes, cats .. £1/£2/£3

Propaganda (*See* MILITARY)
Anti-British—Boer War .. ..£6/£10/£15

101

Anti-British—WW1 (incl. Zeppelin Kommt) ..	£4/**£6**/£8
Hamster Erlebnisse (post-War Black Market) ..	£3/**£5**/£7
Red Cross	£4/**£5**/£6
Wir Barbaren (WW1)	£3/**£4**/£5

Romantic Scenes
Couples, dancing, etc. .. .. £3/**£4**/£5

Sporting Scenes
Billiards, bowling, football, horseracing, hunting, roller-skating, tennis, and tobogganing .. .. .. £3/**£5**/£7

Topical Themes

Komet Kommt (Halley's Comet, 1910)	£6/**£8**/£10
Zeppelin Kommt (Peacetime)	£4/**£6**/£8

Others .. .. £2/**£5**/£12

THOMAS, HERBERT SAMUEL (BERT) (1883–1966)
Born in Newport, Wales, the son of a sculptor, he started work in London for a small advertising agency. He also contributed to comics and magazines like London Opinion *and* Punch. *During WW1 he served as a private in the Artists' Rifles and during the War did the picture that was to bring him fame—' 'Arf A Mo, Kaiser!', for the* Weekly Despatch *Tobacco Fund for Troops (Pub. Gale & Polden)—which raised £250,000. After the War he continued to contribute to magazines and newspapers (like the* Evening News*) and re-emerged mainly for Tuck in WW2 with ITMA jokes and other timely humour. Mainly comic, his work also includes some striking caricatures and theatre adverts between the Wars (Pub. Odhams).* See Comic.

Price range .. .. 75p/**£2.50**/£8

TURNER, J. A.
One of Australia's most popular and sought-after artists, who specialised in portraying bush scenes, similar in style to J. Hutchings, but of greater clarity. He was little regarded in the general art world until one of his oil paintings recently fetched a record price in Australian auction. Period 2.

Pub. Robert Jolley
Various designs .. .. £3.50/**£5**/£7
'Panel' cards with gilt edges and greetings messages .. ..
.. .. £3.50/**£5**/£9

Pub. 'P.S. & Co.'
Swallow and Ariell's adverts .. .. .. £2.50/**£3.50**/£6

TWELVETREES, CHARLES H.
Prolific American artist of babies and cute kids, crosspatches and comic animals, fatties and teddy bears. His work spanned from about 1907 until well into the 1930s. Many cards are signed with the initials 'C.T.' only, some are unsigned but

instantly recognisable (although many attempts were made to fake his popular style). The snappy captions are an integral part of the design.

Twelvetrees also drew some glamour, seasonal greetings and WW1 patriotics. In the USA the majority of his work was published by Edward Gross, the House of Art and Reinthal and Newman; in the UK by 'Alpha'.

U.S. Publishers

Edward Gross, N.Y.	75p/**£1**/£1.50
House of Art, N.Y.	50p/**75p**/£1
Illustrated Postal Card & Nov. Co.	50p/**75p**/£1
Reinthal & Newman	50p/**75p**/£1

Cards Distributed in UK
Pub. Alpha. Entitled 'Comic', 'Smile Messengers' or 'Twelvetrees'. Printed Ed. Gross, NY.

A list of these cards was given in the third edition of this catalogue, pp. 95–96.

Price range .. .. 75p/**£1.25**/£2.50

Pub. Alpha. Smile Messengers with no 'Edward Gross' markings.

Price range .. .. 50p/**£1**/£1.50

Pub. Ullman Co.
National Cupids, 1906. incl. England, France, Germany, Holland, Italy, Scotland, United States .. £2.50/**£4**/£5

UPTON, FLORENCE (1873–1922)
Creator of the golliwog in 1893, Florence Upton illustrated a children's book using her original character called The Adventures of Two Dutch Dolls; *it was an instant success. In 1903 Tuck bought the rights to the book and reproduced the illustrations as postcards. Sadly Florence Upton was too naïve about business to profit much from the international success of her creation.*

Pub. Tuck (from 1903). About 15 sets of 6, many overprinted with Christmas Greetings .. .. £5/**£6**/£7

VILLON, JACQUES (Gaston Duchamp) (1875–1963)
French artist who contributed to many satirical publications, like Le Rire, L'Assiette au Beurre, *etc. His postcard output was small and therefore much sought after. First and foremost a poster artist he contributed 7 cards to the Gala Henri Monnier series and his design for the* Collection des Cent (see COLLECTIONS) *is the most highly rated of all.*

Price range .. .. £50/**£100**/£250

WAIN, LOUIS (1860–1939)

Louis Wain is known as 'The Cat Man' par excellence. *His cats which remain typically feline while displaying uncannily human characteristics, first brought fame to their creator as illustrations for children's books. He also drew dogs, birds and other animals with equal competence. His postcard output, for a variety of publishers, was large—500–600 designs have been identified; his most successful association was with Tuck, especially in the 'Amewsing Write-Away' series. Most of his work bears at least a trace of almost zany humour and his cards are popular with collectors in several fields—animals, humour, or themes like diabolo, ping-pong, etc.* See ANIMALS: Cats.

Price range   ..   .. £4/**£8**/£20

WALL, BERNHARDT (1872–1956)■CH 1

Born in Buffalo, N.Y., Wall studied at the Art Students League but soon outgrew his teachers and opened his own art school. He enlisted in the Spanish-American war and on his return took a job with the Ullman Publishing Co. He was reputed to have started the company's postcard production and he went on to publish most of his cards with them. Over 15 identified publishing companies printed his cards, as well as many unnamed companies. Wall went on to become a proficient etcher, illustrating many historical biographies. During WW1 he designed many patriotic cards.

Pub. Ullman
     Busy Bears (*No. 79*), In Holland (*87*), Little Coons (*59*).
       Overall Boys, Sunbonnets (perhaps his most famous
       design)   ..   .. 75p/**£1.50**/£4
     Greetings designs, incl. April Fool (*156*). Hallowe'en (*143*),
       Independence Day (*124*)   ..   ..   .. 75p/**£1.50**/£3
     North Pole Series (*2564–2567*) celebrating Peary's feats
       (*1909*) ..   .. £1.50/**£3**/£5
Pub. Valentine
     Hudson-Fulton Celebration set of 6. 300th Anniv. of
       discovery of Hudson River (1909) 3 versions, 1 embossed
       per card   ..   .. £1.50/**£3**/£4
Other Pubs.
     Various designs   ..   .. 75p/**£1.50**/£3

WALTZ, J. J. (Hansi) (1897–1910)

Waltz was an Alsace-Lorrainer, who had fled to France in the summer of 1914 to escape punishment at the hands of the German authorities for his 'seditious' propaganda. He then organised the French propaganda machine against the Germans. Waltz, or 'Hansi', as he preferred to be known, used the popular folk art of the postcard as part of his campaign. Periods 2/3.

Price range   ..   .. £3/**£7.50**/£15

WARD, SIR LESLIE (Spy) (1851–1922)
Amongst the most reproduced of all caricatures are those drawn by 'Spy', the pseudonym of Sir Leslie Ward, for the satirical magazine Vanity Fair. *It was launched in 1868 as a rival to* Punch, *but did not survive long. 48 of the cartoons were reproduced as postcards by Stewart and Woolf in 4 sets of 12 in 1902.*

Price range   ..   ..   **£2/£3/£4**

WENNERBURG, BRYNOLF
Versatile German artist, whose work ranged from early UB *chromo-litho bathing beauties* (see SOCIAL HISTORY) *through comic tennis players to sentimental WW1 scenes of lovers/ nurses* (see MILITARY) *He also contributed to the famous* Lustigen Blätter *series.*

Price range   ..   ..   £1.50/**£8**/£15

WHEELER, DOROTHY (1891–1966)
From an artistic family and trained at Blackheath Art School, Dorothy was a successful illustrator of magazines and books (incl. Enid Blyton stories).

Pub. Black, A. & C. (*c.* 1926). English Nursery Rhymes   ..
..   ..   £1/**£1.50**/£3
Pub. Milford, Humphrey. Day at the Fair series   £1/**£1.50**/£3
Pub. Salmon, J. Several series   ..   ..   ..   75p/**£1**/£1.50

WHITE, FLORA
Best known for her patriotic children designs during WW1 (see MILITARY) *mostly published by Photochrom.*

Price range   ..   ..   75p/**£1.50**/£3

WIEDERSEIM, GRACE (1877–1936)
American artist best known for her chubby, pop-eyed children. She also signed cards by her married name, Grace Drayton. Most of her designs were published by Reinthal & Newman and Tuck in Period 2. She was also famous for being the creator of the 'Campbell's Kids'.

Comic children, general   ..   ..   £2/**£4**/£8
Campbell's soup ads. ..   ..   £3/**£5**/£10

WIELANDT, MANUEL (1863–1922) ■A 32
German artist who studied at Karlsruhe and Stuttgart. His love of travel (to Capri, France, Italy, Malta, etc.), resulted in some fine water-colour views. Over 100 designs have now been identified of the French and Italian Rivieras, Lakes, Gulf of Venice, Germany and Switzerland, many UB. *Publishers include Moser, Nister, Schmidt-Staub and Velten.*

Price range   ..   ..   **£2/£3/£4**

■A32 Pub. J. Velten, Karlsruhe. Artist Manuel Wielandt. 'Cannes'. Early Period 2 £4

WILLEBEEK le MAIR, HENRIETTE (1889–1966) ■A 33
Dutch-born artist of a wealthy family. She enjoyed a privileged upbringing but found her own commercial success at an early age. Augener Ltd., the music publishers, soon recognised her talents and published her drawings to illustrate a series of children's books, reproducing some of them as postcards. A checklist of her cards, compiled by George Eimermann of Den Haag, Holland appears in the section supplement.

Price range   . .   . .   £2/**£4**/£6

■A33 Pub. Augener Ltd. Artist Henriette Willebeek le Mair. 'The Merry Peasant'. Period 4 £6

WILLIAMS, MADGE
Daughter of a Suffolk rector, she illustrated several children's books. Her WW2 postcards for J. Salmon epitomised British 'pluck' through the medium of appealing children.

Price range   . .   . .   50p/**75p**/£1

WILLRICH, WOLF
*In Hitler's campaign against 'degenerate art', Willrich was one
of the few artists approved by the National Socialist Regime.
His work depicted idealistic, sturdy, Aryan, thoroughly
approved, Germanic characters—soldiers, sailors, airmen,
mothers, fathers, Hitler Youth types, etc. His fine line-drawing
portraits are reminiscent of the work of Albrecht Durer as is
his spindly, distinctive signature, a 'W' interspersed with the
date of the drawing.*

Deutscher Blutadel in Aller Welt (German Aristocracy of
Blood Throughout the World incl. 'Carinthian Farmer's Wife;
Lower Saxony Maiden; Old Bavarian Countryman;
Westphalian Country Girl. Periods 4, 5.
b & w	£1.50/**£2**/£2.50
col.	£2/**£2.50**/£3

Fallschirmjager (Parachutists). Fine col. series, incl. Sgt.
Arpke, Col. Brauer, Capt. Delicia, Maj. Koch. Period 5 ..
.... £6/**£8**/£15

Fundraising cards for National Socialist causes, e.g.
V.D.A.—Volksbund fur das Deutschtum in Ausland (League
of Expatriate Germans). Subjects similar to 'Deutscher Blutadel'. Periods 4, 5.
b & w	£1.50/**£2**/£2.50
col.	£2/**£2.50**/£3

Heer und Panzer (Army and Tanks) Period 5. Fine series of
portraits, incl. Oberst Brauer, Obltn. Brenner, Dietl, Fulda,
Goricke, Guderian, von Lutzow, Rommel, von Rundstedt
.... £5/**£8**/£15

Luftwaffe (Airforce) Period 5. Airborne personalities, incl.
Graf Kageneck, Hanna Reitsch .. .. £6/**£9**/£14

Marine (Navy) Period 5. Similar series of naval portraits incl.
Donitz, Endrass, Kretschmer, Prien, Raeder, Schepke,
Schuhart .. .. £6/**£9**/£11

WIMBUSH, HENRY B.
*An accomplished landscape artist, his most productive period
was from 1881 to 1908. He painted views of the British Isles
and the Channel Isles, illustrating books as well as designing
postcards. Most of his postcard work was reproduced by Tuck
in the 'Oilette' range and by A. & C. Black. Period 2.*

Price range .. .. 50p/**£1**/£1.50

WOOD, CLARENCE LAWSON (1878–1957)
*Coming from a distinguished artistic family, he studied at the
Slade School of Fine Art and Calderon's School of Animal
Painting. He was a member of the London Sketch Club and a
friend of Tom Browne. His postcard production spanned from
Period 2 to Period 4. The early work is characterised by 'stock'
characters—the cheeky boy, the rotund policeman, etc. Also
famous were his 'Prehistoric' series. After the war his greatest
success came with the creation of 'Gran'pop', an engaging
chimpanzee. Parrots were another favourite theme.*

Pub. Allen, David. Theatre Poster Advert (1903). Beauty and
  the Barge   ..   ..   **£3/£6/£8**
Pub. Brown & Bigelow (B & B), USA. Period 4, 'Gran'pop'
  Calendar cards for the J. E. Fricke Co.   ..   ..   **£2/£3/£4**
Pub. Carlton Pub. Co. Period 2 Comics   ..   75p/**£1/£1.50**
Pub. Davidson Bros. Period 2. 'Prehistoric' series   ..   ..
..   ..   75p/**£1/£1.50**
Pub. Dobson, Molle & Co. Period 3. Patriotics   **£1/£1.50/£2**
Pub. Henderson. Weather Forecasts   ..   ..   75p/**£1/£1.50**
Pub. Inter-Art. 'Artistique' series/'Comique' series (children)
..   ..   50p/**75p**/£1
Pub. Lawrence & Jellicoe. Period 2. London Opinion series
..   ..   **£1/£1.50/£2**
Pub. Pictorial Stationery Co. 'Prehistoric' series 75p/**£1/£1.50**
Pub. Salmon, J. Period 3 designs   ..   ..   75p/**£1/£1.50**
Pub. Stiebel, Alfred. Modern Humour series   75p/**£1/£1.50**
Pub. Valentine. Periods 2, 3. Several series; Period 4.
  Gran'pop/Parrots   ..   ..   75p/**£1/£1.50**

WOOD, STANLEY L. (1866–1928)
Best known for his WW1, dashing military pictures, he exhibited at the Royal Academy and his paintings fetched £100 in his heyday.

Price range   ..   ..   50p/**£1/£1.50**

YOUNG, WALTER HAYWARD (Jotter) (1868–1920)
Much research has been done on the life and works of this popular, prolific postcard artist by, among others, Brian Lund, Marjorie Nielson-Jones (Young's daughter) and Hewson Osborne (see Picture Postcard Annual 1982). Over 800 postcard designs have so far been identified, probably starting with the Tuck Oilette series that made him so well known.

Price range:
Children/comic/glamour (often signed 'Hayward Young')
..   ..   50p/**£1.25/£2**
Oilette-type scenes (usually signed 'Jotter')   25p/**75p/£1.50**
Hotel/Railway ads.   ..   ..   75p/**£1.50/£3**

ZEC, PHILIP
Powerful cartoonist, whose WW2 Daily Mirror cartoons were often controversial and anti-Establishment. However, many of them were reproduced as postcards for propaganda purposes and distributed through the Lisbon British Embassy in neutral Portugal.

Period 5 Propaganda ..   ..   75p/**£1/£1.25**

ZILLE, H.
The Berlin artist par excellence, whose output includes finely observed Berlin types—prostitutes, traders, urchins, etc. He was described by the rightwing newspaper Fridericus *as 'The Berlin portrayer of toilets and pregnancy'. He contributed to the famous German series,* Lustigen Blätter.

Price range   ..   ..   **£3/£5/£8**

SECTION SUPPLEMENT – ARTISTS

1. DINAH CARDS

Pub. Tuck Oilettes
Dates postally used in parentheses

9A.	We must hand it to the RAF
9B.	For evermore
9C.	?
9D.	Home Grown
9E.	Can it be true?
9F.	?
9G.	Here is the news (1943)
9H.	?
9J.	Good Morning! Nice Day! (1943)
9K.	?
9L.	On Leave (1943)
9M.	?
10F.	No basic? We should worry (1944)
11A.	Inside information
12.	Good Egg
13.	Who care a darn
67.	A little bit of overtime

Longing to see you (1943)
A piece of cake
I'll make short work of this
Free Press (1945)
Refresher Course
News from the front (1945)
For the love of Mike (1944)
TNT – Today Not Tomorrow
The Home Front (1944)
I'll walk beside you (1944)
Is my journey really necessary (1944)
Good night, Forces
Early Birds! (1945)
A pleasant reflection
Deep in the heart of Texas
I'll (k)not forget you (1945)
Making a stir (1945)
Why worry? (1945)
Swell! (1945)
Mary and her little Lamb (1945)
Monday night at Eight (1945)
Washing up (1945)
A little bit behind
Trying it on (1945)
I've come to the conclusion (1945)
Ladies in waiting
Food flash
Long distance call
Boots! Boots! Boots!
There's a good time coming (1944)
The Girl Friend (1944)
Booked!

Engaged!
Chin chin!
Oh what a beautiful morning!
Happy to greet you
In clover
Between you and me
Sew what!
Watch your step
Two to one on (1947)
For Auld Lang Syne (1949)
Well, I'm blowed!
Between You and me
Cashing in
Cheerio!
Early Birds
Fishing!
Short Wave!
In the pink
Long Pants
Love and Kisses
Mooning by spoonlight
Two to one on
Why worry?

Mason's Alpha Series 'Dinah' Series

12/1   'Housewive's Choice'
12/3   'Skiffle Your Blues Away'
12/7   'Jam Session'
12/9   'Men! I Hate 'Em'
12/12 'When a Body Meets a Body'

2. CHECKLIST OF THE POSTCARDS OF H. WILLE-BEEK LE MAIR

Small Rhymes For Small People
See, saw, Margery Daw
Dance-a-baby, diddy
Baby mine
Dance to your Daddy
The babes in the wood
Lazy sheep
Three mice went to a hole to spin
Sleep baby sleep
Goosey gander
Where are you going to my pretty maid?
Little Jumping Joan
Lavender blue

Schumann's Children's Pieces
First loss
Catch me if you can
Soldiers' march
Roundelay
The poor orphan
Dreaming
Melody
The merry peasant
Vintage
Perfect Happiness

Sicilienne
Romance

More Old Nursery Rhymes
A frog he would a wooing go
O, dear, what can the matter be?
Girls and boys come out to play
The crooked man
Bedtime
A happy family
Curly locks
What are little boys made of?
Three little kittens
Hush-a-by baby
There was a little man
Ride a cock horse

Little Songs of Long Ago
Young lambs to sell
There came to my window
Little Polly Flinders
Little Tom Tucker
Old King Cole
I had a little nut tree
The north wind doth blow
Dame, get up and bake your pie
London bridge has broken down
I saw three ships a sailing
Simple Simon
Over the hills, and far away.

The Children's Corner
Secrets
The garden city
A cosy corner
Last year's frock
Poor baby
Hair cutting
Fishing boats
Troublesome children
The invalid's birthday
Greedy
Buying hats
Persevering Dicky
Out in the snow
Baby's fright
The dove's dinner time
Queen of the birds
Dreadfully busy

Old Rhymes with new Pictures
Jack and Jill
Little boy blue
Yankee Doodle
Humpty Dumpty
Polly put the kettle on
Lucy Locket
Three blind mice
Mary, Mary quite contrary
Twinkle, twinkle little star
Little Jack Horner
Little Mother
Little Miss Muffet
Sing a song of sixpence

Little People
Dressing baby
The little culprit
In the garden
Paying calls
A critical moment
In the belfry
Hide and seek
Evening prayer
Time to get up
Johnny's breakfast
Good evening Mr. Hare
The bride

Old Dutch Nursery Rhymes
The stork has brought a little
 brother
Turn round, turn round
Follow my leader
Weekday and Sunday
The marionettes
Polly Perkins
Our baby prince
Jacky stand still
The tiny man
A basket full of nuts

English and Dutch Rhymes
In the church
Four and twenty tailors
The first walk
In the park
Poor doggie
The wise horses
The christening
The wooden shoes
A fairy tale
In Holland stands a house

Our Old Nursery Rhymes
I love little pussy
George Porgy
Here we go round the mulberry
 bush
Oranges and lemons
Dickory, dickory dock
Little Bo-peep
Baa, baa, black sheep
Pat-a-cake
O, where is my little dog gone?
Pussy cat, pussy cat
Mary had a little lamb

AVIATION

Postcards were carried aloft during the siege of Paris in 1870. They and their modern equivalents, like those transported by Concorde, attract a specialist range of collectors. Frequently postal history attributes such as time and place of posting, cancellation, etc. are the decisive factors in assessing the value of a card. Some examples are given under the heading 'Flown' below. Real photographic cards tend to be the most highly valued. Interest also remains strong in cards depicting balloons or Zeppelins and they usually deserve a high valuation. Artistic impressions should not be ignored, however, and the early Tuck series are prized.

Cards of WW1 and WW2 are listed under MILITARY.

Accidents

Aircraft. Blackpool, 7 September 1935	..	..£8/**£12**/£15
Aircraft. Period 2	.. ..	..£6/**£12**/£20
Aircraft. Others..	.. ..	£3/**£5**/£7.50
Airships	.. ..	..£6/**£10**/£15

Aircraft (Photographic Types)

Period 2	.. ..	£3/**£5**/£8
LL 'Nos Aeroplanes' series ..	.. .. ..	£2/**£4**/£6
Period 4	.. ..	£3/**£5**/£7.50
Periods 6, 7	.. ..	25p/**50p**/£2

Airfields (Photographic Types)

Period 2. General view	.. .. ..	£2/**£4**/£6
Period 2. With aircraft	.. .. ..	£3/**£5**/£8

Airships (Photographic Types)

British. Period 2	.. ..	£4/**£7**/£10
British. Period 4	.. ..	£6/**£8**/£10
British. Other periods	.. .. ..	£4/**£5**/£6
Foreign. Period 2	.. ..	£4/**£7**/£8
Foreign. Other periods	.. .. ..	£3/**£5**/£6

Artist Drawn

Bannister, Derek
Pub. J. Salmon. Faithful drawings of contemporary aircraft.

Periods 2, 4	.. ..	£1/**£2**/£3
Pub. Tuck. Oilette. 'Famous Aeroplanes' series	..	£2/**£3**/£4
'In the Air' series	.. ..	£2/**£3**/£4

Handville, R.
US National Air & Space Museum Series. Pub. Dexter. Subjects Amelia Earhart, Charles Lindbergh, Wright Brothers, etc. 25p/**50p**/75p

Others .. .. 75p/**£5**/£7

Balloons (Photographic Types)

Period 1	.. ..	..£5/**£10**/£15
Period 2	.. ..	£4/**£7.50**/£10
Other periods	.. ..	£3/**£4**/£5

British Commemorative/First Flights/Meetings (in chronological order)

Detailed listings of these cards were given in the third edition of this catalogue, pp. 105–106.

Manchester & Salford, August 1903.
Lifeboat Saturday. Unflown (See also *Flown*)   £30/**£50**/£75

Doncaster Meeting, October 1909
Blackpool Meeting, October 1909
Wolverhampton Meeting, June–July 1910
Bournemouth Meeting, July 1910
Blackpool Meeting, July–August 1910
Lanark Meeting, August 1910
Doncaster Meeting, September 1910
Burton-on-Trent Meeting, September–October 1910

Price range   ..   ..£5/**£10**/£20

First UK Aerial Post (1911). London to Windsor £12/**£15**/£20
First UK Aerial Post (1911). Windsor to London £20/**£30**/£60
Daily Mail circuit. Pictures of competitors with their machines plus facsimile signatures of Salmet, etc. 1912
    .. ..   £4/**£5**/£6
Daily Mail. Multi-portrait cards. Artist Henry Laussucq
    ..   ..   £10/**£12**/£18

British montage cards 1910 ■AV 1
Made from agency photographs and sold at aviation meetings, these usually features a pilot, an aircraft and a background view of the meeting location.

Price range   ..   ..   £1.50/**£3**/£6

A listing of Blackpool montage cards was given in the fourth edition, pp. 114–116.

■AV 1 Pub. E. R. G. Blackpool. Photomontage No. 27. A. V. Roe in Flight. Period 2 £3

Commomorative Issues ■AV 2, 3
Cards produced to commemorate first, or historic, flights, British and Foreign (other than Concorde – see below)

Period 2	..	..	..	..	..	..	..	.. £3/**£6**/£10
Periods 3–6		..	..	..	..	..	..	.. £2/**£4**/£6
Period 7	..	..	..	..	..	..	..	25p/**50p**/£1

■AV 2 Pub. Rotary Photo Co. M. Bleriot's Landing at Dover. Period 2 £6

■AV 3 Official U.S. Postal Stationery Card. 28c. stamp 1981. 50th Anniv. of first Trans-Pacific flight by Pangborn and Hendon 50p

Concorde
Listings of commemorative postcards for various Concorde test and inaugural flights (flown and unflown) were listed in the third and fourth editions of this catalogue (pp. 107 and 116–117 respectively). Valuations vary according to the postmarks used. The higher valuation is for flown items on special flights.

Price range   ..   ..   **£1/£5/£15**

Fantasy/Photo-Montage
Artist drawn visions of future air transport   75p/**£1**/£1.50
People photographed in 'Flying Machines' ..   £1/**£2**/£2.50
Photographic scenes with superimposed aircraft   £1/**£2**/£2.50

Flown ■AV 4
Beckenham, 1902. Pub. Tuck. Edward VII Coronation. Over-printed, 'Despatched from the Clouds', 9 August 1902 (see above)   ..   ..   **P/A**

Daily Graphic Expedition, 1907
    Flown   ..   ..   £75/**£125**/£300
    Not Flown   ..   ..   £25/**£35**/£40
Friedrichshafen, 1931. Official card. Printed 8pfg stamp. Centenary of the airfield. Flown in the L.S. Graf Zeppelin, 27 August 1931   ..   ..   £35/**£40**/£50
Johannesburg, 1936. Empire Exhibition Airmail 'Last Day Card'. 18 Jan. 1936. On front RP Rand Airport   £5/**£10**/£15
Luxembourg, 1927. International Stamp Exhibition Commemorative. U/S. Flown by balloon, 8 September 1927
  ..   ..   £6/**£8**/£10
Manchester & Salford, 1903. Life-Boat Saturday. Card carried by Balloon Post during fund raising for the Lifeboat Service. Valuation very subject to condition, 29 August 1903   ..
  ..   ..   £500/**£700**/£900

Zeppelin Centenary, 1938. LZ129 Hindenburg. Flight from Frankfurt to Denmark, 8 July 1938   ..   ..   **£8/£9/£12**

■AV 4 Pub. 'G.P.S.' S.A., Johannesburg Empire Exhibition. Flown last day commemorative card with exhibition cancellation 18 Jan. 1936 £15

Personalities ■AV 2, 3, 5
R.P. cards tend to be most highly valued, particularly if both aviator and aeroplane are featured in close-up. Most cards are Period 2.

Alcock & Brown, Period 4 ..   ..   £2/**£4**/£6
Aubrun   ..   ..   £3/**£4**/£5

Audemars ..	.. ..	..	£5/**£7**/£8
Barnes	.. ..	..	£3/**£5**/£6
Bielovucie ..	.. ..	..	£3/**£4**/£5
Blackburn, Harold	.. ..		£3.50/**£4**/£5
Blériot, Louis			
Pub. 'LL'. Landing at Dover	.. ..	..	£2/**£4**/£6
Others	.. ..	..	£2/**£6**/£8
Breguet	.. ..		£2.50/**£3**/£4
Cody, Col. ..	.. ..	..	£2/**£5**/£6
Drexel	.. ..	..	£3/**£5**/£6
Dubonnet ..	.. ..	..	£4/**£7**/£8
Dumont, Santos ..	.. ..	..	£4/**£6**/£9
Earhart, Amelia (Period 4)	.. .. ..	..	£3/**£4**/£5
Farman	.. ..	..	£3/**£7**/£9
Ferber	.. ..	..	£2/**£4**/£5
Gilmour	.. ..	..	£4/**£5**/£6
Godden	.. ..	..	£3/**£4**/£6
Grace	.. ..	..	£2/**£3**/£5
Grahame-White ..	.. ..	..	£2/**£3**/£5
Hamel, Gustav ..	.. ..	..	£2/**£4**/£5
Hawker, H. G. ..	.. ..	..	£2/**£3**/£5
Hucks, B. C.	.. ..	..	£1/**£2.50**/£5
Johnson, Amy	.. ..	..	£3/**£5**/£7
Latham	.. ..	..	£2/**£6**/£7
Lindbergh, Charles A.	.. .. ..	..	£3/**£5**/£6
McArdle	.. ..	..	£3/**£5**/£6
Pangborn, Clyde & Herndon, Hugh	..	..	50p/**£1**/£4
Pegoud	.. ..	..	£3/**£4**/£5
Prosser	.. ..	..	£1/**£2**/£3
Reitsch, Hanna (Period 4) ..	.. ..	..	£5/**£10**/£20
Roe, A. V.	.. ..	..	£5/**£7**/£9
Rolls ..	.. ..	..	£2/**£3**/£5
Rougier	.. ..	..	£1/**£2**/£4
Salmet, H. ..	.. ..	..	£2/**£6**/£7
Sopwith	.. ..	..	£2/**£4**/£5
Valentine ..	.. ..	..	£1/**£2**/£4
Wright Bros.	.. ..	..	£1.50/**£3**/£5
Zeppelin, Count von	.. ..	..	£2/**£2.50**/£5

■AV 5 Pub. Tuck. Miss Amy Johnson C.B.E. 'Real Photograph' Postcard No. 3867. Period 4 £5

CHILDREN/TOYS

Dutch dolls, golliwogs and, increasingly, teddy bears, are still much collected. There is an enthusiastic following for many of the artists of this genre.

ARTISTS

American Artists (Periods 2, 3) ■CH 1

Mainly 'Cute Kids', often chubby and wide-eyed (even 'pop'-eyed), 'Kewpie' dolls (a corruption of 'Cupid') and 'Sunbonnet' children. The most brilliant exception is the superb work of Jessie Willcox Smith. Publishers include Gabriel, Sam; Gross, Edward (New York); House of Art (New York); Reinthal & Newman; Rose, Chas.; Rotograph; Tuck; Ullman.

Anderson, V.C.†	50p/**£1**/£1.50
Brundage, Frances†	.. **£2**/**£4**/£8
Clapsaddle, Ellen†	.. £1/**£3**/£10
Corbett, Bertha (Sunbonnets)	£1/**£2.50**/£4
Drayton, Grace (*see* Wiederseim)	
Dixon, Dorothy (Sunbonnets)	.. £1/**£2**/£3
Dwiggins, C. W.† ('Dwig')	.. **£2**/**£4**/£6
Gassaway, Kate	75p/**£1.50**/£3
Griggs, H. B. (signed also 'H.B.G.')	.. 50p/**£1**/£2
O'Neill, Rose† (Kewpies)	..£3/**£10**/£35
Outcault, Richard Felton†	£1.50/**£3**/£6
Smith, Jessie Willcox† (incl. *Art Deco*) ..	.. £3/**£8**/£15
Twelvetrees, Charles†	50p/**£1.50**/£5
Wall, Bernhardt† (incl. Sunbonnets)	.. **£2**/**£4**/£6
Weiderseim, Grace†	.. **£2**/**£4**/£10

■CH1 Pub. Ullman Artist Bernhardt Wall. 'Week Day' Series No. 23 'Tuesday Sunbonnet'. 1905 £4

European Artists (Periods 2, 3) ■A 6

Many of these well-known artists did general designs as well. Publishers include Davidson Bros.; Faulkner, C. W.; Hildesheimer; Inter-Art; Millar & Lang; Tuck.

Barber, C. W.	25p/**50p**/75p
Barribal, W.†	£2/**£4**/£6
Bertiglia, A.† (It.)	£2/**£3**/£6
Brundage, Frances†	£2/**£4**/£8
Butcher, Arthur	50p/**75p**/£1
Caldecott, R.†	50p/**75p**/£1
Dexter, Marjorie†	25p/**50p**/75p
Ebner, Pauli	£1/**£2**/£4
Feiertag, K.	£1/**£1.50**/£2.50
Gilson, T.†	50p/**75p**/£1.50
Goodman, Maude	75p/**£2**/£6
Greenaway, Kate	£20/**£40**/£50
Hardy, Florence†	£1/**£2**/£4
Hassall, John† (Nursery Rhymes)	£1/**£2**/£5
King, Jessie, M.† (incl. *Art Deco*)	£10/**£20**/£50
Kinsella, E.P.† (cricket/tennis)	£1/**£3**/£5
Mallet, Beatrice	50p/**75p**/£1
Nash, A. A.†	£1/**£1.50**/£2
Parkinson, Ethel	£2/**£3**/£4
Poulbot, F.†	75p/**£2**/£4
Richardson, Agnes†	£1/**£2**/£3
Upton, Florence†	£5/**£6**/£7
Wanke, Alice	£3/**£5**/£15
White, Flora†	75p/**£1.50**/£3

Unsigned European Artists (Early Period 2)

Many delightful and beautifully produced early chromo-litho studies (some embossed or silvered) were produced by publishers like Meissner & Buch; M. Munk (Vienna); Nister; Stewart & Woolf; Tuck and many foreign unnamed publishers.

Price range	£1/**£2**/£4

Wish I could buy you somefink, but here's good wishes for a NO COUPON **HAPPY BIRTHDAY**

■CH2 Pub. Regent Pub. Co. Artist Kit Forres. No. 6187. Period 5 £1.50

European Artists (Periods 4, 5) ■CH 2, A 4, 18
Publishers include Bamforth; Lychgate Ltd. (Worthing); Millar & Lang; Photochrom; Regent Pub. Co.; Salmon; Tuck; Valentine.

Attwell, Mabel Lucie† (also Periods 2 to 3)	£1/**£1.50**/£3
Birch, Norah Annie	25p/**50p**/75p
Brisley, Nora	50p/**75p**/£1
Broo, Piet (Dutch)	£1/**£2**/£4
Comicus (Harry Parlett)†	25p/**50p**/75p
Cooper, Phyllis	50p/**75p**/£1
Dean, Dora	50p/**75p**/£1
'Dinah'†	50p/**75p**/£2
Forres, Kit	50p/**75p**/£1.50
'Henry' (Belg)	75p/**£1**/£1.50
Mallet, Beatrice	50p/**75p**/£1
Patterson, Vera	50p/**75p**/£1
Richardson, Agnes†	75p/**£1**/£1.50
Rose, Freda Mabel	25p/**50p**/75p
Taylor, Arnold	50p/**75p**/£1
Tempest, D.	50p/**75p**/£1
White, Brian ('Nipper')	50p/**75p**/£1
Williams, Madge	50p/**75p**/£1
Young, Gwen Hayward	50p/**75p**/£1
Unsigned Belgian, British, Dutch, French and Italian artists	50p/**£1**/£3

'Nursery' Artists (Period 4) ■CH 3, ART 1, A 33
The popular British children's cards of the 1920s and 1930s depict more ephemeral creations than the robust American children and they often feature elves, fairies, nursery rhymes and whimsical animals. Many of the artists were first and foremost children's book illustrators, and often their postcards were distributed by their publishers to promote books. The best artists of this genre show a distinct Art Deco influence. Publishers include Augener Ltd.; Black, A. & C.; Faulkner, C. W.; Liberty & Co.; Medici Society; Milford, Humphrey; Millar & Lang; Tuck; Valentine; Vivian Mansell.

Allen, Daphne†	£2.50/**£4**/£5
Barham, Sybil	75p/**£2**/£4
Barker, Cecily M.	£1/**£2**/£2.50
Bowden, Doris	75p/**£1**/£1.50
Brett, Molly	75p/**£1**/£1.50
Briggs, Barbara	£1/**£2**/£4
Caldecott, Randolph†	50p/**75p**/£1
Cloke, René†	£1/**£1.50**/£2
Cooper, Phyllis	75p/**£1.50**/£2
Cowham, Hilda†	£1/**£1.50**/£2
Cramer, Rie	£3/**£5**/£10
Folkard, Charles†	£2/**£3**/£4
Govey, Lilian A.	£1/**£2**/£3
Jacobs, Helen†	£2/**£3**/£4
James, Ivy Millicent†	£1/**£2**/£3
King, Jessie M.†	£20/**£40**/£60
Marsh-Lambert, H. G. C.	£1/**£2**/£3
Margetson, Hester	75p/**£1.50**/£2
Mercer, Joyce†	£1.50/**£3**/£5

Miller, Hilda T.						£1.50/**£3**/£5
Nixon Kathleen†						£1/**£2**/£3
Outhwaite, Ida Rentoul†						£1.50/**£3**/£8
Pearse, Susan Beatrice						£1/**£2**/£3
Preston, Chloë						75p/**£1.50**/£2
Richardson, Agnes†						£1/**£2**/£3
Shand, C. E.†						£2/**£4**/£6
Sowerby, Millicent†						£2/**£4**/£5
Tarrant, Margaret†						50p/**£1**/£1.50
Tempest, Margaret T.†						50p/**£1**/£1.50
Wheeler, Dorothy†						£1/**£1.50**/£2
Willebeek le Mair, Henriette†						£2/**£4**/£6

■CH3 Pub. A. M. Davis & Co. Artist H.G.C, Marsh Lambert. 'Flower Fairies'. Series No. 519 'Michaelmas Daisy'. Period 4 £3

COONS ■CH 4
A popular theme during Period 2. Artists include:

Burbrook (Coon series)
Gilson, T.† (Pub. Hey, E. J.)
Hyde, Graham (Pub. Tuck. 1906)
Sandford, H. Dix (Pub. Tuck 'Happy Little Coons', etc.)
Twelvetrees, C.† (Pub. Reinthal & Newman)
Wood, Lawson† (Pub. Valentine)
Unsigned artists
Pub. Coe—Collotype, Bradford
Pub. Davis, A. M. ('Little Darkies')
Pub. Ettlinger (various 'Coon' designs)
Pub. Inter-Art (Quaint Kids, etc.)
Pub. Tuck ('Coon Town Kids', etc.)
Pub. Watkins & McCombie (Coon series)

Price range .. .. £1/**£2**/£4

■CH4 Pub. Tuck Artist 'H.D.S.' (H. Dix Sandford) Oilette No. 9049. 'Happy Little Coons'. PU 1910 £2

DOLLS/GOLLIWOGS/OTHER TOYS

Artist drawn Periods 2 to 4

Pauli Ebner—toys with children	..	..	..	£2/**£3**/£4
Rose O'Neill 'Kewpies'	..	..	..	..	£2/**£3.50**/£5
Florence Upton 'Golliwoggs'	..	..	..	..	£5/**£6**/£7

Others (value according to calibre of artist and period)

.. .. 75p/**£2.50**/£5

Mirror Grange, miniature house for Pip, Squeak and Wilfred, Artist A. B. Payne. Pub. Tuck. Period 4.

Sepia	..	..	..	..	..	..	75p/**£1**/£1.50
Col.	..	..	..	..	..	..	£1/**£1.50**/£2

Nudekins (British version of the 'Kewpie' Doll) Pub. Tuck.

Periods 2, 3	..	..	..	..	..	50p/**75p**/£1
Posed photographic. Periods 2 to 4	..	..	50p/**75p**/£1.50
Others	..	..	..	..	..	..	50p/**£1.50**/£3

PHOTOGRAPHIC PORTRAITS OF CHILDREN

Thousand of posed portraits of children, ranging from the very appealing to the coyly sentimental, were produced in Periods 2 to 4. Publishers include Birn Bros.; Carlton Pub. Co.; Davidson Bros.; Ettlinger; Hildesheimer; Knight Bros.; Rotary; Schwerdtfeger; Tuck; Wildt & Kray; as well as foreign and other British publishers.

Price range .. .. 25p/**50p**/£1

TEDDY BEARS ■CH 5

These are highly collected in the USA, the country of their origin (named after President Theodore Roosevelt, who puportedly saved the life of a bear cub on one of his hunting expeditions). They were popularised as a symbol for Roosevelt

Children/Toys

in the 1907–8 Presidential campaign as opposed to Taft's animal representative, Billy Possum. The craze spread to Europe and many Period 2–4 bears are to be found on cards by continental and British publishers.

American Bears
A full listing of the American publishers and their postcards appeared in the fourth edition of this catalogue, pp. 22–23.

By well-known artists   ..   ..   **£4/£6/£8**
Others   ..   ..   **75p/£1.50/£3**

European bears
Artists include: Ellam; 'Jotter'; McGill, Donald; Wood, Lawson.

Price range   ..   ..   **75p/£3/£6**

Period 7
Many pleasing Teddy bear postcards, often in sets of series, are being produced today. Publishers include: Art Unlimited (The Teddies); Athena (incl. 'Winnie the Pooh'); Camden Graphics; Steiff (originators of 'Teddy' Ads).

Price per card **25p**

■CH5 Pub. Margarete Stieff, Geingen. Ad. for their famous range of Teddy bears and other toys. Christmas 1985 25p

The Stanley Gibbons Postcard Department is at 399 Strand, London, WC2. Open Mon – Fri. 9.30 am – 5.30 pm; Sat. 10.00 am – 12.30 pm.

COLLECTIONS: The Great Series

On the Continent there exist several well-documented, artist drawn, 'Classic Collections' of picture postcards—the most prized and sought after cards in existence. Cards from these beautiful series are collected today all over the world, although the prices they command vary from country to country. Recent UK auction prices have moved up towards the previously higher continental and US valuations.

The three most famous series of all—the *Collection des Cent, Concours Byrrh*, and *Wiener Werkstätte* were listed in detail in the Second Edition (pp. 105–107).

Austrian
Ver Sacrum
1898. Postcards reprinted from the journal of the same name.

Price range (10 cards)   ..   ..   £50/**£75**/£100

Wiener Werkstätte
Literally 'The Vienna Workshop'. Produced in Vienna between 1908 and 1913, this superb collection is the showcase for a style that foreshadowed Art Deco, *Existentialism, Cubism and Surrealism. Like the famous German Bauhaus, the* Wiener Werkstätte *was a workshop with over 100 craftsmen engaged in a variety of arts and crafts—pottery, glass, furniture, architecture, fashion and metal work. The most highly priced examples were drawn by Oskar Kokoscka and Egon Schiele. The elegant ladies of Mela Koehler and Maria Likartz are extremely popular in Britain* (see Artists). *Subjects include Christmas, Easter and New Year Greetings, Months of the Year (Low-Lazar) and illustrated proverbs (Luksch-Lazar). The postcards from the series can easily be recognised as they all clearly state* Wiener Werkstätte *on the reverse. Some oversize square cards were produced for the series by Mela Koehler, also several $1^1/_2$ times normal postcard sized examples.*

For a complete listing see Second Edition, p. 107.

Most examples	£20/**£30**/£50
Jung, Koehler, Likarz, Loffier	£30/**£50**/£80
Kokoshka, Schiele	£150/**£300**/£450
Textile designs (some with Jewish texts) ..	£10/**£15**/£20

Philipp & Kramer Early Series
Pub. Philipp & Kramer, Vienna. Over 100 series of 10 cards each have been identified, of which the first 30 are the most sought after, drawn by Hoffman, Kainradl, Kurzweil, Moser and Olbrich. Other superb artists include Gerlach, Hampel, Hedley, and Kirchner.

Price range   ..   ..   £30/**£60**/£80

Austrian/German ■ROY 1
Das Grosse Jahrhundert
A vast series of postcards (a total of 612 cards has been suggested, although not authenticated) to chart the achievement of famous men and women of the 19th century as that

123

century drew to a close. Printed in the 1890s, they record international figures of literary, military, musical, political, theatrical and other spheres of fame, e.g. Sarah Bernhardt, Edison, Engels, Marx, Pasteur, etc.

A checklist of this series was given in the third edition of this catalogue, p. 120.

Price range .. .. £3/£8/£15

British ■C 1

Most of the British cards which qualify to be listed under this heading were published by Britain's foremost postcard publishers, Raphael Tuck. Details of the following Tuck series are found under PUBLISHERS: Celebrated Posters; Empire Series; Heraldic Series; Kings and Queens of England and Proof Limited Editions. A listing of Warner Gothard cards was published in the third edition of this catalogue.

■C1 Pub. David Allen Artist E. P. Kinsella. Theatre poster ad for 'A Chinese Honeymoon'. Period 2 £10

David Allen Theatre Postcards

The famous family firm of David Allen celebrated its centenary in 1957 and is still operating in Harrow, Middlesex. Their speciality is the printing of high quality theatre posters. The best commercial artists of the day were commissioned to design the posters, but frustratingly, many of their studies are unsigned. They included: Bruce Bairnsfather, Barribal, John Stuart Browne, (not to be confused with Tom Browne), Buchel, Dennis Dorian Fitzsimmons, John Hassall, Edward Patrick Kinsella, Albert George Morrow, Andrew Murray, Lance Thackeray and Will Owen. Many of the posters were reproduced, from c. 1903 onwards, as postcards. They seem, however, to have been considered as of minor importance to the firm. Experts deduce that postcards were probably printed for the majority of titles, some being produced for theatre managers, overprinted with their theatre's name. Postcards were known to have been produced at least to 1927.

The supplement to this section continues the list of plays with known postcards which was started in the fourth edition of this catalogue, pp. 128–130.

Price range .. .. £4/**£8**/£20

French

Cocorico
Probably the rarest of all the French series, only 12 cards, of which very few examples exist today. The artists are: Does; Faverot; De Feure; Kienerk; Kupka; Léandre; Michael; Mucha; Popineau; Roubille; Steinlen; Willette.

Price range (Highest valuation for De Feure and Mucha.)
.. .. £100/**£250**/£500

Collection des Cent
Pub. Greningaire. Literally 'The Collection of the One Hundred'. Actually 99 designs have been identified. They started to appear from 1 Nov. 1901 in packaged sets of 10. It is thought that about 500 examples were printed of each of the early numbers, and less than 100 of the later series. The contributors were amongst the finest illustrators of the day and included Steinlen, Boutet, Mucha, Caran D'Ache, Grasset, Lélée, Villon, Gaston Noury, Chéret, Fernel, Jossot & Orens.

Price range
    Most examples .. .. £50/**£60**/£75
    Boutet, Capiello, Caran D'Ache, Grasset, Orens, Roubille, Steinlen .. .. £65/**£100**/£150
    Mucha, Villon, Vogel .. .. £150/**£300**/£500

Concours Byrrh
French prize competition (1906) for advertisements for the aperitif Byrrh, a fortified wine with alleged tonic qualities. The competition attracted the very best artists of the day. One hundred and thirteen prizewinning designs were published as postcards. Each design had to incorporate the words, Byrrh, Tonique, Hygiénique, à base de quinquina et de vins généraux. Several prize-winners were announced for each prize—two 1st prizes, two 2nd, six 3rd, five 4th, thirty-one 5th and sixty-five 6th. Contributors included Kirchner, Kienerk, Péan, Denis and Valloton.

Most examples .. .. £30/**£40**/£50
Artists named above .. .. £60/**£150**/£200

Editions Cinos (1898) ■C 2
Reproductions of posters by the top artists of the day such as Chéret, Mucha, Noury, Redon and Toulouse Lautrec. Thirty-five designs have so far been identified, only the last 9 being numbered.

Collections

The cards were listed in the third edition of this catalogue, pp. 120–121.

Price range (highest for the Lautrec) ..   ..   £55/**£100**/£650

■C2 Pub. 'Editions Cinos'. Artist Anon. UB. 1898 £55

Job ■C 3

Reproductions of posters/calendars by the cigarette paper manufacturer, 'Job'. Five different series were printed:
1903 (horizontal) Beautiful series of 12 cards
1905 (horizontal) 1 poster, 7 calendar designs
1907 (horizontal) 8 calendar designs
1911 (horizontal) 3 posters, 21 calendar designs
1914 (vertical) 8 posters and 22 calendar designs.
Artists include: Asti, Cheret, Léandre, Mucha.
Nearly 100 different designs have now been identified. Several perfect collections of 'Job' postcards have come up in auction in 1985 and achieved uniformly high prices.

Price range (highest fo earliest series and sought after artists like Mucha) ..   ..   £15/**£35**/£100

■C3 Pub. 'Job' (cigarette paper manufacturers). Artist A. Asti. Postcard version of 1899 Calendar £25

Maîtres de la Carte Postale (1898–1900)
*Superb postcards, issued in several editions, of designs by some
of the most talented current artists, which first appeared in the
magazine* La Critique.
*Artists include: Auburtin; Biais; Bradley; de Caldain; Chap-
ront; Christiansen; Couturier; Delatre; Detouche; Durangel;
D'Espagnat; Jordic; Jossot; Lebègue; Lyongrun; Misti;
Mouclier; Paraf-Javal; Sloog; Thibaut; Thomen; Valtat and
Vibert.*

Price range (highest for the Valtat)   ..   .. £100/**£150**/£200

Germany

Bauhaus
*The rarest of all German collections, 20 designs, of which only
25 examples are said to have been printed.*

*The Bauhaus movement was started by Walter Gropius in
Weimar in 1919, incorporating artists of all classes, several
nationalities and varying skills and crafts in the fields of pure
art, architecture, carving, furniture and interior design, metal
work, pottery, etc.*

*The Bauhaus postcards were produced in 1923. The artists
who designed them are: 1 & 2 Feininger; 3 Kandinsky; 4 & 5
Klee; 6 Marcks; 7 Moholynagy; 8 Schlemmer; 9 & 10
Baschant; 11 & 12 Bayer; 13 Haberer; 14 Helm; 15 & 16
Hirschfield-Mack; 17 Molnar; 18 & 19 Schmidt; 20 Teltscher.*

The whole of this exclusive collection of original lithographic
postcards came up in auction in Cologne in 1985, most
reaching record prices. The highest valuation is for the Klee's.

Price range   ..   ..   £150/**£500**/£2500

Jugend (1899)
*Three series of 25 cards each. Artists include Bernuth, Caspari,
Christiansen, Eichler, Hoess, Munzer, Seitz, Weinhold,
Zumbach.*

Price range   ..   ..   £20/**£40**/£65

Lustigen Blätter
*Postcards reproduced from the famous newspaper of the same
name in Berlin. Artists include Wennerberg† and Zille† and
many of them are anti-British, incl.* Kriegs-Karte *during
WW1.*

Price range   ..   ..£8/**£12**/£25

As it is difficult to date a card precisely, a period
system has been used in this catalogue.
For a full explanation of the system see page viii.

SECTION SUPPLEMENT – COLLECTIONS

DAVID ALLEN THEATRE POSTCARDS ∎C 1

Checklist continued from fourth edition, pp. 128–30.

Abbreviations
B = Box Office Card
C = Corner Card, Picture is in one corner only
P = Photographic Picture
The naming of an artist does not mean that all cards were by him.

Autumn Manoeuvres	1	L. Barribal
Dancing Mistress	2	L. Barribal
Girl in the Train	2	L. Barribal
Hamlet	1	
Henry V	1	
Her Second Time on Earth	2	
His Excellency	2 + B	
Hypocrites, The	1	Hocker
If I were King	1	
If Winter Comes	1	
Island King, The	2	
It Pays to Advertise	1	
Jack and the Beanstalk	2 (+ 4 *page card*)	
Jacko	1	
Jack the Giant Killer	2	
Just Like Callaghan	1	
Katja the Dancer	2	
King Amongst Men	1	
King of Cadonia	1	
Kismet	1	J. Harker
Kiss Call	1	
Kiss for Cinderella, A	1	
Kitty Grey	1 + B	
La Poupee	1 + B	
Lady Huntsworth's Ex.	1 + C	
Lady Madcap	2 + B	
Lady of Ostend	4	
Lady of the Rose	1	E. P. Kinsella
Ladies' Paradise	2	
Lady of Sherry	2 + B	
Lash, The	1	
Letty	2 + B + C	
Lido Lady	1	
Lilac Domino	1	
Lilac Time	1	
Little Bit of Fluff, A	1	W. Owen
Little French Milliner,	1 + C	

The Little Grey Home in the West	1	
Little Michus	8 + B	E. P. Kinsella, A. Morrow
Little Red Riding Hood	3 + C (+ 4 *page card*)	J. Hassall
Lord Richard in the Pantry	1	T. E. Stephens
Message from Mars, A	1	Morrow
Messenger Boy, The	1	
Miss Elizabeth's Prisoner	1	C. A. Buchel
Miss Hook of Holland	4	S. Brennick, Morrow
Morals of Marcus, The	1	
Mother Goose	1	Hassall
Mousme, The (Maids of Japan)	1	
Mrs. Gorringe's Necklace	1	
Mummy, The & The Hummingbird	1	
Old Heidelberg	1	J. S. Browne
Omar Khayam	1	
Only Way, The	1	Hassall
Orchid, The	4	Hassall, A. Murray
Orlando Dando	1	
Our Miss Gibbs	1	
Paola	2	
Passers By	1	
Peggy	2	
Peter's Mother	1 + B	
Peter Pan	1 + B	
Pride of the Regiment	1	
Private Secretary	1	
Public Opinion	1 + B	
Quaker Girl	1	
Quality Street	2	Buchel, Morrow Browne
Quo Vadis	2	Browne
Raffles	1	
Resurrection	2	Buchel, Morrow
Robin Hood	2 + B	J. Cameron
Robinson Crusoe	5 + C (+ 4 *page card*) + CNR CD	D. D. Fitz- simmons, Murray
Runaway Girl, A	1	Hassall
San Toy	2 + B	Morrow
Sands of Time	B O	
Saturday to Monday	1	
School Girl, The	1 + B	Morrow
Scrape o' the Pen	1 (P) (*photo*)	
See-See	B	
Sergeant Brue	1	Hassall
Sherlock Holmes	2 + B	
Shop Girl, The	1	
Silver King	1 (P) (*photo*)	

Sinbad the Sailor	2 (+ 4 *page card*)	
Sleeping Partner	1	
Smile it Smile	1	
Smith, Brown, Jones & Robinson	2 + B	W. True
Soldier of France, A.	1	W. True
Soldiers Wedding	8 (*mostly photos*)	
Spring Chicken, The	2	Morrow
Storm	1	Kinsella
Sunday	1	
Swiss Express	1	
Talk of the Town	2 + B	
Taming of the Shrew	1	Morrow
Tempest, The	1	
Three Little Maids	2 + B	Browne
Tilly of Bloomsbury	1 (*photo*)	
Tina	2	Kinsella
Tonight's the Night	2	Barribal, Kinsella
Toreador, The	1	Murray
Treasure Island	1	
Unforseen, The	1 + B	
Veronique	2 + B	Murray
Walls of Jericho, The	1	
What the Butler Saw	2	
When Knights were Bold	2	Browne, Hassall
Where the Rainbow Ends	1	
Whip, The	1	
White Chrysanthemum	2 + B	
Whitewashing Julia	2 + B	
Why William Lied	1	
Wildflower	1	Kinsella
Within the Law	1	
Worst Woman in London	8 (*mostly play stills*)	Kinsella, W. E. Morgan
You Never Can Tell	1 (*photo*)	
Zaza	1	Morrow

Three Band Pricing System

Left Hand Band: The lowest price you will probably
be asked to pay for this card.
Middle Band: What you will normally be asked to pay
for this card: its average, reasonable price.
Right Hand Band: The highest price you will probably
be asked to pay for this card.
For a full explanation of the system see page ix.

COMIC

This is the type of postcard at which the British excelled during the 'Golden Age' of collecting. It was typically British, as were *Art Nouveau* and topographical French, *Gruss Aus* German and patriotic/political Italian. No other country has such a rich vein of humour in its postcard production. No area of Edwardian life seemed immune from the humorous artist, and the wealth of comic artistic talent was extraordinary.

Cards in most collecting categories were given the humorous treatment. To list them all here would make this section unwieldy. Therefore many 'comic' cards are described under other main headings, notably:

CHILDREN,
MILITARY,
POLITICS,
SOCIAL HISTORY

Most comic cards, however, are collected because of their artists, many of whom came to postcard design from the poster, or book and magazine illustration, and have a reputation far beyond their postcard output.

Listed in this COMIC section are many of the minor, but highly collectable, comic artists, examples of whose work can still be found for a modest price. Comic cards are also collected by virtue of their publisher, and some of the main comic publishers are listed here, as are some of the important comic series and the comic 'themes', often drawn by competent but unsigned artists.

N.B. Many of the cards by the following artists may have higher valuations in other sections. The following prices are for their comic designs only.

ARTISTS (Signed) ■COM 1–4, A 3–5, 15, 18, 19, 31, AN 13, SH 3

'A.A.'	25p/**50p**/75p
Adams, Will	50p/**£1**/£1.50
'A.E.' *see* English, Archibald	
Anderson, Martin (Cynicus)† *(Highest valuation for early Period 2 and 'Court' size)*	£1.50/**£2.50**/£10
Aris, Ernest	75p/**£1**/£2
Attwell, Mabel Lucie†	£1/**£1.50**/£3
Austerlitz, E.	75p/**£1.50**/£2
Bairnsfather, Bruce†	£1/**£2**/£3
Bamber, George A.	50p/**75p**/£1
Barnes, G. L.	75p/**£1**/£1.50
Bateman, H. M.†	£1/**£2**/£3
Bee, Noah	50p/**75p**/£1.50
Belcher, George†	£3/**£4**/£5
Biggar, J. L.	50p/**75p**/£1
'Bob' (*Irish and other humour*)	50p/**£1**/£1.50
Bradshaw, P. V.† (*also signed 'PVB'*)	£3/**£4**/£6
Browne, Tom† (*also signed 'Tom B.'*)	£2/**£3**/£5
Buchanan, Fred†	75p/**£1.50**/£2

Bull, Rene†	£2/**£3**/£4
Buxton, Dudley†	75p/**£1.25**/£2.50
Cameron, Archie	25p/**75p**/£1
Carter, Reg†	75p/**£1**/£2
Carter, Sydney†	50p/**£1**/£2
Christie, G. F.† (*also signed 'G.F.C.'*)	50p/**£1**/£2
Comicus *see* Parlett, Harry	
Cook, Charles K.	75p/**£1.50**/£3
Crombie, Charles	75p/**£1**/£2
Cynicus *see* Anderson, Martin	
'Dauber'	75p/**£1**/£1.50
Davey, George†	75p/**£1.50**/£2
'Dinah'†	50p/**75p**/£1.50
Duncan, J. A. ('Hamish')†	50p/**75p**/£1
Dwiggins, C. V. ('Dwig')†	£2/**£4**/£6
Earnshaw, Harold†	75p/**£1**/£1.50
Ellam, W. H.†	£1/**£2**/£4
Elliott, Harry	£2/**£4**/£6
English, Archibald ('A.E.')†	50p/**75p**/£1.50
Esmond (*'Germs', etc.*)	75p/**£1**/£4
'F.S.' *see* Spurgin, Fred	
Fitzpatrick, Brian (*Bamforth*)	25p/50p
Fleury, H.	50p/**75p**/£1
Fuller, Edmund†	£2/**£4**/£6
Gibson, Charles Dana†	£1/**£2**/£3
Gill, Arthur†	£1/**£1.50**/£3
Gilson, T.†	50p/**£1**/£2
Gothard, Fred ('Spatz')†	25p/**50p**/£1
'Graeff'	50p/**75p**/£1
Greenall, Jack (*'Useless Eustace'*)	50p/**75p**/£1
Grisset, Ernest	75p/**£1**/£1.50
Gunn, Gwennet†	50p/**75p**/£1
'Guy L'	50p/**75p**/£1
Hardy, Dudley†	£2/**£4**/£5
Hassall, John†	£2/**£4**/£6
Heath-Robinson, W.†	£2/**£3**/£4
Huber, G.†	50p/**£1**/£2
Hyde, Graham	£1/**£2**/£4
Ibbetson, Ernest†	£1/**£2**/£4
'Karaktakus'	25p/**75p**/£1
'K.S.'	25p/**75p**/£1
Leete, Alfred†	£1/**£1.50**/£2
Ludovici, Anthony†	£2/**£3**/£4
MacBean, L.	50p/**£1**/£1.25
McGill, Donald†	50p/**£1.50**/£3
Martin, Phil	25p/**50p**/75p
Maurice, Reg†	75p/**£1**/£2.50
May, Phil†	£2/**£3**/£4
'Mich'	£1.50/**£2.50**/£3.50
Moreland, Arthur†	£1/**£1.50**/£2
Morgan, F. E.	25p/**50p**/75p
Morton, Alfred (*'Imps'*)	£2/**£3**/£4
Noble, Ernest	25p/**50p**/£1
Opper, Frederick Burr	50p/**£1**/£2
Outcault, Richard Felton	£1.50/**£3**/£6
Owen, Will†	£1/**£2**/£4
Parlett, Harry ('Comicus')†	50p/**75p**/£1

■COM 1 Pub. Tuck. Artist 'P.V.B'. (Percy Bradshaw). Humorous Series No. 1324. 'Cricket Illustrated' 'Cover Point!'. PU 1904 £4

■COM 2 Pub. Anon. Artist T. Gilson. No. 1214 Period 2 £1.50

■COM 3 Pub. Tuck. Artist Gilbert Wilkinson. 'What a War'. Courtesy of the *Daily Herald*. Period 5 £1.75

■COM 4 Pub. Anon. Artist C. Lawson Wood. 'Prehistoric types'. Period 2 £2.50

Payne, G. M.†	50p/**75p**/£1.50
Pirkis, Albert George†	75p/**£1.50**/£3
'PYP'†	£1.50/**£2**/£2.50
Reynolds, Frank†	75p/**£1.50**/£3
Rob, A.	75p/**£1**/£1.50
Rowland, Ralph	50p/**£1.50**/£3
Rowntree, Harry	£1/**£2**/£4
Schonpflug, Fritz†	£1/**£2**/£3
Shaw, W. Stocker	50p/**75p**/£1
Shepheard, George Edward†	75p/**£1**/£2
'Spatz' *see* Gothard, Fred	
Spurgin, Fred† (*also signed 'F.S.'*) ..	£1/**£1.50**/£3
Starr Wood, H.†	£1/**£1.50**/£3
Studdy, George†	£1.50/**£2**/£4
Taylor, Arnold	25p/**50p**/75p
Tempest, Douglas	50p/**75p**/£1
Thackeray, Lance†	£2/**£4**/£6
Thiele, Arthur†	£2/**£4**/£8
Thomas, Bert†	75p/**£1.50**/£3
Wain, Louis†	£6/**£8**/£15
Ward, Dudley	25p/**50p**/£1
Ward, Sir Leslie†	£2/**£3**/£4
Wilkinson, Gilbert	75p/**£1**/£1.50
Wood, Lawson†	£1/**£2**/£3
Zimmerman, H. G.	75p/**£1.50**/£2

ARTISTS (Unsigned/Minor)
Periods 2 to 6 .. .. 25p/**50p**/£1.50

COMIC PUBLISHERS/SERIES/THEMES

Addled Ads. *see* Misch & Stock

Bamforth & Co.
Many posed humorous song and other series of photographic origin. Periods 2 to 4.
    Single cards and sets of 2, 3, 4 .. .. 50p/**75p**/£3
    Similar cards by other publishers 25p/**50p**/75p

Couples, Courtship
On of the favourite butts of comic ards.
Artist drawn 25p/**50p**/75p
Photographic in origin (esp. by Pub. 'J.W.S.') 25p/**50p**/75p

'Dam' Family
Pubs. Crockers, Fraser & Jenkinson, others 25p/**50p**/75p

Davidson Bros. ■P 1
Undoubtedly the 'kings' of the comic card.
Periods 2, 3 .. .. 50p/**75p**/£5

Ethnic/Regional Humour (*see* SOCIAL HISTORY)
Irish humour ('Paddy' jokes, many local pubs.) 25p/**50p**/£1
Jewish humour ('mean' jokes, etc.) .. .. £1/**£2**/£3

| Scottish humour (artists like 'Hamish', pubs. like Millar & Lang) .. .. | 25p/**50p**/75p |

Welsh humour ('jawbreaking' placenames, pubs. incl. Valentine) 25p/**50p**/75p

Others 25p/**50p**/75p

Marriage

'Is Marriage a Failure?'. Pub. Millar & Lang   25p/**50p**/75p

Mrs. Caudle's Lectures (various pubs.) ..   50p/**75p**/£2

Others 25p/**50p**/75p

Military Humour

See MILITARY.

Price range .. .. 50p/**£1**/£3

Misch and Stock

This publishing house produced many fine series of comic postcards, using some of the most popular comic artists of the day, in early Period 2.

A listing of these cards was given in the third edition of this catalogue, p. 127.

Price range .. .. 75p/**£1.50**/£4

Punch Cartoons

Early Period 2/Period 3 (various pubs., *see* MILITARY and POLITICAL).. .. .. £1/**£1.50**/£3

Sporting Humour

Cricket, Golf, Ping Pong, Skating, etc. (*see* ARTISTS) .. ..

.. .. 75p/**£1.75**/£3

Tuck ■COM 1

Britain's foremost publishing house produced many fine humorous series, far too numerous to list in total. They used artists of the calibre of: Ernest Aris; 'Dwig'; Ellam; Dudley Hardy; John Hassall; Graham Hyde; Phil May; G. E. Shepheard; Lance Thackeray and Louis Wain.

Series include: Coon Series (Various); Game Birds (Political); Humour in Life; ITMA Wisecracks (Period 5); 'Nudekins' (Period 3); School Days & others (Dwig); Sporting Terms, Illustrated; Vanity Fair Cartoons; and perhaps the most famous of all, 'Write Away'.

Periods 1–3 .. .. £1/**£3**/£6

Periods 4–6 .. .. 50p/**£1**/£3

Undivided-back Comics

Period 1/Early Period 2, often chromo-lithographs   £2/**£3**/£4

'Wordy' Humour

The pseudo 'essay' or 'poem' on humorous topics, often in dialect. Various pubs. .. .. 25p/**50p**/£1

Southsea
Collectors Fair

St. Simons Church Hall
Albert Road, Southsea, Hants.

10 am – 5 pm

On the Last Saturday Bi-Monthly of
January, March, May, July,
September, November

 Its mostly postcards!

Visit Point Collectors Centre and see our
fine collection of old postcards at

Broad Street, Old Portsmouth
Details of Opening Hours:
Telephone (0705) 814992

LOOKING FOR BARGAINS?

When you go shopping for old picture postcards be sure to visit us at our shops. You
will see choice cards in a wide range of
categories. We are also keen to buy pre-1925
cards in collections and miscellaneous lots,
old maps of the world and stamp collections.
Good prices paid.

J. A. L. FRANKS LTD.

7 New Oxford St., WC1A 1BA
(01–405 0274/5)

22 BOND STREET, BRIGHTON,
Sussex, BN1 1RD
(Brighton 686120)

COMMEMORATIVE

This was undoubtedly one of the most important classifications in the postcard collecting of the 'Golden Age'. Then the picture postcard fulfilled the function which TV and radio do today in recording events and anniversaries. Some particularly beautiful commemorative cards were produced in Period 1 and early Period 2. Commemorative postcards have been listed in detail in previous editions of this catalogue and examples of fine cards of this genre appear in EARLY CARDS, EXHIBITIONS, MILITARY, POLITICAL and ROYALTY. Period 7 Commemorative issues feature in MODERNS. A summary appears below. (N.B. Special handstamps often raise values considerably.)

PERIOD 1 (Many are court sized)

Austria (e.g. 25th Anniv. of the postcard, 1894)	£20/**£40**/PA
Britain (e.g. Nile Expedition, 1898)	£40/**£60**/£100
Canada (e.g. USS Maine Memorial, 1898) ..	£10/**£20**/£30
Germany (e.g. Death of Bismarck, 1898) ..	..£5/**£10**/£30
Italy (e.g. 25th Anniv. Liberation Rome 1895)	£5/**£10**/£20
Others	..£5/**£10**/£40

PERIOD 2 ■COMM 1, 2

Britain (e.g. Tuck Empire Series 1900 and Wrench's Links of the Empire 1901)	£10/**£30**/£100+
Austria (e.g. Assassination of Arch Duke Ferdinand 1914)	..£5/**£10**/£25
Australia (e.g. Foundation of Commonwealth 1901)	.. £5/**£8**/£15
Bulgaria (e.g. Declaration of Independence 1908)	£3/**£5**/£10
France (e.g. Millenaire Normand 1911) ..	.. £1/**£5**/£12
Germany (e.g. Official new century cards 1900) ..	£1/**£5**/£10
Italy (e.g. 50th Anniv. Kingdom 1911) ..	.. £1/**£3**/£10
USA (e.g. Wedding of Alice Roosevelt 1906) ..	£1/**£3**/£8
Others	.. £1/**£5**/£10

PERIOD 3 First World War – see MILITARY

PERIOD 4

Britain (e.g. Opening of Mersey Tunnel 1934)	75p/**£1.50**/£5
Canada (e.g. Winnipeg Jubilee Parada 1924)	75p/**£1.50**/£3
Germany (e.g. Hindenburg's 80th Birthday 1927)	£3/**£5**/£10
Switzerland (e.g. International Disarmament Conf. 1932)	£1.50/**£3**/£5
Others	75p/**£1.50**/£5

PERIOD 5 Second World War – see MILITARY

PERIOD 6

France (e.g. 40th Anniv. of Armistice 1958) ..	£1/**£3**/£5
USA (e.g. 85th Anniv. Gettysburg Address 1948)	£2/**£4**/£6
USSR (e.g. 50th Anniv. of October Revolution 1969)	£2/**£4**/£6
Others	75p/**£3**/£5

■COMM 1 Pub. Anon. Austria. RP. Arrest of bomb thrower Cabrinovic. 28 June 1914 £10

■COMM 2 Official German postcard with 5pfg. stamp. The year 1900. UB £5

Three Band Pricing System

Left Hand Band: The lowest price you will probably be asked to pay for this card.
Middle Band: What you will normally be asked to pay for this card: its average, reasonable price.
Right Hand Band: The highest price you will probably be asked to pay for this card.
For a full explanation of the system see page ix.

COMPETITIONS/CRAZES/HOBBIES

BEAUTY COMPETITIONS
Daily Mirror 1908. Pub. C. W. Faulkner
Daily Mirror 1919. Pub. Daily Mirror & Rotary
Daily Express & Seymour Hicks. Pub. C. W. Faulkner
Others

Price range .. .. 75p/**£1.50**/£2

BICYCLING
*Bicycling flourished in Victorian and Edwardian times, as
well as being a viable means of transport. Advanced young
ladies shocked society with their bicycling bloomers; cycling
clubs sprang up around the country, rallies, gymkhanas and
races regularly took place.*

*High quality Real Photographic (R.P.) cards attract higher
valuations than general photographic origin postcards.*

See ADVERTISING.

Artist Drawn
Pub. Pascalis Moss & Co. (1901/1902). Cyclists of All Nations.
   Series of 12 col. caricatures .. .. .. £1.50/**£3**/£5
Pub. Tuck. Period 2. Artist. Leslie Willson. 'The Scorcher's
   Progress'. Set of 6 witty cycling jokes .. £1.50/**£2**/£4

*Most of the well-known comic postcard artists of Period 2
designed series of postcards on cycling themes, notably Browne,
F. S. and Pirkis, A. G.*

Signed artists .. .. £1/**£2**/£5
Unsigned artist drawn .. .. 50p/**£1**/£2

Cycling Champions
Periods 2, 3 .. .. 75p/**£1.50**/£4
Periods 4 to 6 .. .. 50p/**£1**/£2

Cycling Clubs
Photographic origin/RP Periods. 2 to 4 .. .. 75p/**£1**/£4

Cycling Gymkhanas
Photographic origin/RP Periods. Periods 2 to 4 .. 75p/**£1**/£4

Cycling Races/Rallies
Artist drawn. Period 2 souvenir cards .. .. £2/**£4**/£6
Artist drawn. Others .. .. £1/**£2**/£4
Milk Race. Periods 6, 7 .. .. 25p/**50p**/75p
Tour de France. Periods 2, 3 .. .. £2/**£4**/£6
Tour de France. Periods 4, 6 .. .. £1/**£2**/£3
Photographic. Edwardian cyclists—posed portraits .. ..
.. .. 75p/**£1.50**/£3
Poster type ads .. .. £10/**£15**/£25
Others .. .. 50p/**£1.50**/£2

CROSSWORD PUZZLES (Period 4, c. 1924/5)
The last of the great 'crazes' illustrated on the postcard.

'Crosswords' series. Artist Donald McGill .. 75p/**£1.50**/£3
Pub. Tuck. Oilette 3514. 'The Crossword Craze' 1924 .. ..
.. .. 75p/**£1.50**/£2
Others .. .. 50p/**75p**/£3

DIABOLO (Period 2, from 1906)
The craze boomed from the invention of an aerodynamically efficient 'devil' (and there are many diabolo jokes which play on this word), by Gustave Phillipart in 1906.

Artist drawn
Browne, Tom. Pub. Davidson (Series 2627, 2631)   £2/**£3**/£4
Christie, George Fyffe, Pub. Wm. Ritchie & Sons (W.R. & S.)
.. .. 75p/**£1**/£1.50
Cross, J. Pub. Tuck .. .. 50p/**75p**/£1.50
Kinsella, E. P. Pub. Langsdorff .. .. £1/**£2**/£4
McGill, Donald .. .. 75p/**£1**/£1.50
Wain, Louis. Pub. Tuck .. ..£6/**£10**/£15
Other artists/publishers, including Birn Bros., H. Vertigen &
Co... .. .. 50p/**£1**/£1.50

Greetings cards featuring Diabolo
Various publishers .. .. 75p/**£1.50**/£3

Photographic Diabolo cards
Various publishers .. .. 75p/**£2**/£4

LIMERICKS (Period 2, mainly 1907/8) ■CCH 1
The craze followed the competition in London Opinion *to complete the last line of a limerick. Soon other competitions and even specialist magazines appeared.*

■CCH 1 Pub. Millar & Lang. Artist Anon. 'The Limerick Craze'. PU 1908 £1.50

Comic cards
Pub. Davidson Bros. Artist Dudley Hardy. Nos. 3008/9. 'Limericks'
      £2/**£4**/£6
Pub. Gottschalk, Dreyfus & Davis (G.D. & D.). Artist 'KS' (*c.* 1906) ..   ..   50p/**75p**/£1.50
Pub. Hildesheimer. Artist 'Kyd' (1905) ..   ..   £1/**£2**/£4
Pub. W. & A. K. Johnston. Series 112, 119 (1905) 50p/**75p**/£1
Knight Series. Jingle Cards (1905) ..   ..   75p/**£1**/£2
Pub. Millar & Lang. 'The Limerick Craze' (1907) 75p/**£1**/£2
Pub. Shamrock & Co. The Limerick Lunatic with appliqué 'noose' ..   ..   50p/**75p**/£2
Pub. Tuck. Limerick postcards with appliqué checked material. Nos. 9568, 9596/7 ..   ..   ..   50p/**75p**/£2
Pub. J. Welch & Co. (1907) ..   ..   ..   75p/**£1**/£2
Other pubs. ..   ..   50p/**75p**/£1

Competition cards
Palantine Limerick Postcard ..   ..   ..   £1/**£1.50**/£2
Valentine & Sons (1907) ..   ..   £1/**£1.50**/£2

Novelty cards
Artist Ralph Ruttley. Pub. Shamrock & Co. (Set of 5 views and 1 Limerick card with last line to complete.)

Per set ..   ..   £3/**£5**/£7.50

POSTCARD COLLECTING
The greatest hobby-cum-craze of the Golden Age of the postcard was, of course, collecting post cards! Many cards alluding to postcard collecting can be found spanning the 7 Periods.

Postcard Clubs
Period 1. International Poste Carte Club (IPCC). Series of 12 cards designed by artists of the calibre of Jossot, etc.
  ..   ..   £50/**£100**/£200
Period 1. Other Clubs ..   ..   ..   £10/**£20**/£40
Period 2. Various Clubs ..   ..   £3/**£5**/£15

Postcard Competitions

C. W. Faulkner (Period 2)
611 prizes from 10s. 6d. to £100 for putting in order the best 6 cards from a packet of 12.

Price range ..   ..   £1/**£2**/£4

St. Paul's Hospital Competition (1924)
To raise funds for a new hospital. Set of 12 sepia view cards of London.

Per set **£1.50**
Per set complete with detachable entry coupons **£5**

Shurey's Great Prize Competition (Period 2)
Delittle Fenwick & Co. per 6 cards ..   ..   50p/**£1.25**/£2

Raphael Tuck & Sons
Raphael Tuck & Sons. Competitions. Advert cards.
(see edition four of this catalogue for list of dates)

By well-known artists	.. £2/**£5**/£10
Unsigned artist drawn	£1.50/**£3**/£5
Advertising on reverse only	.. 75p/**£1**/£2
Sheffield Weekly Telegraph Kodak DIY postcard competition.	
Prizes in Tuck postcards	75p/**£1.50**/£3
Other Competitions	.. 50p/**£1**/£3

Postcard Exhibitions (*see* EXHIBITIONS)

Period 1
Venice 1894, Berlin 1896, Leipzig, Munich, Zürich 1898, Nice,
  Berlin & others 1899 .. .. £20/**£30**/£75
Period 2
Paris 1900, Paris 1904, Nuremberg 1907 .. ..£5/**£10**/£25
Others .. ..£5/**£10**/£15

Period 7
Century of British Postcards 1970.
With Exhibition Postmark .. .. £3/**£4**/£5
Unused .. .. £1/**£1.50**/£2
Others see MODERN

■CCH 2 Pub. Anon. Facsimile of Besnardeau 1870 postcard,
1904 £40

Postcard 'Inventors' ■CCH 2
Besnardeau (now hotly disputed 'inventor' of the picture card)
  cards from 1870/71 .. .. £75/**£100**/£125
Besnardeau reprints (1903) .. .. .. £20/**£25**/£30
Dr. Hermann (instigator of the postcard)
Jubilee of the postcard (1894) .. .. .. £75/**£100**/£150
1952 Austrian official issue commemorating Hermann ..
  .. .. £10/**£12**/£15

Postcard Week ■CCH 3
1984 16–24 June (UK)
1985 5–11 May (USA)
1986 4–10 May (UK)

Various designs.

Price range 25p/50p

■CCH 3 Pub. Anon. USA Postcard Week. 5–11 May 1985.
50p

RINKING (Period 2)
*The great roller skating craze (which reached its zenith in 1909
as far as postcard production was concerned) swept the United
States, Britain and Europe. The great entrepreneur C. B.
Cochran opened rinks in Olympia, throughout the UK, in
Paris, Berlin, Hanover, Hamburg, Antwerp and Nice. Magaz-
ines like* The World on Wheels, Roller Skating Record *and*
The Rinking World *were published.*

Artist drawn cards
Browne, Tom. Pub. Davidson. Series 2623/1   ..   £4/**£5**/£6
Carter, Reg. Pub. Verdier ..   ..   £1/**£1.50**/£2
'F.S.' ..   ..   75p/**£1**/£2
Thackeray, Lance. Pub. Tuck. Set No. 9919   ..   £2/**£3**/£5
Wiederseim, Grace   ..   ..   £1/**£1.50**/£3
Other signed artists ..   ..   75p/**£1**/£1.50

Publishers of comic 'Rinking' cards
Artist drawn. Davidson Bros., Inter-Art, local publishers,
    McGlennon, Millar & Lang, Wm. Ritchie & Sons, Philco,
    Tuck   ..   ..   75p/**£1.50**/£2
Photographic. Bamforth & Co. (premium for complete set)
    ..   ..   50p/**75p**/£1.50

Skating Rinks
Photographic. Various publishers   ..   ..   ..   £1/**£2**/£4

Skating Rink Managers
Reprinted from *Rinking World*, Artist T. H. Smith   ..   ..
..   ..   £1.50/**£2**/£4

Skating Champions
Photographic. Various publishers   ..   ..   ..   £1/**£2**/£4

CURIOUS/MISCELLANEOUS

In this section are described the odd and the unusual: human freaks, natural phenomena, quaint buildings, record breaking attempts and postcards that do not fit into any of the traditional groupings

CODES/CYPHERS

Many strange devices were used to disguise the messages on postcards to avoid their being read by postmen, servants, etc. If a postcard has its message written in code, in cyphers, in 'mirror writing', in shorthand, in Greek or Latin, or otherwise disguised, add a premium of 50p to £1 to the card, depending on the complexity of the system used.

CURIOSITIES

Animal Curiosities
Cards of photographic origin, usually by local publishers, may show animals with one leg too many or too few; animals with two heads; animals working treadmills; birds' nests in strange places, etc.

Price range   ..   ..   £1/**£1.50**/£2

Human Curiosities
Many of these appeared on the stage, or in sideshows at circuses (like Barnum & Bailey) or fairs, or in C. B. Cochran's 'Midget City' at Olympia. The cards carry a premium of 25% if they have been hand autographed by the subject.

Dwarfs/Midgets
Anita the living doll (26 in. high); Asra, 'der lebenden Puppe'; Baron Ernesto Magri; Baron Paucci (62 cm. high); Count Primo Magri; Madame Pauline, the Miniature Comedienne; Major and Mrs. Mite; Major Newell; General Tom Thumb; Mrs. Tom Thumb (née Lavinia Warren, Mrs. Magri by her second marriage); Troupe Lilliputienne Zeynard; Willy Pantzer and his Wonderful Midgets.

Price range   ..   ..   £1.50/**£2.50**/£3

Freaks
Bearded ladies; Siamese twins; Various physical deformities.

Price range   ..   ..   £1/**£2**/£3

Giants
Abomah, the Tallest Lady in the World; Hassan Ali, the Egyptian Giant (8 ft. 2 in); Machnow, the Russian Giant; The Nottingham Giant Girl.

Price range   ..   ..   £1/**£2**/£3

Odd Characters
Bird Charmers of Hyde Park Corner/Tuileries, Paris; Cave dwellers; Others.

| Price range | .. | .. | .. | .. | .. | .. | 50p/**£1.50**/£3 |

Unusual Performers
Conjurers; Contortionists; Escapologists; Hypnotists; Illusion-
ists; Mind Readers; Snake Charmers; Spiritualists and
Ventriloquists.

| Price range | .. | .. | .. | .. | .. | .. | £1.50/**£3**/£6 |

Man-made Curiosities
Mannekin Pis, Brussels: many series, comic and photographic,
    some in booklet form
Models in icing sugar, made from matchsticks, etc.
Odd-shaped houses, 'smallest' houses and other curious
    buildings
Ossuaries (e.g. cemetery of Capucin Monks)
Sand sculptures

| Price range | .. | .. | .. | .. | .. | .. | 50p/**£1**/£1.50 |

Natural Curiosities

Crocodile Rock, Millport, USA or other strange rock		
formations		25p/**50p**/75p
Double trees (e.g. beech and oak joined) ..		25p/**50p**/75p
Giant trees		25p/**50p**/75p
Grottoes/underground caverns		25p/**50p**/75p
Halley's Comet. 1910. German. Set of 6		
Col. signed K. Hesse		£2/**£4**/£6
Others		75p/**£1.50**/£3
Others		25p/**50p**/75p

■CUR 1 Pub. Ernest Schmidt, Lübeck. Feldgen and Beiss's
6 year Round Europe trip overland and water in the Rotorship
Buckau 1926–32. Period 4 £4

FEATS/RECORD-BREAKERS/WAGERS ■CUR 1
Allen, W. C.—Walking 2000 miles in 44 days—trained on
  Bovril (1904)
Belbin, H. W. G.—Riding his land & water cycle
The Crusader walking round the world (£500 reward)
Leach, Bobby—Going over Niagara Falls in a barrel (1911)
Rolling a barrel from Vienna to Paris (1900)

Round Europe. 6 years by Rotorship *Buckau* (1926–32)
Schilling, Geo.—Walking round the world in an airship
Walking round the world in an iron mask (£21,000 wager)
Walking from Vienna to Paris, pushing wife and child (*c.* 1900). Pub. Baumann, pram manufacturer, Vienna

Price range .. .. £1.50/**£2.50**/£5

GAMES OF CHANCE

Playing Cards
Various designs. Periods 2–4 .. .. £2/**£4**/£6
Periods 5–7 .. .. 50p/**75p**/£1.50

Roulette and other Gambling Games
For casino buildings *see* SOCIAL HISTORY.
Croupiers/gamblers. Clear pictures photographic in origin with good detail of people .. .. £1/**£2**/£3
French. Rules of Roulette/other gambling games at Monte Carlo and other Casinos .. .. £2/**£3**/£4
Others .. .. 75p/**£1**/£3

INTERNATIONAL LANGUAGES ■CUR 2

Braille
Price range .. .. 75p/**£1.50**/£2

■CUR 2 Pub. A. Farges. Director of the Esperanto Office, Lyon. Artist Jean Robert. The Chivalrous Zamenhof fights the dragon 'Ido'. Period 2 £8

Deaf and Dumb Sign Language
Price range .. .. 75p/**£1.50**/£2

Esperanto

For cards with messages written in Esperanto add 50p to £1 to value, the earlier the card the higher the premium.

Esperanto Congresses

Price range   ..   .. 75p/**£3**/£8

Esperantists

Bourlet	£2/**£3**/£5
Cunningham	£2/**£3**/£5
Zamenhof, Ludwig (1859–1917) (inventor of Esperanto) ..	
.. ..	£3/**£5**/£8
Others	75p/**£3**/£5

Ido

Revised form of Esperanto, from the initials International Delegation (1907). For cards written in Ido add 50p to £1 to the value of the card, the earlier the card the higher the premium.

Congresses

Price range   ..   .. 75p/**£1.50**/£5

Ido-ists

Marquis de Beaufront, Louis (Inventor)	£1/**£3**/£5
Others	75p/**£1.50**/£3

Propaganda cards

Price range   ..   .. £1/**£3**/£5

■CUR 3 Pub. J. M. Cubart. *Rite Ecossais Ancien et Accepté.* Period 7 35p

MASONIC (and other secret societies) ■CUR 3

Artist Drawn
Pub. Millar & Lang. Comic col. series 'Are You a Mason?' 24
  cards. Period 2 .. .. £2/**£4**/£6
Other comic series .. .. 75p/**£1**/£3

Photographic Origin
Masonic regalia .. .. £1/**£2**/£4
People in masonic regalia .. .. £1/**£3**/£5

Other Societies
Price range .. .. 50p/**£1**/£2

MISTAKES ON POSTCARDS
For wrongly printed captions, postcards printed the wrong
way round or other mistakes, add 50p to £1 to the value of
the card.

'WANTED' CARDS
Pub. USA. with and without stuck on photo of wanted person
.. .. **P/A**

PICTURE POSTCARD MONTHLY

The hobby's top magazine

News. Features. Book Reviews. Articles.
Lively Postbag. Club News. Diary of Events.
Fully Illustrated

Subscription by post £10 p.a.

PICTURE POSTCARD ANNUAL
superb reference work for collectors £3.50

both available from

REFLECTIONS OF A BYGONE AGE
15 Debdale Lane, Keyworth,
Nottingham NG12 5HL

EARLY CARDS: Period 1/
Early Period 2

These are the postcards between 1869 and 1903. Soon after
the first postcard was produced in Austria in 1869 line drawn
adverts started to appear. Gradually the pictures developed
into vignettes, colour was added and the picture postcard
became a work of art. Often superbly printed on high quality
board, with a distinct 'silky' feel, these early cards are to be
found in many sections: ADVERTISING, ART, COMMEMORATIVE,
EXHIBITIONS, ROYALTY, etc. The majority of chromolitho cards
was produced on the continent until 1899, when Raphael Tuck
entered the postcard business and the British trade flourished.
The main types are described below, and are to be found in
three sizes: 'Court', 'Intermediate' and full UPU size. The
earlier the card, the higher the valuation, and condition is all
important.

CHROMO-LITHO CARDS

The majority of these cards were printed on the Continent
during Period 1 and early Period 2. They are readily recognised by the excellence of the colour printing (*see* 'Chromo-
litho' in the Glossary), are frequently undivided backs and
often have vignettes in the design. We list below the major
printers/publishers of chromo-litho cards. Their postcards are
listed and valued under the three headings that follow below:

Printers/Publishers
Bechtold, Rudolph (*Wiesbaden*); Berardi, E. (*Milan*); Cham-
penois (*Paris*); Dietrich (*Brussels*); Franzl, L. (*Munich*);
Frey & Sons (*Zürich*); Hendelsohn, G. (*Berlin*); Huardel, P.
G. (P.G.H. & Co.); Juxberg, F. W. (*Frankfurt*) (F.W.J.); Köhn,
Brüder (*Vienna*) (B.K.W.); Meissner & Buch (*Leipzig and
London*); Menke-Huber (*Zürich*); Miesler, J. (*Frankfurt*);
Moss, Henry (H.M. & Co.); Munk, M. (*Vienna*) (MM); Nister,
Ernest (*London and Nuremberg*); Pascalis, Moss & Co.;
Philipp & Kramer (*Vienna*); Pictorial Stationery Co.
(*London*); Pinkau, Emil (*Leipzig*); Ricordi (*Milan*); Rosenblatt
(*Frankfurt*); Roth, Ludwig (*Berlin*); Schmidt, Staub & Co.
(*Nuremberg*); Stengel (*Dresden*); Tuck, Raphael & Sons;
Winkler & Schorn (*Nuremberg*); Zieher, Ottmar (*Munich*)

General Designs/Views
Period 1	..	..	..	..	..	..	..	£3/**£5**/£8
Others	..	..	..	..	..	..	£1/**£1.50**/£3

COURT CARDS ■EC 1

The Court Size postcard measures approx. 115 × 89 mm in
contrast to the 122 × 75 mm of the normal Periods 1 to 3
cards. Full UPU size in Periods 1 to 3 was 140 × 89 mm.
Court cards are indigenous to Britain (though similar size
Continental cards exist) and were used from *c.* 1895 until
early in Period 2. Court size views of Edinburgh published by
George Stewart in 1894 have sometimes been proposed as the

first British produced picture postcards, although privately produced court cards were not recognised by the Post Office until the issue of the first official court card (21 January 1895).

Publishers of British Court Cards include:
Beechings (whose views of London and Manchester now command a considerable premium) Blum & Degen; Faulkner; Frith; Photochrom; Pictorial Stationery Co.; Sandle Bros.; Stewart, Geo.; Valentines.

Gruss Aus types

Chromo-litho	..	..	..	..	..	..£8/**£12**/£25
Col. (not chromo-litho)		..	..	..	..	.. £6/**£8**/£10
B & w/sepia	..	..	..	..	..	£3/**£5**/£8

Thematic (Advertising, Commemorative, Exhibitions, Royalty, etc.) see the appropriate subject sections in this catalogue. The older the card the higher the value.
General views/vignettes

Chromo-litho	..	..	..	..	..	..£8/**£15**/£35
Col. (not chromo-litho)		..	..	..	..	£3/**£5**/£8
B & w/sepia	..	..	..	..	..	£1.50/**£3**/£5

■EC 1 Pub. Pictorial Stationery Co. Court card. Col. Ramsgate. Vignette. UB. Period 1 £15

GRUSS AUS TYPE ■EC2

Literally 'Greetings from . . .'. A type of card popularised in Germany in the 1880s, showing small, one colour line drawings/vignettes—pictures of a beauty spot or a town and its inhabitants—often in an elaborate border of flowers, scrolls, etc. By the mid-1890s these were also being produced in colour, often chromo-litho. Variations on the German words of greeting (according to the language of the country of origin) are: 'Greetings from . . .' (Britain & Colonies incl. India), *Gruss aus* . . . or *Gruss vom* . . . (Germany and Colonies), *Memorias de* . . . (Spain and Spanish-speaking countries), *Ricordi di* . . . and *Saluti di* . . . (Italy), *Souvenir de* . . . (Belgium, France and Colonies, Switzerland). The type was also produced in Russia! Generally speaking the earlier the card and the more obscure the country of origin (e.g. Heligoland) the more valuable it will be. Ultimately, however, the value of a *Gruss Aus* type card will be determined by its sheer appeal and beauty—and beauty is in the eye of the beholder.

Court Size—*see above*

Period 1 pre-1890

Chromo-litho	£10/**£20**/£30
Col. (not chromo-litho)	.. £8/**£12**/£18
B & w/sepia	.. £5/**£8**/£12

Line drawn, letterpress or intaglio black views on buff official cards. Picture occupies a third or less of the card   ..   ..
   ..   ..   £13/**£15**/£25

Period 1 post-1890

Chromo-litho	.. £3/**£6**/£18
Col. (not chromo-litho)	.. £2/**£5**/£10
B & w-sepia	£1.50/**£3**/£5

Early Period 2

Chromo-litho	.. £2/**£3**/£6
Col. (not chromo-litho)	£1.50/**£2**/£4
B & w/sepia	£1/**£1.50**/£2

■EC 2 Pub. A. Schmittner. Artist J. Puntky. Full UPU size 'Gruss Aus' card from Furth, Bavaria UB. Embossed £12

INTERMEDIATE SIZE

Unlike their continental counterparts, the British Post Office was loath to lift restrictions on the size of officially permitted postcards. By 1898 pressure was strong from British manufacturers and collectors alike and the Post Office was forced into permitting a larger sized card. In November 1899 full Universal Postal Union sized postcards gradually become redundant, disappearing by 1902.

Chromolitho vignettes	.. £5/**£10**/£15
B & W/sepia	.. £2/**£4**/£6

ENTERTAINMENT

CINEMA

CINEMA ADVERTISING ■E 1

Periods 2 to 4 .. .. £1/**£2**/£4
Periods 5 to 7 .. .. 30p/**£1**/£2
Italian artist Nanni. Superb *Art Deco* poster portraits of stars
  like Vittorio di Sica, Elsa Merlini .. .. £9/**£12**/£15

■E 1 Pub. Editions *Humour à la Carte*. 'Diva' poster ad.
Period 7 30p

CINEMAS/BIOSCOPES (Buildings)
Periods 3 to 5. Sharp photographs .. .. ..£5/**£10**/£20

FILM STARS
Many durable stars' careers spanned two or three postcard
periods. A listing of such stars was given in the fourth edition
of this catalogue, pp. 152–153. There has been an upsurge in
interest in Period 6, 7 recently.

Price range
Periods 2, 3. sought-after stars .. .. £1/**£2**/£4
Periods 2, 3. others .. .. 75p/**£1**/£1.50
Periods 4, 5. sought-after stars .. .. £2/**£4**/£8

Periods 4, 5. others	.. ..	75p/**£1.50**/£3
Periods 6, 7. sought-after stars	.. ..	£1/**£3**/£8
Periods, 6, 7. others	.. ..	50p/**75p**/£1.50

Hand autographed cards will always attract a premium.

Animated Film Characters (Periods 4 to 6)
Disney: scenes/characters

Pub. Valentine Period 4 ..	.. .. ..	£2.50/**£4**/£7
Published with Fr or Ger text	.. ..	£2/**£3.50**/£6
Others		£1.50/**£3**/£5
Felix the Cat		£1/**£2**/£4
Others		75p/**£1**/£2

FILM STILLS (with postcard backs)
Value according to Period and stars .. .. .. £2/**£3**/£4

CIRCUS

The modern circus has its origins in England in the late 18th-century when Philip Astley popularised trick riding. Showmen moved in from the declining fairs with their varying acts. Soon circuses started in America and by the turn of the century had spread throughout Europe and the USA. Permanent buildings housed some European circuses and a theatrical element crept in. By 1900 the circus was thriving throughout the world. Showmen like P. T. Barnum and James A. Bailey in the USA, and C. B. Cochran in Britain put the circus on a more business-like basis. During Periods 1 and 2 the popularity of the circus gave rise to some of the most fascinating and beautiful of postcards. The delicate chromo-litho drawings, the colourful poster type adverts and the intriguing photographs are all to be found in this category.

ACTS
These often have unusual and emotive names, e.g. Madame Alaska and her Performing Seals; Capt. Alphonzo, the Intrepid Lion-Tamer; The Sarrasani; Waldemeer, the Modern Hercules; Zarmah the Wild Animal Trainer.

Period 1/Early Period 2.

Chromo-litho drawings		£2/**£4**/£7.50
Photographs		£2/**£4**/£7.50
Poster type ads.		£2/**£4**/£7.50
Periods 2 to 4		£1/**£2.50**/£5
Periods 5 to 7		75p/**£1**/£1.50

NAMED CIRCUSES
Barnum & Bailey

Illustrations by Courmont and Franzl ..		£3/**£5**/£7.50
Poster type ads. Periods 2, 3		£10/**£20**/£25

Various photographic cards of acts	£2/**£4**/£6
Wolfgang Holzmour, Lord of the Lions. Period 7	
.. ..	75p/**£1.50**/£3

Buffalo Bill's Wild West Show

Poster type ads	£10/**£15**/£20
Various photographic cards of acts	£2/**£5**/£10

Busch Circus

Colourful poster type ads. Period 2	£5/**£7**/£10

Circus Althoff

Early Period 2. 'Gruss Aus'	£2/**£3.50**/£5

Circus Cesar Sideli

Colourful poster type ads. Period 2	£3/**£5**/£8

Cirkus Varieté, Copenhagen. Period 2. Acts, etc.	£2/**£3**/£5

Hagenbeck's Circus

Various animal and other acts	£2/**£4**/£6
Ringling Bros. Period 2. Poster ads.	£4/**£8**/£10

Royal Netherlands Circus

Early Period 2 vignettes	£2/**£3**/£5

Zirkus Krone, Zirkus Lorch, Zirkus Semsrott. Period 2 ..	
.. ..	£1.50/**£3**/£6
Others	£1.50/**£3**/£8

SITES/TENTS

Artists impressions	£1.50/**£3**/£5
RPs	..£5/**£10**/£20

THEATRE

This section describes actors, actresses, advertising, theatre buildings and stills from theatrical productions. It also includes cards dealing with 'fringe theatre' acts like Punch and Judy, etc. Freaks, and other strange phenomena who entertained the public in circus or fair side shows and theatres are described under CURIOUS.

ACTORS AND ACTRESSES ▇E 2

Literally hundreds of thousands of portrait postcards were published during the Edwardian era of the stars of the legitimate stage, music hall and panto. A comprehensive listing of the run-of-the-mill and the great performers was printed in the fourth edition of this catalogue. pp. 156–157.

Price range Common stars	50p/**75p**/£1.50
Great performers	£2/**£5**/£8

Hand autographed cards will always attract a premium.

ADVERTISING

Poster Types

See ARTISTS for details of theatrical work by Tom Browne (the 'Arcadians'), Raphael Kirchner (Geisha, Mikado, San Toy).

Pub. David Allen & Sons Ltd., Belfast & Harrow. *The largest publishers of theatre posters who reproduced many of their full size posters as postcards from about 1903.*
See COLLECTIONS.

Price range   ..   ..£5/**£15**/£30

■■E 2 Pub. Beagles. Dan Leno. Hand autograph pasted on. Period 2 £5

Pub. Haycock-Caale Co. Camberley. *Productions include* Mr. Wu; *artists include Bert Thomas.*
Price range   ..   ..   **£2/£4/£8**

Pub. John Waddington. Leeds & London. *A company which produced some fine poster adverts during Periods 2 to 4. Play titles include*:
'Extra Special'; 'Flying Colours' (Artist Bairnsfather); 'Joy Bells'.
Price range   ..   ..   £5/**£15**/£30+

Other Publishers.
Price range   ..   ..£3/**£8**/£15

Advertising on Reverse/Play Stills
A list of the publishers who produced such cards was printed in the fourth edition of this catalogue, p. 158.

Periods 2–4   ..   ..   £1/**£3**/£5
Periods 5–7   ..   ..   50p/**75p**/£1.50

DANCERS ■E 3

Artist Drawn
Price range   ..   ..   50p/**£2.50**/£12

Ballet—Real Photographic
Dolin, Anton
Genée, Dame Adeline
Karsavina, Tamara
Markova, Alicia
Massine
Nijinski
Pavlova
Price range   ..   ..   £2.50/**£5**/£10

Other Types of Dancer
Duncan, Isadora
Fuller, Loi
Graham, Martha
Goulue, La
Hari, Mata (Mrs. McLeod)
Price range   ..   ..   £2/**£8**/£15

Hand autographed cards will always attract a premium.

■E 3 Pub. Reliance Printing Co. 'The Original Southend Jolly Boys'. Period 2 £2

PUBLISHERS
Productions vary from matt photographic to highly glossy, ornate borders and frames, photomontages, etc.
Pub. Aristophot; Davidson Bros.; Dennis; Faulkner; Hartmann; Lillywhite; Knight Bros.; Philco; Rapid Photo; Rotary; Tuck; Valentine; Wrench.
Price range for common stars   ..   ..   ..   25p/**75p**/£3

Pub. Rotary. Real photo stamp postcards with adhesive backs
..   ..   £1/**£1.50**/£3
Pub. Silberer & Bros. Leading artists of the American stage
..   ..   50p/**75p**/£1.50

THEATRE BUILDINGS
Good close ups of photographic origin of opera houses, theatres

on piers and in towns. Publishers include: Excelsior Fine Art
Co., Knight Bros., Local Publishers, Rotary, Valentine.

Exteriors .. ..£5/**£10**/£15
Interiors .. .. £2/**£4**/£6

WIRELESS

Artist-Drawn Cards With Wireless Interest
Periods 2 to 7; Value according to artist.
Price range .. .. 50p/**£2**/£6

Broadcasters: Groups & Portraits

Periods 2, 3, 4
*Often showing groups of musicians from the days of early
broadcasting with the station number ('2LO', etc.), some
showing good detail of microphones, equipment, etc.*
Price range .. .. £1.50/**£2.50**/£4

Period 5
*Stars from the popular war-time shows, like Arthur Askey,
Tommy Handley, etc.*
Price range .. .. £1/**£1.50**/£2

Comic Wireless Cards

Periods 2 to 4
Various artists, value according to artist and period .. ..
.. .. 75p/**£1**/£2

Period 5
Incl. 'ITMA' jokes by Bert Thomas and others £1/**£1.50**/£3

Other Wireless Subjects
Price range .. .. 75p/**£1**/£1.50

Three Band Pricing System
Left Hand Band: The lowest price you will probably
be asked to pay for this card.
Middle Band: What you will normally be asked to pay
for this card: its average, reasonable price.
Right Hand Band: The highest price you will probably
be asked to pay for this card.
For a full explanation of the system see page ix.

EXHIBITIONS/EXPOSITIONS/
TRADE FESTIVALS/
WORLD FAIRS

The first of the great International Exhibitions was held at the Crystal Palace in Hyde Park in 1851. At the 1882 Nuremberg Exhibition an official commemorative card bearing a photo-litho vignette view was issued—produced by the printer Zrenner who afterwards claimed that it was the first true 'picture' postcard. Whether it was or not, it was at the Paris Exhibition in 1889 that the privately produced picture post-card made the enormous public impact that began the collecting frenzy. After that date every exhibition (or exposition) had its official and privately produced cards. This is a popular collecting theme, particularly for Period 1 and early Period 2 events when the cards produced were often well designed and printed by chromo-lithography. Generally speaking, the higher values relate to especially designed artist drawn cards or novelty cards like silks. Cards bearing Exhibition postmarks will command a premium.

Nuremberg (1882)	£25/**£35**/£40
Turin (1884)	£25/**£30**/£40
Paris (1889)	£15/**£20**/£30
London (1890). Penny Postage Jubilee	£3/**£4**/£5
London (1891). Royal Naval. Eddystone Lighthouse	
.. ..	£30/**£60**/£80
Vienna (1892). International Music. Vignette. Artist Kronstein. PS back	£5/**£9**/£11

Chicago (1893). *The first commercially produced picture post-cards in America were made by Charles W. Goldsmith for the World's Columbian Exposition in Chicago. They are superb chromo-litho prints on an oversize official card. The first set comprised 10 cards all of which are numbered. In a second printing two of the cards, Nos. 6 and 7, had totally new views. These are shown in brackets below.*

1. Government Building	£10/**£12**/£15
2. Administration Building	..£8/**£10**/£12
3. Manufacturers & Liberal Arts	..£8/**£10**/£12
4. The Agricultural Building	..£8/**£10**/£12
5. The Electrical Building	£8/**£10**/£12
6. Horticultural Building	£10/**£12**/£14
(Fine Art Building).	£6/**£8**/£10
7. Mines Building	£10/**£12**/£14
(Machinery Building)	.. £6/**£8**/£10
8. The Fisheries Building	..£8/**£10**/£12
9. The Womans Building	..£8/**£10**/£12
10. Battle Ship Illinois	£8/**£10**/£12
London (1893). Gardening & Forestry. Eddystone Lighthouse	
.. ..	£50/**£70**/£100
Milan (1894). Philatelic	.. £6/**£8**/£10
Venice (1894). Postcard Exhibition	£15/**£25**/£50
Berlin (1896)	.. £6/**£8**/£10
Budapest (1896)	.. £6/**£8**/£10

Nuremberg (1896). Chromo-litho	£7/**£8**/£9
Ditto. Photo-origin	£8/**£9**/£10
Brussels (1897)	£5/**£7**/£10
Central American (1897)	£5/**£7**/£10
Dresden (1897). Artist drawn. Col. litho ..	£6/**£9**/£12
Hamburg (1897)	£6/**£8**/£10
Leipzig (1897)	£3/**£4**/£5
London (1897). Victorian Era Exhibition, Earls Court ..	
.. ..	£35/**£50**/£60
Nuremberg (1897)	£3/**£4**/£5
Toronto (1897). Victorian Era Exposition ..	£10/**£25**/£40
Bergen (1898). Artist Carl Dotzler	£16/**£19**/£21
Vienna (1898). Jubilee	£3/**£4**/£5
Ghent (1899)	£5/**£7**/£9
Nice (1899). Exposition de Cartes Postales ..	..£7/**£10**/£12
Period 1. General	..£3/**£6**/£10
Paris (1900). Artist Jack Abeille	£10/**£15**/£20
Ditto. Postcard entrance pass	.. £6/**£8**/£10
Ditto. Meteor transparancies ▐▐EX 1 ..	..£8/**£10**/£12

▐EX 1 Pub. 'Meteor'. Hold to Light. Paris Universal Exhibition, 1900. The Eiffel Tower. £10

Salzburg (1900). Fishing	£2/**£4**/£5
Berlin (1901). Official cards pub. by Klimoff and Co. At least 3 series of 6	£2/**£3**/£5
Buffalo NY (1901). Pan American. Over 12 pubs. including Livingston & Strauss	£1/**£4**/£6
Dresden (1901)	£2/**£3**/£5
Glasgow (1901)	
Artist Cassiers, pub. Dietrich	£3/**£4**/£5
Other publishers	£1/**£2**/£2.50
Cork (1902)	£1/**£2**/£3
Wolverhampton (1902)	£1/**£2**/£2.50
Bradford (1904)	£1/**£2**/£2.50
St. Louis (1904). Louisiana Purchase World's Fair.	
Artist H. Wunderlich	£1/**£3**/£5
Chromo-litho vignettes	75p/**£1**/£1.50

Hold to Light	£3/**£5**/£6
Monochrome views	**50p**
Photo-origin views	25p/**50p**/75p
Silver finish views	25p/**50p**/£1
Others	25p/**50p**/£1
Liège (1905)	£1/**£2**/£5
Milan (1906). Gilded cards	£1.50/**£3**/£5
Others	50p/**75p**/£1.50
Nuremberg (1906)	£1/**£2**/£3

Dublin (1907). Irish International.

General	£1/**£1.50**/£2
Woven silk. Pub. Grant, W. H.	£12/**£15**/£20

Jamestown (1907). 300th Anniv. of first English settlement
in America .. .. £2.50/**£5**/£8

Prague (1908). Radiotelegraphic. R. P. cards £1.50/**£3**/£4

White City (1908). Franco-British.

Comic designs by named artists like Crombie, Sarg ..	
.. ..	50p/**£1**/£1.50
Designs by artist A. K. Macdonald .. .. ..£5/**£10**/£15	
Famous people at the Exhibition	50p/**75p**/£2
Flip Flop	50p/**75p**/£1
General views	**50p**
Hagenback's Circus	75p/**£1**/£1.25
Mucha advertisement for Job Cigarettes with Exhibition overprint	£25/**£50**/£75
Ornamental/Patriotic coloured borders ..	75p/**£1**/£1.50
Oversize views	50p/**75p**/£1
Trade stands	£1/**£1.50**/£2
Unusual designs	£1/**£3**/£8

Frankfurt (1909). Poster type. Artist Correggio .. £5/**£7**/£8

Argentine (1910). Republic Centennial. Poster type £3/**£5**/£7

Vienna (1910). Hunting. Poster type. Artists Kalmsteiner,
Lenhard, Puchinger .. .. £2/**£4**/£6

White City (1910). Japan-British. *General categories and
valuations as for Franco-British above.* ■EX 2

Artist Fred Spurgin. Pub. Paternoster ..	75p/**£1.50**/£2
Artist Mortimer Menpes. Pub. Tuck ..	75p/**£1.50**/£2

Crystal Palace (1911). Festival of Empire. Rotary Photo Series
No. 6799. Over 30 cards in series .. .. 50p/**75p**/£1

Turin (1911). International. Poster type. Artist A. de Karolis
.. .. £1.50/**£2**/£3

Chelsea (1912). Royal International Horticultural. Poster type
.. .. £4/**£6**/£8

Breslau (1913). Artist drawn .. .. .. £4/**£5**/£7

Leipzig (1913). International Architecture.

Art Deco poster types	£6/**£9**/£11
Other artist drawn	£1.50/**£2**/£3

Leipzig (1914). Artist drawn .. .. £2.50/**£3**/£4

San Diego (1915). Panama-Californian. At least 14 different
pubs. identified

Pub. Detroit Pub. Co.	75p/**£1**/£1.50
Pub. Fred Harvey	£1/**£1.25**/£2
Others	25p/**50p**/£1

San Francisco (1915). Panama-Pacific International. Over 30
different pubs. identified. ■EX 3

Pub. H. S. Crocker. Pre-Exhibition poster ..	£2/**£5**/£8
Others	£2/**£5**/£10

■EX 2 Pub. Tuck. Artist Mortimer Menpes. Souvenir Japan British Exhibition 1910 (from *Japan Illustrated* by Menpes) £2

■EX 3 Pub. Anon. Underwood typewriter ad. on San Francisco Panama-Pacific Exhibition 1915 £10

Blackpool (1916). Loos Trenches. Recreation of battlefield at
Loos. Two different pubs. identified   ..   £1/**£1.75**/£2
Wembley (1924/25). British Empire. ■EX 4
Exhibitors' cards by Tuck included Anglo-Persian Oil Co.,
Bryant & May, Canadian National Railways, Canadian
Pacific Railway, the Catholic Oratory, Idris, Imperial
Airways, North British Rubber Co., Schweppes, Sharpe's
Toffee and South African Wine   ..   ..   50p/**£1**/£1.50
General views/art studies, e.g. Artist Ernest Coffin ..   ..
..   ..   25p/**50p**/£1
Named artists e.g. Harry Payne   ..   ..   ..   £1/**£3**/£7
Tuck Oilettes ..   ..   £1/**£2**/£3
Overprints or sepia views for product advertising, incl.
Anglo-Persian Oil Co., Eno's Fruit Salts, Express Dairy,
Mersey Docks and Pears Soap   ..   ..   50p/**75p**/£2
'Super Circus' poster ads, pub. Waterlow   £18/**£20**/£26
Paris (1925). Decorative Arts. Five different pubs. identified
..   ..   25p/**50p**/75p

161

■EX 4 Pub. Tuck. Artist Charles E. Flower. Bryant & May Cottage. British Empire Exhibition, Wembley 1924 £4

Philadelphia (1926). 150th Anniv. of the founding of the USA.
.. .. 25p/**50p**/75p
Strasbourg (1927). International Philatelic. Poster type an
official, pre-stamped card .. .. .. £3/**£5**/£6
Newcastle-on-Tyne (1929). North East Coast .. 50p/**£1**/£3
Antwerp (1930). International 25p/50p
Liege (1930). International .. .. .. £1/**£1.50**/£3
Milan (1930). Poster type. Fiat. Artist Mizoli £1/**£2**/£2.50
Vienna (1930). Philatelic. Artist drawn .. £1.50/**£3**/£5
Paris (1931). International Colonial .. .. 25p/**50p**/£1
Chicago (1933). World's Fair .. .. .. 50p/**£1**/£1.25
London (1934). Ideal Home. Photo cards of Heath Robinson
exhibits .. .. £1.50/**£2**/£3
Breslau (1935). Col. poster type .. ..£9/**£10**/£12
Dresden (1936). Olympic Year Stamp Show .. £7/**£9**/£10
Paris (1937). International Arts & Crafts .. 25p/**50p**/75p
Glasgow (1938). Empire. Pubs. Valentine's and at least 3
others .. .. 25p/**75p**/£1
Wellington (1939). New Zealand Centennial. Five different
pubs. identified .. .. 50p/**£1**/£1.50
San Francisco (1939). Golden Gate. At least seven pubs.
identified .. .. –/**25p**/50p
New York (1939). World's Fair 25p/**50p**/75p
New York (1947). Postal Centennial. 'Souvenir Postal Card',
Pub. Lee C. Cray Printed stamp. Illus. both sides .. ..
.. .. £1/**£1.50**/£3
London (1951). Festival of Britain. Pubs. include Salmon,
Tuck, Jarrolds & Valentine's. Most cards are photo type
.. .. 25p/**50p**/75p
New York (1964). World's Fair. Most cards pub. by Dexter
Color **50p**
Montreal (1967). Expo '67. Various, incl. col. photos, repro. of
Exhibition stamp 25p/**50p**/75p
New Orleans (1984). World's Fair. Range of artist drawn/
photographic cards. **25p**
Liverpool (1984). Art of the Beatles ■EX 5 .. .. **50p**

■EX 5 Pub. Merseyside County Council. Artist David Oxtoby. 'The Art of the Beatles' Exhibition 1984 50p

BATTLEFIELD & ANCIENT HISTORY TOURS
Organised by Europe's leading Experts
MAJOR & MRS. HOLT

Destinations include:
WW1: Ypres, Vimy, Somme, Mons, Cambrai, Hindenberg Line, Verdun, etc.
WW2: Normandy Beaches, Arnhem, Rhine Crossing, Anzio, Berlin, Munich, El Alamein.

U.S. CIVIL WAR   WATERLOO
EGYPT, GREECE, ITALY
AGINCOURT, CRECY, PORTSMOUTH

Full tour commentary, luxury coach, 3 star hotels, Maps, Literature, all combined to transport you back in time.

Brochure from:
**Major & Mrs. Holt's Tours,
15 Market St, Sandwich, Kent CT13 9DA.**

EXPEDITIONS/EXPLORATION

The period covered by the 'Golden Age' of the picture postcard, 1869–1914, was one of intense activity in the field of exploration and adventure. Happily, the course of many of these exciting expeditions was charted on the postcard—from Nansen's 1893 Arctic expedition by sea, to Byrd's historic flight over the North Pole in 1926 and Andrée's exploits in the same area in a hot air balloon, ending with his tragic death in 1930. Other historic characters, like Captain Scott and Amundsen, became postcard heroes too, and expeditions from the Sahara Desert to Victoria Falls were featured on the newsworthy, topical medium of the picture postcard. This is a fascinating area of collection, fast growing in popularity and appreciation. Record prices were achieved in auction during 1985 for signed cards in this section, notably Wrench's 1901 'Links of the Empire' signed by Capt. Scott. Autographed cards always command a high premium to the following prices, as will postmarks from places on the itinerary.

EVEREST

1922. Gen. the Hon. C. G. Bruce. Everest Expedition. Sepia. RP of named party of 12: Bruce, Crawford, Finch, Longstaff, Mallory, Morris, Morshead, Noel, Norton, Somervell, Strutt, Wakefield .. .. £1/**£2**/£4
1924. Gen. the Hon. C. G. Bruce. Everest Expedition. Film ads.

Facsimile signature (unsigned)	£5/**£7**/£10
Signed	£10/**£15**/£25

GENERAL

Pub. Anon. Set of 12 cards. UB. Continental backs. Fine col. and printing. Early Period 2. See fourth edition of this catalogue p 166 for list.

Per card	£2.50/**£5**/£8
Per complete set	£50/**£75**/£100

POLAR ■EXP 1–3

1893. Nansen's Expedition to the North Pole in *The Fram*

Composite set—*see* NOVELTY
Pub. Aristophot. Period 2. Portrait of Nansen .. £6/**£8**/£10
Pub. Meissner & Buch. (1898). Series 1016 of 12 chromo-litho. *Aus Nansen in Nacht und Eis.* Artist Goldberg.

The cards were listed in the Third edition of this catalogue, p. 162.

Per card	..£8/**£12**/£15
Per set	£95/**£195**/£225
Others	.. £5/**£8**/£10

■EXP 1 Pub. H. Abel. Portrait of Fridtjof Nansen. 1899 £5

■EXP 2 Pub. Armanino, Genova. Rare card of Duke of Abruzzi's expedition to North Pole. 1899. UB £12

■EXP 3 Pub. Anon. Ger. Satyrical comment on 1908–9 rivalry between Cook & Peary. Period 2 £8

1897. Adrien de Gerlache (Belg) Antarctic Expedition
Pub. Nels. Series of 10 .. ..£8/**£12**/£15
Return of Expedition (1899) .. ..£8/**£15**/£20
Others .. ..£5/**£10**/£15

1897–1930. Andrée (Fr). Expedition to the North Pole by hot air balloon
Pub. Bergeret, Nancy. Set of 25, showing the expedition ships, the hot air balloon, scenes in Norway, Denmark, etc.
    Per card .. ..£8/**£12**/£15
    Per set .. .. £200/**£250**/P/A
Portraits of Andrée, etc. when his body and diary were found
    (1930) .. .. £3/**£5**/£7

1899–1900. Duke of Abruzzi/Capt. Cagni (It) Arctic Expedition in the *Stella Polare*
Various expedition cards .. ..£5/**£10**/£12
Rome Conference/Subscription cards (1901) ..£8/**£12**/£18

1901. British National Antarctic Expedition. Capt. Scott and *The Discovery*
Pub. Wrench. 'Links of the Empire'. Series of 4
Posted from ports of call .. .. £75/**£100**/£150
Unposted .. .. £25/**£50**/£75

1901. Otto Sverdrup's Arctic Expedition in the *Fram*
Price range .. ..£8/**£10**/£12

1901. De Drygalski (Ger) South Polar Expedition on the *Gaus*
Price range .. .. £5/**£8**/£12

1903–05. Dr. J. B. Charcot. (Fr) Expedition to Antarctic in the *Français*
Launch of the *Français*. 27 June 1903. St. Malo £8/**£10**/£15
Pub. Tuck. Souvenir card of subscribers .. £15/**£30**/£40
Series of 20 Expedition cards. Per card .. .. £5/**£8**/£10
Others .. .. £3/**£5**/£10

1904. Scottish National Antarctic Expedition
Pub. Wm. Ritchie. Probably 12 cards in set .. £6/**£8**/£10

1908–36. Dr. J. B. Charcot (Fr) Expeditions to Antarctic in the *Pourquoi Pas*?
Launch of the *Pourquoi Pas*?. Several versions £8/**£10**/£12
Series of 1908 Expedition. incl. return to Rouen. Pub. E.L.D.,
    N.D. and others .. .. £5/**£8**/£10
Series of 1910 Expedition. Pub. E.L.D., N.D. and others
    .. ..£6/**£10**/£20
Shipwreck (1936) .. .. £5/**£8**/£10
Funeral of Charcot (1936) .. .. £10/**£15**/£20

1908. Capt. Robert E. Peary (USA) Expedition to North Pole in the *Roosevelt* and controversy with Dr. Frederick A. Cook in the *John R. Bradley*
Pub. *Hampton's Magazine*
    13 'North Pole Gravure Series'. Per card .. .. £4/**£6**/£8

Pub. Kawin & Co. Chicago
Set of 50 b & w photos .. .. £3/**£5**/£6
Pub. Taggart
Series of sepia photos .. .. £2/**£4**/£5
Pub. Tuck.
Oilettes by A. Operati .. .. £3/**£5**/£7
Pub. Ullman
North Pole series 162 by Bernhardt Wall .. £3/**£4**/£6
Series of 3 official postcards of SS *Roosevelt* with inset Peary
portrait. PU. Coastal T.P.O. 12 Sept. 1909. Per card ..
.. .. £50/**£75**/£100
Various comic/satirical designs highlighting the rivalry
between Cook and Peary .. .. £3/**£5**/£8

1908. Shackleton's Expedition to Antarctic with *Nimrod*
Price range (Highest value for adverts) .. .. £5/**£8**/£10

1910. Amundsen's Antarctic Expedition
Price range .. ..£8/**£10**/£12

1910. Capt. Scott's Antarctic Expedition (with Bowers, Evans, Oates, Wilson)
Ad. for Fry's Cocoa. Col. Poster type .. .. £30/**£40**/£50
Expedition scenes .. .. £5/**£8**/£10
In Memoriam cards .. ..£8/**£10**/£12
Portraits .. .. £5/**£7**/£8

1911. Australasian Antarctic Expedition with SY *Aurora*
Price range .. .. £1/**£2**/£5

Period 2. Scientific Expedition in the Hot Air Balloon *Princess Alice*
Set of 24, showing Alfonso XIII of Spain and the Prince of
Monaco, etc. in Spitzberg
Per card .. .. £5/**£8**/£12
Per set .. .. £160/**£200**/P/A

1914. Shackleton's Antarctic Expedition
Price range .. .. £4/**£8**/£15

1918. Amundsen's attempted drift over N. Pole in the dirigible *Maud*
Price range .. .. £10/**£15**/£20

1925–26. Flights over the N. Pole in airships/dirigibles by Amundsen, Bennett, Byrne, Ellsworth, Nobile
Price range .. .. £12/**£20**/£25

1926. Commander Richard Evelyn Byrd (USA) Flight over North Pole
Series of 18 cards. Per card .. ..£5/**£10**/£15

1934. Commander Byrd (USA) Antarctic Expedition
Price range .. ..£7/**£12**/£20

SAHARA

1921. Captain Angus Buchanan (UK) Expedition to cross the 'Great Sahara' ■EXP 4

Set of 12 photo postcards showing Capt. Buchanan, other members of his team, animals, salt cones, oasis, nomads, etc.

Per card	£1/**£2**/£2.50
Per complete set	£13/**£25**/£35

Other Expeditions

Price range	£1/**£3**/£5

■EXP 4 Pub. Anon. Transporting big game specimens to camp during Capt. Buchanan's 1921 'Great Sahara Expedition'. Autographed on reverse by 2 of the subjects Period 4 £2.50

FREE POSTCARD OFFER!

Stanley Gibbons have commissioned a special series of 'Familar Figures of London' cards mirroring those which have appeared on all four editions of the Stanley Gibbons Postcard Catalogue. Number **3** in the series, **'The Flower Seller'** was given free with the 'Picture Postcard Monthly' and 'The British Postcard Collectors Magazine' as well as being distributed through Postcard Collectors Clubs.

Number 4, 'The Shoeblack' is available only to purchasers of this catalogue. In order to obtain your copy of this exclusive limited-edition card please clip off the coupon on the corner of page xiii and send it together with a stamp addressed envelope to:

Postcard Offer,
Stanley Gibbons Publications Limited
Parkside,
Ringwood, Hampshire BH24 3SH.

Remember the number of cards available is strictly limited and that they can only be obtained in exchange for the coupon.

Look out for card Number 5.

GLAMOUR

The general term 'Glamour' classifies postcards depicting
feminine and/or masculine charms, from the nude, through
the scantily dressed to the fully clothed. The earliest
'Glamour' postcards are to be found in Period 1 and are
usually of bathing beauties (*cf.* Jack Abeille). During Period
2 the pictures became more daring and more popular, with
the French the undisputed leaders in the field. The work of
Xavier Sager, the most prolific of all the 'Glamour' artists,
epitomises the genre. The type blossomed anew during Period
3, when the term 'pin-up' was coined (*see* MILITARY). During
Period 4 the best artists survived by adapting to the new
decorative art style (*Art Deco*) and the most striking designs
in this era are to be found in Italy.

AMERICAN GIRL (THE) ■G 1, A 9, 20, GR 1
A species unique to that country, of bright, outgoing, athletic,
socialite or collegiate types. Her sophistication is tinged with
innocence, in direct contrast to the coy, lingerie-clad creations
of the European glamour genre. Main artists include:

Banks, E. C.	£1/**£1.50**/£2
Boileau, Philip†	£2/**£4**/£8
Christy, F. Earl†	£2/**£3**/£4
Christy, Howard Chandler†	£1/**£2**/£4
Dewey, Alfred James	£1/**£2**/£3
Elliott, Kathryn	75p/**£1.50**/£2
Farini, May	£1/**£2**/£3
Fidler, Pearle (*married name Le Munyan*) ..	£1/**£2**/£4
Fidler, Alice Luella	£1/**£2**/£3
Fisher, Harrison†	£2/**£4**/£6
Flagg, James Montgomery†	£1/**£2**/£4
Gilbert, Allen	75p/**£1**/£2

■G1 Pub. Edward Gross
(overprinted Alfred Stiebel).
Artist Penly Stanlaws.
Period 2 £3

Gunn, Archie†	£1/**£2**/£3
Hare, J. Knowles†	75p/**£1**/£2
Hunter, Lillian Woolsey	£1/**£1.50**/£2
Kimball, Alonzo†	£1.50/**£2.50**/£3.50
King, H.†	75p/**£1**/£2
Kinneys, The	£1/**£2**/£3
McFall, J. V.	75p/**£1**/£2
Mayer, Lou	£2/**£4**/£5
Powell, Lyman C.	75p/**£1.50**/£2
Ralph, Lester	£1/**£2**/£3
Reiter, Brill G.	75p/**£1**/£1.50
Reynolds (*Wild West Flavour*)	£1/**£2**/£4
Schmucker, Samuel†	£3/**£5**/£8
St. John	75p/**£1**/£2
Stanlaws, Penly	£1/**£2**/£3
Underwood, Clarence†	£1/**£1.50**/£3
Waskow, Edward G.	75p/**£1**/£1.50

EROTIC/PORNOGRAPHIC
Cards in this section vary from the gently titillating to the blatantly erotic.

Deshabille/Lingerie (Periods 2 to 4)
Artist drawn, unsigned/photographic origin	25p/**50p**/£1.50
RP	50p/**£1**/£2

Erotic
Phallic symbols like asparagus, bananas, flutes, towers, swans, trees, etc. and lesbian interest. The 'suggestive' rather than the explicit.
Artist drawn	75p/**£1.50**/£3
Photographic origin	£1/**£3**/£5

Eunuchs and Harems
Artist drawn	£1/**£2**/£5
Photographic origin	£2/**£5**/£8

Fantasy
Girls as neckties. French series	£5/**£10**/£20
Heads composed of beauties *en déshabillé*	£4/**£5**/£8
Mechanical incl. Blow-up bosoms and posteriors/ Spanking—*see* NOVELTY	£2/**£4**/£6
Photomontage	£2/**£4**/£6

House of German Art
Period 5. Hitler-approved Aryan beauties.
B & w	75p/**£1.50**/£3
Coloured	£2/**£3**/£5

Nudes
Artist drawn	£1/**£3**/£15
Photographic (Paris Salon, etc.)	£1/**£3**/£5
Seldoms and other stage acts	£1/**£2**/£4

Pornographic
Artist drawn	£3/**£5**/£10
Photographic origin	£3/**£5**/£10

Prostitution

Brothels (interior and exterior)	£2/**£4**/£5
Prostitutes	£2/**£4**/£5

■|G2 Pub. James Henderson. Artist C. Dana Gibson. 'Pictorial Comedy'. No. 164. PU 1908 £2.50

EUROPEAN ARTISTS ■G 2, 3, A 1, 6, 24, 27, AD 3, 9, C 2

These fall into three types—the slightly risqué, often scantily clad; the robust, bosomy Asti types; and the elegant Gibson-girl types.

Abeille, Jack (*Fr*)†	£10/**£20**/£25
Asti, Angelo (*It*)† (Highest for 'Job')	£1/**£2**/£30
Aveline, F.†	75p/**£1**/£1.50
Balfour-Kerr (*Gibson types*)	75p/**£1**/£1.50
Barber, C. W.	75p/**£1.50**/£2
Barribal, W.†	£2/**£4**/£6
Bayard-Jones (*Gibson types*)	75p/**£1**/£1.50
Bertiglia, A. (*It*)	£1/**£2**/£3
Bettinelli (*It*)	£1/**£2**/£3
Bianchi (*It*)	£1.50/**£2.50**/£4
Blanchard	£1/**£2**/£3
Bompard, Luigi (*It*)†	£1.50/**£2.50**/£4
Bonora (*It*)	75p/**£1**/£2
Bonzagni, Aroldo (*It*)	£1/**£3**/£5
Brisley, E. C.	75p/**£1.50**/£2.50
Brown, Maynard	75p/**£1.50**/£2
Brunelleschi, Umberto (*It*)†	£25/**£50**/£70
Busi, Adolfo (*It*)	£4/**£6**/£8
Butcher, Arthur	75p/**£1.50**/£2
Calderara, C. (*It*)†	£1.50/**£3**/£6
Capiello, Leonetto (*It*)	£1/**£1.50**/£2
Cenni, Elda (*It*)	£1.50/**£3**/£4
Cherubini, M. (*It*)	£1/**£2**/£3
Collins, G. T. (*Asti types*)	75p/**£1**/£1.50
Colombo, E. (*It*)	£1/**£2**/£4
Corbella, Tito (*It*)†	£1.50/**£3**/£5

■G3 Pub. 'L. E.' Paris. Artist R. Kirchner. 'Yes, I'm waiting'. PU 1916 £15

Dedina, Jean (*Czeck*)†	£2.50/**£5**/£8
Dudovich, Marcello (*It*)	. .£5/**£10**/£15
English, Archibald	50p/**75p**/£1
Fabiano (*Fr*)	£2/**£4**/£6
Fontan, Léo (*Fr*)	£2/**£4**/£6
Gayac (*dancers a speciality*)	£3/**£4**/£6
Gibson, Charles Dana (*American, but with strong European connexions*)†	£1/**£1.50**/£3
Grosze, Manni (*silhouettes*)	£1/**£2**/£4
Guerzoni, C. (*It*)	£1/**£2**/£4
Harbour, Jennie (*crinoline types*)	£2/**£4**/£6
Haviland, Frank	£2/**£3**/£4
Hérouard (*Fr*)	£3/**£5**/£6
Horrell, Charles†	£1/**£1.50**/£2
Horsfall, Mary (*colourful, elegant girls*)† ..	£1/**£2**/£3
Icart, Louis (*Fr*)	£2/**£4**/£6
Jarasch, A. (*Fr*)	£3/**£5**/£6
Jozsa, K. (*Aust*)	£15/**£25**/£35
Kez ('*Simplissimus*', etc.)	£2/**£3**/£4
King, W. R. (*Gibson types*)	75p/**£1**/£1.50
Kirchner, Raphael (*Aust*)†	. .£7/**£15**/£30
Léonnec (*Fr*)	£3/**£5**/£6
Longley, Chiltern	. .£5/**£10**/£15
Maréchaux, C. (*Fr*)	£1/**£2.50**/£5
Mauzan, Achille (*It*)†	£2/**£3**/£4
Meunier, Suzanne (*Fr*)	£4/**£5**/£6
Millière, Maurice (*Fr*)	£3/**£4**/£5
Monier, M	£2/**£4**/£6
Monestier, C. (*It*)	£2/**£3**/£4
Montedoro, M. (*It*)	£3/**£8**/£15
Muggiano (*It*)	£1/**£2**/£3
Nanni, Giovanni (*It*) (*Fashion*)†	£2/**£4**/£5
Ney (*Fr*)	£4/**£5**/£6
Peltier (*Fr*)	£2/**£3.50**/£5

Pénot, A. (*Fr*)	..	..	..	..	..	..	..	£2/**£4**/£6
Pépin (*Fr*) ..	..	..	..	..	..	..	..	£2/**£4**/£5
Péras (*Fr*) ..	..	..	..	..	..	..	..	£1/**£2**/£3
Peraux, Lionel (*Pub. Tuck*)				..	..	..	..	£1/**£3**/£5
Plum, A. ..	..	..	..	..	..	..	..	£1/**£2**/£3
Popini	..	..	..	..	..	..	..	£2.50/**£4**/£6
Rappini (*It*)	..	..	..	..	..	..	..	£2/**£3**/£4
Rauh, Ludwig	..	..	..	..	..	..	..	£4/**£8**/£10
Sager, Xavier (*Fr*)†	..	..	..	..	..	..	£2/**£4**/£10
San Marco (*It*)	..	..	..	..	..	..	£1/**£2.50**/£5
Simonetti, A. M. (*It*)	..	..	..	..	..	..	£2/**£3**/£4
Spurgin, Fred†	..	..	..	..	..	..	75p/**£1.50**/£3
Tam, Jean ..	..	..	..	..	..	..	..	£3/**£5**/£6
Turner (*Gibson types*)		..	..	..	..	50p/**75p**/£1
Usabal (*Ger*)	..	..	..	..	..	..	£1/**£1.50**/£3
Wennerberg, Brynolf (*Ger*)†		..	..	..	..	£4/**£6**/£8
Unsigned ..	..	..	..	..	..	..	..50p/**£3**/£10

LANGUAGE OF . . .

Type of code or message card to convey an amusing/loving/sexual meaning. Subjects include: *babies, eyes, knots and vegetables. The best known artist seen on this type of card is Maurice Boulanger.*

Price range   ..   ..   50p/**75p**/£4

MALE GLAMOUR

Boxers/wrestlers in 'beef-cake' or fighting poses—named, e.g. A. Aberg (Russian champ.), Launceston Elliott, Gruhn, Hackenschmidt, Tom Jenkins, Eugen Sandow, others   ..
   ..   .. £1/**£2**/£4
He-man poses, body-builders, boxers, wrestlers, etc.—unnamed   ..   ..   75p/**£1.50**/£3
Publishers of the above include Beagles. Rapid Photo Co., Rotary.
Homosexual interest ..   .. £2/**£3**/£5

ROMANCE/SENTIMENT

Many sentimental wartime postcards exist (notably the embroidered silks) with appropriate verses (see MILITARY*). Pre- and post-war series exist in their thousands, of varying merit and artistic quality. Many with* Art Deco *and* Art Nouveau *interest are well above average quality as are early Period 2 chromolithos, accounting for the highest valuations. The romantic theme was often given the comic treatment (see* COMIC*).*

Anonymous or Minor Artist Drawn
Beauties, courtship, kisses. Periods 1 to 6. Value according to artistic merit and age.
Price range   ..   ..   50p/**£2**/£5

Photographic in Origin
Posed subjects as above, many hand-tinted, many of Continental origin by anonymous publishers.
Price range   ..   ..   50p/**75p**/£1.50

GREETINGS/HOLIDAYS

One of the most under-estimated categories of postcard collecting, this section contains examples of some of the printer's finest work. Greetings cards vary enormously in appeal and quality, and are often highly ornate. Where a wide price range is given, the lower band applies to mediocre designs (photographic origin or artist drawn), probably b & w. The middle band applies to an attractively designed card, probably col., perhaps with some 'Novelty' factor. The higher band applies to fine early chromo printing, to heavy gilding/embossing or other novelty decoration or to the work of an important named artist.

Some of the best postcard illustrators designed greetings or had their general designs over-printed with seasonal messages.

Because many of the Greetings cards refer to public holidays, the genre is often known as 'Holidays' in the USA, and merges or overlaps with COMMEMORATIVE and 'Patriotic' in many cases. As transatlantic trading increases, more of these colourful, often amusing, postcards are now becoming available and collected in Britian.

AMERICAN
GREETINGS/HOLIDAYS/PATRIOTICS

Several festivals and holidays are celebrated more in America than in Europe, with resultant appropriate greetings postcards.

Decoration Day/Memorial Day (April); Ground Hog Day (2 February); Hallowe'en (31 October); Independence Day (4 July); Jewish New Year (September) *(Rosh Hashana);* Labor Day (September); Lincoln's Birthday (12 February); Rally Day; St. Patrick's Day (17 March); Thanksgiving Day (November); Washington's Birthday (22 February).

Price range .. .. 75p/**£3**/£6

APRIL FOOL/POISSON D'AVRIL
A day celebrated more on the postcard in France than any other country, with their 'April Fish' jokes.

British publishers 25p/**50p**/75p
French publishers .. .. 50p/**75p**/£1

BIRTHDAY ■GR 1
Cards by well-known artists command a premium.

Period 1/Early Period 2 UB
Chromolitho artist signed, sometimes embossed .. £1/**£3**/£5
Chromolitho unsigned, sometimes embossed .. 75p/**£2**/£4

Periods 2, 3
Artist drawn .. .. 50p/**£1**/£3
Appliquéd, embossed, gilded, silvered, tinselled, etc. .. ..
.. .. 50p/**75p**/£1.50
Others 25p/**50p**/75p

Periods 4, 5
For specified ages/friends/members of family   25p/**50p**/75p
Photographic, often with deckle edges or embossed edges,
    sometimes hand-tinted **50p**
Others 25p/**50p**/75p

■GR1 Pub. Edward Gross (Overprint Alphalsa Pub. Co.). Artist 'The Kinneys'. 'Kinney No. 9'. PU 1929 £3

CHRISTMAS ■GR 2
Themes include angels, animals, bells, children, food and drink, robins, Santa Claus (qv), *religious subjects, snow scenes, etc.*
Price range   ..   .. 25p/**£1**/£5

■GR2. Pub. Tuck. 'Christmas' Postcard. No. 8609. Embossed, gilded Santa. PU 1905 £8

EASTER
Themes include angels, chickens, flowers, rabbits, religious subjects.
Price range   ..   ..   25p/**75p**/£1.50

FAITH, HOPE & CHARITY
Often known as 'FHC' or 'The Virtues'. Some beautiful series on this theme of Victorian/Edwardian virtues exist, often extending to Innocence, Patience, Prudence, Purity and others.
Artist drawn, signed ..   ..   50p/**75p**/£2
Artist drawn, unsigned 25p/**50p**/75p

GENERAL GOOD WISHES ■GR 3
Themes include Forget-me-not, friendship, hearty greetings, kind thoughts, 'sorry', 'write to me', etc.
Price range   ..   ..   25p/**75p**/£3

■GR3 Pub. 'P.F.' 'Loving Greetings'. Embossed, gilded £3

GREETINGS FROM/GRUSS AUS/SOUVENIR DE *see*
EARLY CARDS

HANDS ACROSS THE SEA
Type of card which came into prominence with the wave of emigrations to the Commonwealth and other countries in early Period 2. They are amongst the most colourful and exuberant postcards printed. They show clasped hands, means of transport and national symbols.
Price range   ..   ..   75p/**£1.50**/£2

KRAMPUS
Mid-European version of the devil who became the dark alterego of Santa Claus. Where Father Christmas rewarded good children, the Krampus beat, or otherwise punished, naughty ones.
Artist drawn, signed ..   ..£7/**£15**/£25
Artist drawn unsigned   ..   ..   £3/**£7**/£10

LARGE LETTER

Alphabet Series ■GR 4

Actresses with *Art Nouveau*/Fantasy letters   50p/**75p**/£1.50
German *Art Nouveau* series, incl. children/fantasy/females
Period 2

Per set of 26	£35/**£50**/£70
Multi-Baby Alphabets	75p/**£1**/£1.50
Photo Printing & Pub. Co. ABC postcards ..	£1/**£1.50**/£3
Rotary Photo Co.	50p/**75p**/£1
Tuck. Cupid's Alphabet	75p/**£1.50**/£3
Others	50p/**75p**/£1

■GR4 Pub. Philco. Name Series. 'Elsie', photomontage
actresses. Period 2 £1.50

Calendar Cards

Various designs, incl. New Year   ..   ..   .. 50p/**£1**/£3

Dates

The year, often with New Year greetings. Various designs

..   .. £1/**£3**/£6
25 December (Premium if posted on that date)   75p/**£1.50**/£3
1 January (Premium if posted on that date)   50p/**£1**/£1.50

Days of Week

Birn Bros. series   ..   .. 75p/**£1**/£1.50
Others (value according to artist or style)   .. 50p/**£1.50**/£5
Many American sets of Teddy Bears, Sunbonnet Children, etc.
 see ANIMALS, CHILDREN.

Leap Year

Various comic series ..   .. 50p/**£1**/£3

Mizpah

'God be with you till we meet again'. Various designs   ..
..   .. 25p/**50p**/75p

Names

Made up of flowers, photomontages of actresses, etc. Various
designs   ..   .. 50p/**75p**/£1.50

Numbers (1–10, etc.)

Musterschutz (Ger. Pub.) *Art Nouveau*/Children/Fantasy/
Females. Period 2.

| Per set of 10 | .. | .. | .. | .. | .. | .. | £17.50/**£25**/£30 |
| Others | | .. | .. | .. | .. | .. | .. 50p/**£1**/£2 |

Towns
Made up of photomontages of views, etc.

| Various designs.. | .. | .. | .. | .. | .. | 50p/**£1**/£1.50 |

MONTHS OF THE YEAR
Many well known artists, from Sydney Carter to Mucha, produced sets of 12 of the months, making this a highly desirable type, especially if the set is complete. Value according to the artist.

| Per set | .. | .. | .. | .. | .. | £6/**£24**/P/A |

MOTTOES/PROVERBS/SAYINGS

| Various designs.. | .. | .. | .. | .. | 25p/**75p**/£1.50 |

MOURNING/SYMPATHY CARDS
To announce a death, or offer sympathy—rare subjects.

| Price range | .. | .. | .. | .. | .. | 75p/**£1.50**/£5 |

NEW YEAR
Themes include angels with trumpets, calendars and dates.

| Price range | .. | .. | .. | .. | .. | 50p/**£1.50**/£10 |

SANTA CLAUS (Father Christmas) ■GR 2

| Period 1/Early Period 2. Highly decorative .. | | .. | £2/**£4**/£8 |
| Later designs | .. | .. | .. | .. | .. | .. | £1/**£2**/£3 |

SEASONS, THE
Many artists have treated this attractive subject of the 4 Seasons—Spring, Summer, Autumn, Winter. There also exist fine, unsigned sets in distinct Art Deco *or* Art Nouveau *style. Artist signed—value according to artist.*

| Per set | .. | .. | .. | .. | .. | .. | £8/**£30**/P/A |

Well-designed, unsigned sets.

| Per set | .. | .. | .. | .. | .. | .. | ..£4/**£12**/£20 |
| Others | .. | .. | .. | .. | .. | .. | .. 50p/**£2**/£3 |

VALENTINES

Comic Designs

| Artist drawn, value according to artist | | .. | 75p/**£1.50**/£3 |
| Photographic origin | .. | .. | .. | .. | 25p/**50p**/75p |

Sentimental

| Early chromolithographic, embossed, etc. | .. | .. | £1/**£2**/£4 |
| Later designs | .. | .. | .. | .. | .. | 50p/**75p**/£1 |

WEDDING GREETINGS AND CONGRATULATIONS
Rarely seen on postcards, and then usually in Period 4.

| Early, good quality productions .. | | .. | .. | £1/**£1.50**/£3 |
| Later designs | .. | .. | .. | .. | .. | 25p/**50p**/75p |

LITERARY/MUSICAL

For more details, see *Picture Postcard Artists* (Literary Types) by Tonie & Valmai Holt (1984).

LITERARY REPRESENTATIONS ▌L 1–3

Alice in Wonderland/Through the Looking Glass

Pub. Black, A. & C. Artist Charles Folkard†. Series of Songs from *Alice in Wonderland* and *Through the Looking Glass*. Period 4 .. .. £1.50/**£2**/£2.50

Pub. British PO 1979 Year of the Child 13p stamp—scene from *Alice* (PHQ 37d) **50p**

Pub. Faulkner, C. W. Artist Kathleen Nixon†. Series 1819 set of 6 *Alice* cards. Period 4 .. .. £1/**£2**/£3

Pub. Fuller & Richard. Artist Tenniel. Reproductions of his original illustrations for *Alice*. Set of 8 cards (1910) ..
.. .. £1/**£2**/£3

▌L1 Pub. Anon. Artist A. A. Wall. 'Miss Marie Corelli presents a cup to Stratford-on-Avon Boat Club.' Period 2 £2

Pub. King, Gerald M. Twenty-one cards reproduced from his book, *Alice through the Pillar Box*, all hand stamped and designed. Period 7. The set **£20**

Pub. Guinness. Set of advertising cards with re-written episodes from *Alice*. Period 4 .. .. 75p/**£1**/£1.50

Pub. Lester, Leslie. Artist Mendoza. Set of 6 *Alice* cards by permission of Walt Disney. Period 6 .. £1/**£1.50**/£2

Pub. Merrimack. Reprints of Tenniel's illustrations for *Alice*. Period 7 .. .. **50p**

Pub. R.P.S. Series. Artist Studdy†. *Alice in Wonderland* dog
.. .. £1/**£2**/£3

Pub. Salmon, J. Artist Flora White†. Series No. 1472 .. ..
.. .. 50p/**75p**/£1.50

Pub. Savory Ltd. Cheshire Cat with *Alice* quotation. Period 2
.. .. 75p/**£1**/£1.25

Andersen, Hans

Pub. Henderson. Illustrated Fairy Tales. Artist Sydney Carter†. Period 2 .. .. 50p/**£1**/£1.50

Burns, Robert

Pub. Art Pub. Co. Burns Souvenir cards. Period 2 .. ..
.. .. 75p/**£1**/£1.25
Pub. Johnston W. & A. K. Several series of Burns sets from
1902 .. .. 25p/**50p**/75p
Pub. Stoddart & Co. Burns Pictorial series. Period 2 .. **50p**
Pub. Tuck. Oilette series 7703, 7694 (1918) 50p/**75p**/£1

Byron, Lord

Pub. Tuck. Oilette series 2750 (1918) .. .. 50p/**75p**/£1

Dante's Inferno

Artist Ezio Anichini. *Art Deco* studies in red and black, 18
cards recorded. .. .. 75p/**£1.25**/£2
Artist Kienerk—*see* Artists

■L2 Pub. J. Salmon (Over-
printed J. E. Beale). Artist
Flora White. 'Aladdin'.
Period 4 £3

Dickens, Charles

Pub. Beagles. Centenary of Dickens' birth (1912) £2/**£3**/£4
Pub. Cassell & Co. Character Sketches from Dickens. Artist
Frederick Barnard. Three sets of 6 (1904) 50p/**75p**/£1
Pub. Chapman & Hall. Set of 13 cards reproducing monthly
parts of Dickens' novels (1905) .. .. 50p/**75p**/£1
Pub. Faulkner, C. W. & Co. 'Pickwick' series No. 244. B & w
.. .. 50p/**75p**/£1
Pub. Hildesheimer. B &w Dickens characters. Artist E. F.
Manning UB 25p/**50p**/75p
Pub. Jones, A. V. N. Dickens Characters. Artist Frank
Reynolds .. .. £1/**£2**/£3
Pub. London Stereoscopic Co. Set of 12 cards illustrating the
production of The Only Way (adaptation of *Tale of Two
Cities*) 25p/**50p**/75p

Pub. Stewart & Woolf. Dickens' Characters. 3 sets by Artist
Alfred Crowquill (1902) .. .. 75p/**£1**/£1.25
Pub. Tuck. At least 15 series of 'In Dickens Land' Oilettes
(from 1903) .. .. 50p/**75p**/£1
'With Famous Authors and Painters' (1918). Eight Dickens
sets .. .. 50p/**75p**/£1
Pub. Valentine. Several series of Dickens designs. Period 2
.. .. 25p/**50p**/75p

For the many fine series of Dickens characters by Joseph
Clayton Clark ('Kyd'), *see* ARTISTS

Fairy Tales/Nursery Rhymes
Pub. Anon. (Dutch). Artist Kirchbach. Col. Princess and the
Pea .. .. 75p/**£1**/£2
Pub. B.K.W. Col. Series 885, incl. Pied Piper .. 75p/**£1**/£2
Pub. A. & C. Black Ltd. Series No. 91. 'Nursery Rhymes
and Tales', illustrated by Charles Folkard. Superb col. set of
6—Cinderella; Tom, the Piper's Son; Beauty and The Beast;
Little Bo Peep; Sleeping Beauty; Red Riding Hood.
Price range .. .. £2/**£3**/£5
Pub. Misch & Stock. Series No. 120. Fairy Tales and Panto-
mime Stories, e.g. Little Red Riding Hood, Blue Beard, etc.
.. .. 75p/**£1.50**/£3
Pub. Tuck. 'Art' Nos. 3471/3/5. Cinderella, Puss in Boots,
Hansel and Gretel, Little Snowhite, etc. Period 2 .. ..
.. .. 75p/**£1.50**/£2
Pub. Valentine's. Various artists .. .. 50p/**75p**/£3
Others (incl. Artist Arthur Thiele) .. .. 25p/**£1.50**/£8

Hardy, Thomas
Pub. Tuck. Oilette series 7700, 7755, 7763 (1918) 50p/**75p**/£1

Jerome, Jerome K.
Pub. Blum & Degen. 'Three Men in a Boat' series with Jerome
seal of approval on reverse (1907) .. .. 75p/**£1.50**/£2

■L3 Pub. Tuck. Artist
Harold Copping. 'Shake-
speare' Postcard No. 846.
'Hamlet'. Chromo. UB. Early
Period 2 £4

Lorna Doone
Pub. Photochrom 'Celesque'. Scenes from Lorna Doone. Period
2 .. .. 50p/**75p**/£1
Pub. Valentine. Characters from Lorna Doone. Period 2
.. .. 25p/**50p**/75p
Various scenes from 'Lorna Doone Country', etc. .. **50p**

Milton
Pub. Tuck. Oilette Series 7039, 7420/1 (1918)   50p/**75p**/£1

Omar Khayam
Pub. A & C Black. Art studies by Gilbert James. Set of 6. Per
card .. .. £1/**£1.50**/£3
Pub. Harrop. Art studies by Willy Pogany. Set of 6. Per card
.. .. £1/**£1.50**/£3

One Thousand and One Nights
Kunstlerkarten Series 1102 (Ger). *Marchen aus 1001 Nacht.*
Artist Mackott. Beautiful col. series. UB. PU 1900. Titles
include Aladin, Sinbad the Sailor, Scheherzerade (*sic*) ..
.. .. £1/**£2**/£4

Pilgrim's Progress
Pub. Religious Tract Soc. Four sets of 6 by Artist Harold
Copping† (1911) .. .. 75p/**£1**/£2

Scott, Sir Walter
Pub. Hildesheimer. Sketches from Scott. Artist Sydney
Carter†. Period 2 .. .. 50p/**£1**/£1.50
Pub. Ritchie & Sons. Home & Haunts of Sir Walter Scott.
Artist J. Douglas (1906) .. .. 50p/**75p**/£1
Pub. Ritchie & Sons. Comic characters from Sir Walter Scott
(1907) .. .. 50p/**75p**/£1
Pub. Tuck, Artist J. Finnemore. Nos. 460–5. Vignettes UB
.. .. £1/**£1.50**/£2
Pub. Valentine. Scenes from Scott 25p/**50p**/75p

Shakespeare (*see* ENTERTAINMENT: Theatre)
Pub. Ackermann, Munich. Set of 12 silhouettes, various play.
Period 2 .. .. 50p/**£1**/£2
Pub. Collins, Wm. Shakespeare characters in sepia by Artist
Dudley Hardy†. Period 2 .. .. .. £1/**£1.50**/£2
Pub. Faulkner, C. W. 'Shakespeare Series'. Superb UB
chromolithographed .. .. £1/**£2**/£4
Pub. Hildesheimer. Sketches from Shakespeare. Artist
Sydney Carter. Period 2 .. .. 50p/**£1**/£1.50
Pub. Lyon, Wm. Set of ping-pong cards with titles from
Shakespeare. Period 2 .. .. 50p/**75p**/£1.50
Pub. Nister. Scenes from Shakespeare. Superb col. UB
chromolithographs .. .. £1/**£2**/£4
Pub. Nister. Later series divided backs .. 75p/**£1.50**/£3
Pub. Stewart & Woolf. Comic series with Shakespeare quotes
UB chromolithographs .. .. £1/**£1.50**/£2
Pub. Tuck. Set of 12 cards from *Hamlet* by Artist Harold
Copping† (1901) .. .. £1/**£2**/£4
Pub. Tuck. Merry Wives of Windsor. Vignettes. Nos. 466–477.
UB Early Period 2 .. .. £2/**£3**/£4

Pub. Valentine. Characters from Shakespeare. Several designs. Period 2 .. .. 25p/**50p**/£1

Thackeray, William Makepeace

Pub. Hildesheimer. Sketches from Thackeray. Artist Sydney Carter. Period .. .. 50p/**£1**/£1.50

Pub. Tuck. *Vanity Fair* Oilette series .. .. 50p/**75p**/£1

Tintin

Adventures of Tintin by Hergé

Pub. Anon. Period 4 .. .. £2/**£4**/£8

Pub. Arno. France. Period 7 .. .. **25p**

MUSICAL

Bands

Clear pictures of photographic origin with good detail of people, etc.—Brass bands; Dance bands; Military bands; Pipe bands; Religious groups' bands; School bands.

Price range .. .. 50p/**£1.50**/£3

Bandstands—*see* SOCIAL HISTORY

Comic Musical Cards

Pub. DeLittle, Fenwick & Co. Songs and Singers. Period 2 .. .. 50p/**75p**/£1

Pub. Moss, Henry & Co. Musical Terms up to Date. Artist P. V. Bradshaw† .. .. £2/**£4**/£6

Pub. Ponajowski, E. Humorous Musical Series in Write-Away style. Period 2 .. .. 75p/**£1**/£1.50

Various publishers. Various artists, signed and unsigned. Value according to artist, period, etc. .. 50p/**£1.50**/£6

Composers

Periods 1 and 2 Great Series .. .. £2/**£4**/£6

Novelty cards (e.g. Fantasy Heads) .. .. £10/**£20**/£30

Photo portraits .. .. 25p/**50p**/£1

Others .. .. 50p/**75p**/£1.50

Concerts

Clear pictures of photographic origin with good detail of people.

Indoor views 25p/**50p**/75p

Exterior views .. .. 50p/**75p**/£1.50

Conductors

Big Band .. .. 50p/**75p**/£1

Classical orchestras .. .. 25p/**50p**/£1

Famous names .. .. 50p/**75p**/£1

Instruments

Bells/Bell ringing .. .. 75p/**£1.50**/£2

Orchestral instruments 25p/**50p**/75p

Organs—church 25p/**50p**/75p

Organs—cinema .. .. £1/**£3**/£5

Others .. .. 25p/**50p**/£1

Instrumentalists
Big band bandleaders and musicians (e.g. Count Basie, Bennie Goodman, Glenn Miller, Tommy Dorsey, etc.) Periods 4 to 6 .. .. £1/**£2**/£3

Opera ■L4, 5

Gilbert & Sullivan. Pub. Savoy Co. .. .. £1/**£1.50**/£3
   Other pubs .. .. 50p/**75p**/£1.50
Opera Heroines. Early Period 2. Artist drawn col. vignettes (Ger) .. .. £2/**£4**/£5
Pub. Breitkoff & Hartel. Series of 60 cards of Wagner operas, incl. portraits of conductors, singers, etc. Period 2 .. ..
   .. .. £1/**£1.50**/£5
Pub. Faulkner, C.W. Series of 12 Wagner operas. Col. Period 2 .. .. 75p/**£1.50**/£4
Pub. Meissner & Buch. Wagner series .. .. £1/**£2**/£3
Pub. Ricordi
   Iris by Mascagni (1898). Japanese style chromo-lithos UB
   .. .. £8/**£10**/£15
   Madame Butterfly by Puccini (1898). Japanese style chromo-lithos .. .. £8/**£10**/£15
   Tosca by Puccini (1898). Chromo-lithos .. .. £8/**£10**/£15
Pub. SA Nazionalie del Grammofono, Milano. Period 4. HMV ads. by Artist Nanni, incl. Toti dal Monte as 'Lucia di Lammermoor'.. .. ..£6/**£12**/£18
Pub. Tuck. Period 2. Col. chromo-litho Wagner series. Nos. 691, 693, 694 .. .. £1/**£2**/£4
Others 25p/**50p**/75p

■L4 Pub. F. Guggia. Artists Beggarstaff Bros. Rare invitation from the Countess Albrizzi to a performance of *The Mikado*. March 1900. UB £30

■L5 Pub. C. W. Faulkner. Series No. 1401. Richard Wagner's *Die Meistersinger*. Period 2 £4

Singers

Cabaret/Concert singers (e.g. Dame Clara Butt, Ben Davies, John McCormack, Edith Piaf, Kennerley Rumford, Charles Trenet, etc.) .. .. 50p/**£1**/£2

Jazz singers (e.g. Louis Armstrong) .. .. £1/**£2**/£3

Opera singers (e.g. Enrico Caruso*, Feodor Chaliapin*, Geraldine Farrar, Benjamino Gigli, Dame Nelly Melba, Toti dal Monte, Dame Adelina Patti, Luisa Tetrazini, etc.) .. ..

.. .. 75p/**£2.50**/£5

Other singers 25p/**50p**/75p

(* = commands the highest price)

■L6 Pub. Tuck. Oilette Postcard 1160. 'Illustrated songs'. 'Caller Herrin'. PU 1903 £1.50

Song Cards ■L 6, A 33

Pub. Augener. Little Songs of Long Ago. Artist Henriette Willebeek Le Mair† See ARTISTS for list .. .. £2/**£4**/£6

Pub. Bamforth. Several thousand designs. Periods 2 to 4:

Per pair .. .. 50p/**75p**/£1.50

Per set of 3 .. .. 75p/**£1.25**/£2.50

Per set of 4 .. .. £1/**£2**/£4

Single cards .. .. 25p/**50p**/£1

Pub. Davidson Bros. *See* COMIC. Many series by well known artists .. .. 75p/**£1.50**/£4

Pub. Inter-Art. 3 card song sets .. .. .. £1/**£1.50**/£2.50

Pub. Shamrock. Nearly 400 titles (1908) .. 25p/**50p**/75p

Pub. Tuck. Many Oilette series .. .. 75p/**£1**/£1.50

Pub. Valentine. Several series .. .. .. 50p/**75p**/£1

Other pubs. .. .. 25p/**50p**/£1

National Anthems 25p/**50p**/75p

Songs with Musical Notations/Words

Pub. Musical Post Card Syndicate. Musical Invitations (1903)

.. .. 75p/**£1**/£1.50

Pub. Musical Post Card Syndicate. Popular Songs series

.. .. 25p/**50p**/75p

Pub. Reid Bros. Six sets of 6 (1906) 25p/**50p**/75p

Others 25p/**50p**/75p

Other Musical Series

Price range 25p/**50p**/75p

MAPS

A detailed listing of Map postcards was given on pp. 187–190, of the fourth edition of this catalogue. Since then many interesting Modern map cards have been printed, a comprehensive listing of which has been produced by Ron Griffiths. The following summary is alphabetical by country.

Australia

Periods 2–6	..	..	..	..	..	..	.. 50p/**£2**/£4
Period 7	..	..	..	..	..	..	50p/**75p**/£1

Belgium

Periods 2–6	..	..	..	..	..	..	.. 50p/**£2**/£6
Period 7	..	..	..	..	..	..	50p/**75p**/£1

■MAP 1 Pub. John Walker & Co. Geographical series No. 873. Area of Russo-Japanese War. Engraved by J. Bartholomew. Period 2. £6

■MAP 2 Pub. Thorne Pub. Co. Designer 'Faga'. Series No. 34A M/S *Patricia*. Posted at sea. Period 7 £1.50

Britain ■MAP 1, 2

Ads. ..	..	..	..	..	..	..	..	.. £6/**£7**/£10
Pub. John Walker Geographical. Period 2	..	..	£4/**£5**/£6

Others Periods 2–6 .. .. 50p/**£1.50**/£4
Period 7
Barton, Harvey; Dalkeith; Dennis; Dixon; Faga; Hinde, John;
    Jarrold; Judges; J/V; Murray King; Photo Precision;
    J. Salmon (M. F. Peck); Valentine; Others.   25p/**50p**/£3

Canada
Periods 2–6 .. .. £1/**£2**/£3
Period 7 .. .. 25p/**50p**/£1

France
Ads .. .. £2/**£4**/£6
Periods 2–6 .. .. 50p/**£1.50**/£4
Period 7 .. .. 25p/**75p**/£1

Germany ■MAP 3
Ads/Novelty/War .. .. £2/**£7**/£12
Periods 2–6 .. .. 75p/**£1.50**/£3
Period 7 .. .. 25p/**50p**/£1

■MAP 3 Pub. Emil Pinkau, Leipzig. Area of Anglo-Boer War.
Col. Chromo UB. Period 1 £12

Greece
Periods 2–6 .. .. £1/**£2**/£3
Period 7 .. .. 25p/50p

Holland
Ads .. .. 50p/**£1**/£2
Periods 2–6 .. .. 50p/**75p**/£1.50
Period 7 .. .. 25p/**50p**/75p

Hungary
Novelty .. .. £5/**£7**/£13
Periods 2–6 .. .. £1/**£3**/£5
Period 7 .. .. 25p/**50p**/£1

Italy ■MAP 4
Mil./Pol. .. .. £4/**£6**/£10
Periods 2–6 .. .. £1/**£3**/£5
Period 7 .. .. 25p/**50p**/75p

187

■MAP 4 Pub. Military Geographic Institute, Florence. Italian East Africa. 1935 £8

Malta
Periods 2–6	..	..	..	..	..	..	£1/**£2**/£3
Period 7	..	..	..	..	..	..	25p/**50p**/75p

Portugal
Periods 2–6	..	..	..	..	..	..	50p/**£1**/£2
Period 7	..	..	..	..	..	..	25p/50p

South Africa
Mil. Period 1	..	..	..	..	..	..	£5/**£10**/£15
Periods 2–6	..	..	..	..	..	..	75p/**£1.50**/£3
Period 7	..	..	..	..	..	..	25p/**50p**/75p

Spain
Novelty	..	..	..	..	..	..	£1/**£2**/£4
Periods 2–6	..	..	..	..	..	..	75p/**£1.50**/£3
Period 7	..	..	..	..	..	..	25p/**50p**/75p

Switzerland
Mil. Period 1	..	..	..	..	..	..	£8/**£12**/£20
Periods 2–6	..	..	..	..	..	..	75p/**£1.50**/£3
Period 7	..	..	..	..	..	..	25p/**50p**/75p

USA
Early exhibitions	..	..	..	..	..	..	£3/**£5**/£8
Periods 2–6	..	..	..	..	..	..	£1/**£3**/£4
Period 7	..	..	..	..	..	..	25p/**75p**/£1

Others
Period 1	..	..	..	..	..	..	£2/**£4**/£8
Periods 2–6	..	..	..	..	..	..	50p/**£1.50**/£3
Period 7	..	..	..	..	..	..	25p/**75p**/£1.50

MILITARY

This section deals with cards whose subject matter is, in the main, historical rather than contemporary. The listing is divided into three main groups: *Artists*, *Foreign*, *Publishers* and *Wars*. The last-named section covers 12 conflicts from the Boer War to Vietnam. The major specialist British publisher of military cards was Gale & Polden, although Tucks produced hundreds of titles. Artists who stand out in this field are Richard Caton-Woodville and Harry Payne. Splendid chromo-litho cards were produced in Italy from around 1890 carrying the flags and battle honours of military regiments and these are currently attracting attention.

ARTISTS ■M 1

Caton-Woodville, Richard†	£1.50/**£3**/£5
Ibbetson, Ernest†	£1.50/**£2**/£4
McNeil, John	£1.50/**£2**/£4
O'Beirne, F.	£3/**£5**/£8
Payne, Harry†	£3/**£8**/£25
Others	75p/**£1.50**/£3

■M1 'Imperial Army' series. Artist R. Caton-Woodville. Sepia. 'Trooper, 10th Hussars (Prince of Wales Own)'. 1904 £3

FOREIGN

French
Military figures published by L'H (probably L'Hirondelle) of Paris. Cards are numbered and initialled, 'P.K.' At last 40

cards	£1.50/**£2**/£5.50
Others	50p/**75p**/£1

Italian

Period 1. Chromo-litho. UB.	£4/**£6**/£8
Period 2. Chromo-litho. UB.	£2/**£3**/£4
Others	50p/**75p**/£1

PUBLISHERS ■M 2, 3
The major specialist publisher in this field is Gale & Polden.

■M2 Pub. Gale & Polden. Artist Ernest Ibbetson. 8th (King's Royal Irish) Hussars. 1908 £4

■M3 Pub. Stamp Publicity. (Worthing). Artist Alexandra Baker. 'Private, The Prince of Wales's Own Regt. of Yorkshire 1985' 25p

Gale & Polden
Badge series. Gold border. About 120 cards   £1.50/**£2.50**/£3
British Army (History & Traditions) series. UB. 120 cards in Period 2. Welsh Guards added in Period 3. First issues unnumbered. Artists J. McNeil & Ernest Ibbetson.

No. 1–31 Cavalry	..	..	..	..	£2/**£3**/£4
Nos. 32–104 Infantry	..	..	..	..	£2/**£2.50**/£3
Nos. 105–117 Corps	..	..	..	..	£1.50/**£2**/£3
Lord Kitchener	..	..	..	..	£1/**£2**/£2.50

Sir John French	£1/**£1.50**/£2
Military Mail	£3/**£4**/£5
Nelson series	50p/**£1**/£1.50

Recruiting cards. Regimental recruiting offices used G & P cards picturing their Regiment but changed the text to give details of rates of pay. Many such cards were not postcards. We refer only to postcards printed for HMSO.

Price range	..£8/**£10**/£12

Wellington series. Inset photo-origin cameo views with surrounding artistic military design. UB .. .. £2/**£3**/£4

Others	50p/**75p**/£1

Knight Bros.
Chromo-litho Regimental series .. .. .. 75p/**£1**/£1.25

Salmon, J.
Various military artist-drawn designs (incl. A. R. Quinton)
.. .. 50p/**75p**/£1

Tuck
Our Army/Our Navy. Oilettes	25p/**50p**/75p
Our Generals. Series 68. UB	£1/**£2**/£3

Valentine
The Kings Army. Artotype series 25p/**50p**/75p

Others .. .. 25p/**50p**/£1

BOER WAR (Oct. 1899–May 1902) ■M 4–6
This is a specialist field in which values may fluctuate widely. All cards are UB.

Anti-British Satire
Dutch Pub. J. G. Vlieger Cartoons UB ..	£8/**£10**/£12
French Artist Fredillo UB	.. £6/**£8**/£10
German Pub. Antiquariat Bremen UB ..	.. £6/**£8**/£10

Collectors Publishing Co.
Personalities, photographic origin UB .. .. .. £4/**£6**/£8
Personalities as above plus *The Picture Postcard* magazine
title overprint .. .. £7/**£9**/£10

Peace, Memorials and Reconciliation
Divided back all types .. .. £1/**£2.50**/£5
Joseph Chamberlain Tour Memorial card showing route and
full designs both sides UB .. .. .. £12/**£20**/£25
Peace Conference commemorative UB .. .. .. £5/**£8**/£10

Picture Postcard Co.
Artist drawn battle scenes. Caton Woodville, etc. £4/**£6**/£8
Vignettes of army commanders .. .. £3/**£4**/£6

Sieges
Ladysmith (2 November 1899–28 February 1900)
Natal officials printed during the siege, plus line drawn vignettes in red each side.

■M4 Pub. A. Hembo. Artist H. W. Kuntz. Red, black & white anti-British design. Overprint on reverse 'Postal card in protestation of the englisch war against Transvaal!' (*sic*). PU 26 Aug. 1900 £15

■M5 Pub. Tuck. Artist Harry Payne. Empire Postcard. 'Baden Powell and the Relief of Mafeking'. UB. PU 1900 £15

■M6 Pub. Tuck. Peace Souvenir Postcard – 662. UB. 1902 £12

Used	£100/**£150**/£300
Unused	£25/**£40**/£50
Photo origin views of siege	£10/**£15**/£25

Mafeking (12 October 1899–17 May 1900)

Artist drawn	£8/**£10**/£12
Photo origin	£10/**£15**/£20

Tuck Empire Series

Artist drawn. Berkeley, Payne, Teller, etc.	£7/**£9**/£12
Photographic origin	£5/**£8**/£10

BOXER REBELLION (June 1900–Sep. 1901) ■M 7

Allied soldiers: American, British, Christian Chinese, French, German, Italian, Japanese and Russian.

B & w photo origin poses	£4/**£6**/£8
Artist drawn satire	£10/**£15**/£20

■M7 Pub. Anon. Artist Anon. Fr. Boxer Rebellion satire with Boer War reference. Chromolitho, UB. PU 1900 £20

RUSSO-JAPANESE WAR (Feb. 1904–Sep. 1905) ■M 8

Battle Scenes/Maps/War Portraits

Pub. Hildesheimer

Col. art. Seppings Wright. Ships	£1.50/**£2**/£2.50
War series. Various artists (incl. R. Caton-Woodville)	
	£1.50/**£3**/£5
Pub. J. W. & Co. Russian ships	£2/**£3**/£4
Pub. Knight Bros. Russian navy	£1.50/**£2.50**/£3
Pub. Pictorial Postcard Co. Empire series	£1/**£2**/£2.50
Pub. Tattimoto, Tsujimoto, etc. Art personalities, ships, etc.	
	£1.50/**£2.50**/£3
Pub. Tuck. Oilettes	£1/**£1.50**/£2.50
Pub. Tuck. RP	£2/**£2.50**/£3
Pub. A. J. Young, Harlesden. Action scenes	£1/**£1.50**/£2
Others	£1/**£1.50**/£3.50

■M8 Pub. Tokyo Printing Co. Souvenir of Army Review after Russo-Japanese War. Tokyo handstamp on reverse. 1906 £8

Humour/Satire
Artist Dudley Hardy. Pub. Hildesheimer. Series 3015 ..
.. .. **£4/£5**/£7
French. Artist E. Muller. Pub. P. L. Paris .. .. £2/**£3**/£4
French. Pub. MM, Paris .. .. £2/**£4**/£5
French. 'Le Burin Satirique'. Artist Orens .. £10/**£15**/£20
Others .. .. £1/**£2**/£2.50

Military Review 1906
This was a review to celebrate Japanese success in the war. Special cards with photo montage battle scenes were issued in transparent envelopes in Tokyo and Kobe.
With Tokyo handstamp .. .. £4/**£6**/£8
With Kobe handstamp .. .. £5/**£7**/£10
Without handstamp .. .. £2/**£3**/£5
Transparent envelope .. .. 50p/**£1**/£2

Official Japanese
Communications Department. Post War issue .. £1/**£2**/£3
Post Office 1904 issue. Photo montage. Art borders UB ..
.. .. £3/**£4**/£5
Tuck. Real photographic series no. 5170. 1904 .. £1/**£2**/£3
Tuck. Russo-Japanese series no. 1330 .. .. £1/**£2**/£3

Peace Conference
Pub. Knight Bros. Multi-view .. .. £2/**£3**/£5
Pub. Rotograph Co. New York (1906). 'The Portsmouth Drama' .. .. £3/**£4**/£5

Russian Outrage on Hull Fleet
Anonymous/minor pub. artistic cards .. .. 50p/**75p**/£1
Photographic origin. Damage detail .. .. .. £1/**£2**/£3
Valentines .. .. 75p/**£1**/£1.50

ITALO-TURKISH WAR (Sep. 1911–Oct. 1912) ■M 9
With the object of seizing Libya, and thus counterbalncing French Colonial influence in north Africa, Italian forces invaded from the sea and captured Tripoli and Tobruk. Turkish military resistance was slight and threatened by the impending Balkan War, Turkey negotiated a peace, ceding Libya to Italy.

General scenes ..   ..   £1/£2/£3
Pub. Traldi, Milan. Numbered. RP. At least 17 known   ..
  ..   ..   £4/£6/£8
Higher values for RP cards and unposed military scenes.

■M9 Pub. Traldi, Milan. Turco-Italian War. No. 15, 'Convoy of Arabs (*sic*) prisoners on the route of Tripolis (*sic*)' 1911–2 £6

CHINESE CIVIL WAR (Oct. 1911–Aug. 1917)
Following the Russo-Japanese War, during which most of the fighting had taken place on Chinese soil, the Europeans and Japanese made strong territorial claims upon China. Dissatisfied with the response of their government, Chinese troops mutinied and established the Republic of China. Various internal struggles continued with several changes of President until August 1917 when China joined the Allies and declared war on Germany (WW1).

European and Japanese troops/barracks   ..   £1.50/£2/£3
General art impressions of actions, Hankow, Nanking, etc.
  ..   ..   £2/£3/£4

BALKAN WARS (Oct. 1912–July 1913)
In 1912 Bulgaria, Serbia and Greece joined forces in the Balkan League and moved simultaneously into Turkish European territories, hoping to take advantage of Turkey's war with Italy to extend their borders. Anxious for their own colonial ambitions in the area, the Great European Powers imposed a peace on the combatants in the Treaty of London in May 1913.

RP. Battle scenes. Art borders   ..   ..   ..   £2.50/£4/£5
Others   ..   ..   £1.50/£2/£3

WORLD WAR 1 (4 Aug. 1914–11 Nov. 1918) PERIOD 3
■M 10–13
Higher valuations generally attach to RP cards. French issues tend to be less valuable than others.

Air Warfare

Aces/Personalities
Highest values for RP well known personalities.

British	£1/**£1.50**/£5
French	75p/**£1.50**/£6
German	£1.50/**£2**/£7
USA	75p/**£1.50**/£6

Bomb Damage in Britain

Photographic origin only	£1/**£2.50**/£3
Ramsgate 17 May 1917. Zeppelin Raid ..	£1/**£1.75**/£2.50

Zeppelins
Artistic impressions—general
German propaganda (incl. Thiele *q.v.*)
Zeppelins brought down
Pub. I.V. 'Zepp Slayers'
Pub. Faulkner

Price range	£1.50/**£3**/£4

■M10 Official Red Cross Card. Artist K. Feiertag. 'The Reservist's Farewell'. Period 3 £2

■M11 Pub. C. Harrison Price, Croydon. R. P. 'Recruiting Procession, Oct 2nd 1915' £3

Fund Raising/Welfare
Price range   ..   ..   25p/**50p**/£7

■M12 Pub. 'C.P.C.' Embroidered silk card. 'The Hampshires'. Period 3 £15

■M13 Pub Knackstedt, Hamburg. 'Women in Men's Jobs during the World War. Ticket Collector'. Period 3 £2

Heroes/Personalities/Soldiers

Particularly at the beginning of WW1 it was believed that 'Great Leaders' would decide the outcome. Thus statesmen, royalty, generals and admirals feature on thousands of cards, sometimes in order to raise funds, sometimes for propaganda and frequently because publishers knew that such cards sold well. As the war progressed, heroic deeds became news, and all nations have cards describing individual actions of gallantry, some drawn by fine artists, e.g. Caton-Woodville and Georges Scott.

Price range   ..   ..   25p/**50p**/£4

Land Warfare

The main interest centres upon details of clothing, equipment and general environment. Busy cards of photo-origin are valued most when clear details of motor vehicles, guns and tanks, etc. can be seen. The great mass of French cards showing war damage are little collected. The major British series was published by the Daily Mail.

Daily Mail 176 cards in 22 series. *See* Second Edition (pp. 236–239)   ..   ..   £1/**£1.25**/£2
Others   ..   ..   25p/**£1**/£3

Official Cards

Church Army	25p/**50p**/75p
Field service postcards. AF2042/W3229 ..	50p/**75p**/£1
French with col. flags	25p/**50p**/£1
French with col. flags and border	50p/**£1**/£1.25
German view of captured locality	75p/**£1.50**/£3
Italian with col. flags	25p/**50p**/75p
Regimental issues	75p/**£1**/£1.25
YMCA active service	25p/**75p**/£1
Others	25p/50p

Patriotism/Propaganda/Sentiment

National patriotic fervours in 1914 ran very high in every nation. Postcards in their millions carried waving flags and pretty ladies symbolising allies and alliances. As the war progressed propaganda became more thoughtful, more specific.

Artists

Numerous artists designed such cards—Armitage, Corbello Gunn, Ibbetson, etc., etc.

Price range	25p/**£1**/£8

Publishers

Bamforth song cards	25p/**50p**/75p
Others	25p/**50p**/£1

Over 30 publishers of this genre were listed in the Second Edition (p. 241).

Themes

Certain events provided ideal ammunition for propaganda, e.g. the execution of Edith Cavell and the sinking of the *Lusitania*. Slogans such as 'Ils Ne Passeront Pas', 'Gott Mit Uns', 'Are We Downhearted?—No!' provided emotive patriotic rallying themes.

Cavell, Edith	£1/**£1.50**/£2.50
Recruiting..	50/**75p**/£1.25

Peace/Victory

There was rejoicing everywhere when the war ended—for a while anyway. Here we are concerned only with the period immediately after the war, when references to it continued. Thus we are now in Period 4. Values are low.

Price range	25p/**50p**/£2

Pin-Ups

During WW1 the soldiers pinned up saucy postcards to relieve the horrors of trench life. The ladies became known as pin-ups. Many cards of this type are artists impressions produced in France; the leading exponent being Raphael Kirchner. The most prolific pin-up artist was Xavier Sager.

Déshabillé
Cards showing ladies in various forms of undress. These are generally valued more highly than glamour cards.
Price range .. .. £2/**£3**/£12

Glamour
Cards showing attractive ladies but not undressed, undressing or over-exposing.

Barribal, W.†	£2/**£4**/£6
Bianchi, Alberto (It)	£1.50/**£2**/£3
Boileau, Philip† (USA)	£2/**£2.50**/£3
Bompard, Luigi (It)	£2/**£3**/£4
Busi, Adolfo (It)	£2/**£3**/£5
Colombo, E. (Fr)	£2/**£2.50**/£3
Corbella, Tito† (Fr)	£1.50/**£2.50**/£4
English, Archibald (A.E.)†	75p/**£1**/£1.50
Fidler, Alice Luella (USA)	75p/**£1**/£1.50
Fuchs, R. (Ger)	75p/**£1**/£1.50
Leonnec (Fr)	£2/**£3**/£5
Mauzan, Achille† (It)	£2/**£4**/£6
Nanni, Giovanni†	£2/**£3**/£4
Rappini (It)	£2/**£2.50**/£3.50
Anonymous	75p/**£1**/£1.50

Queen Mary's Collection
Queen Mary, wife of George V, was presented with a quantity of confiscated picture postcards by a postal censor. They are mostly German and Dutch. The total number of cards in the collection, now housed in Windsor, is about 100. This collection was listed in the Second Edition (p. 244).
Price range .. .. 75p to £12

Sea Warfare
The war at sea was a continuous assault by German U-boats upon Allied merchant shipping interspersed by a number of surface actions. In the early months actions were often depicted on postcards, but Germany soon censored these. Britain's best known series by Photochrom showing scenes from the Admiralty film Britain Prepared *was issued in June 1916 the same month as censorship was imposed. Cards produced prior to 1916 tend to be photographic in origin, later cards tend to be artistic impressions. The dates given below are those on which the actions began:*

Photo Origin

Bombardment—Dardanelles. 18 Mar. 1915	£1/**£1.50**/£2
Bombardment—Scarborough. 16 Dec. 1914	75p/**£1**/£1.25
Britain Prepared. 24 cards	£1/**£1.50**/£2
Coronel—1 Nov. 1914	75p/**£1**/£1.50
Falkland Islands—8 Dec. 1914	£1.50/**£2**/£3
Heligoland—28 Aug. 1914	50p/**75p**/£1
Jutland (Skagerrak)—31 May 1916	75p/**£1.50**/£2
Others	25p/**50p**/75p

The Britain Prepared *series was listed in the third edition (p. 288).*

Military: World War 1

Artist drawn
Most artistic impressions rate less than cards of photographic
origin; exceptions are:

Baumgarten, E. V. (Ger)	£3/**£4**/£5
Bohrdt, Professor Hans (Ger).	£2/**£3**/£4
Gribble, Bernard F.	50p/**75p**/£1

Silks
*A detailed listing of these cards was given in the fourth edition,
pp. 204–6.*

Price range

Embroidered

Badges, inserts, etc.	..50p/**£2**/£15
Personalities	.. £2/**£5**/£12

Printed

Flames	.. £2/**£5**/£8
Personalities	50p/**£1.50**/£2

Woven

Flames	..£7/**£10**/£20
Personalities	£10/**£25**/£35

Women at War
*As the men went to fight so women had to take over their jobs.
Interest centres around women performing men's jobs and any
reference to female emancipation. Major publishers on this
theme include Art & Humour, Inter-Art, Noyer (Fr), Photochrom and Tuck. Nursing is the most common theme.*

Artists

Butcher, Arthur	50p/**75p**/£1
Copping, Harold	50p/**75p**/£1
Dupuis, Emile (Fr)	75p/**£1**/£1.50
Edmunds, Kay	25p/**50p**/£2
Horsfall, Mary†	50p/**75p**/£1.50
Leroy (Fr)	£1/**£1.50**/£2
Sager, Xavier† (Fr)	£1/**£2**/£2.50
Skinner, E. F.	50p/**75p**/£2
Spurgin, Fred†	50p/**75p**/£1.50
Wennerburg, B.†	£1.50/**£3**/£4
White, Flora.†	25p/**50p**/75p

Emancipation	.. £2/**£3**/£5

Men's Jobs
Artist drawn:

British	75p/**£1**/£1.25
German	25p/**£1**/£1.50
Others	25p/**50p**/£1

Photographic:

Clear detail	£2/**£2.50**/£3
French posed (Bamforth type)	25p/**50p**/75p
Ger. Pub. Knackstedt. Set of 6	.. 75p/**£1**/£2

Series

'For the Cause' Pub. Tuck	25p/**50p**/75p
La Femme and La Guerre. Pub. Gallais (Fr). Artist Leroy (at least 10 cards)	75p/**£1**/£2
Pub. Merval Corp. (US). Unnamed drawn series showing women at war work (at least 10 cards) ..	50p/**75p**/£1
'Our Own Girls' Pub. Inter-Art. Artist Arthur Butcher ..	
.. ..	25p/**50p**/75p

RUSSIAN CIVIL WAR (Mar. 1917–Dec. 1921)

This is a complicated conflict which began during WW1. At its heart was the struggle between the Red (Bolshevik) and White (Royalist) Russian forces.

Civil strife was triggered by a series of workers' strikes in Petrograd which began in March 1917. Armed conflict spread throughout Russia following the Bolshevik Revolution of November that same year and Russia withdrew from WW1. The Allies intervened in order to prevent war supplies falling into the hands of the Germans. Many other nationalities were involved including Czechs and Poles before Russia signed a peace treaty with the last of its opponents, Italy, in December 1921.

Allied Expeditionary Forces. Photo origin and RP scenes

.. ..	£3/**£3.50**/£6
Red propaganda. Not RP	£1/**£2**/£3
White Russian propaganda. RP	£2/**£3**/£5
Others	£1/**£1.50**/£2

Highest valuations for dated RP cards depicting named events.

THE GRAECO-TURKISH WAR (May 1919–July 1923)

At the end of WW1 Turkey was in a state of near anarchy. To preserve their interests the Allies sent a Greek army into Smyrna thus provoking a patriotic national resistance. Fierce fighting characterised the conflict which ended in a Greek defeat. The Turks re-took Smyrna in September 1922 and the war came to an end with the Treaty of Lausanne in July 1923.

RP scenes. Smyrna	£3/**£5**/£8
Others	75p/**£1**/£3

Three Band Pricing System

Left Hand Band: The lowest price you will probably be asked to pay for this card.
Middle Band: What you will normally be asked to pay for this card: its average, reasonable price.
Right Hand Band: The highest price you will probably be asked to pay for this card.
For a full explanation of the system see page ix.

SPANISH CIVIL WAR (17 July 1936–23 Mar. 1939) ■M 14

Artist drawn—General	£2/**£7**/£10
General Franco propaganda, e.g. Commissariat of Propaganda, Catalonia	£3/**£5**/£10
Nazi. Col. art	£4/**£5**/£8
Photo-origin. *RP action scenes rate highest*	£6/**£8**/£15
Republican propaganda	
Anti-Franco, e.g. Republican Delegation for the defence of Madrid	£2/**£3**/£7
Anti-German	£2/**£4**/£7
Anti-Italian	£6/**£8**/£10

■M14 Pub. Luker, Zaragoza. 'Salute to Franco. Viva España'. Period 4 £8

WORLD WAR 2 (3 Sep. 1939–7 May 1945) PERIOD 5
■M 15–19

This war was essentially a struggle against National Socialism (Nazism). Therefore we have included in this section, under the sub-heading German Propaganda, *information on Nazi cards even though some issues date from Period 4. Sub-divisions used here are broadly similar to those used for First World War cards.*

■M15 Pub. American Red Cross. RP. Period 5 £3

Air Warfare/Airborne Forces

Aeroplanes
These are classified according to their publisher.

German
Official and other cards drawn by von Axster-Heudtlass
.. .. £3/**£7**/£10

Photochrom
'Britain Prepared' photo series. Black and white   £1/**£2**/£2.50
'Britain Prepared' photographic origin series. Brown and
    white   .. .. 50p/**£1**/£1.25
'Colour Photograph' series. Prime Minister's slogan on the
    back   .. .. 25p/**50p**/£1

P.C. Parif (Fr)
Aviation Britannique series   .. .. .. 50p/**£1**/£1.25

Salmon
Artistic coloured impressions by A. F. D. Bannister, about
100 designs all numbered consecutively from no. 4839.
Full out pictures, details on back   .. .. £1.50/**£2**/£3
Details in white strip on the front   .. .. £1/**£1.50**/£2

■M16 Pub. Deutschturmim   Ausland (German Abroad)
No. E49. Artist W. Willrich.   Pilot Hanna Reitsch, Winner
of the Iron Cross. 1st and 2nd   class. Period 5 £25

Valentines
'Real Photograph' series, numbered on front, black and white,
    about 100 cards, action and other scenes .. £1/**£2**/£2.50

Barrage Balloons
Drawn   .. .. £1/**£1.50**/£1.75
Photographic origin .. .. £1/**£2**/£2.50

■M17 Pub. Barnforth. Artist Arnold Taylor. 'Comic' Series No. 830, Period 5 £1

■M18 Official Italian Field Postcard. Fascism unites against Bolshevism. Period 5 £30

Heroes/Personalities/Soldiers
Unless stated valuations are for cards of photo-origin. Higher values for RP.

Belgian
Col. artist drawn portraits ..   .. £2/**£3**/£5

British
Chamberlain	£1/**£2**/£2.50
Churchill	£1/**£1.50**/£3
Montgomery	£1/**£1.25**/£2
Pub. G.P.D. 'For Freedom' series	£1.50/**£2.50**/£3
Pub. G.P.D. 'Victory' series	£1.50/**£2**/£3
Pub. Gale & Polden. Artist Ernest Ibbetson	£1.50/**£2**/£2.50
Pub. Overseas League. VC series	£1.50/**£2**/£2.50
Pub. Photochrom	£1/**£1.50**/£2

Pub. Tuck:
   'Real Photograph' series ..   ..   £1.50/**£2**/£3
   'Royal Portrait' series   ..   ..   £1.50/**£2**/£3.50

Others   ..   ..   £1/**£2**/£2.50

Dutch
Col. art. British commanders, e.g. Dempsey   £10/**£12**/£13

French
Pub. André Leconte. Artist Paul Barbier. *Armée Française*
   series   ..   ..   £1.50/**£2**/£3

German
Artist W. Willrich. Col. o/s   ..   ..   ..   £5/**£12**/£15
Pub. Hoffman, photo series
   Eben Emael paratroopers with Hitler   ..   £30/**£35**/£50
   Others ..   ..£5/**£12**/£15

Italian
Col. Artist drawn o/s ..   ..   £1.50/**£2**/£4

Studio Portraits
German   ..   .. 50p/**£1**/£3
Others   ..   ..   25p/**75p**/£2

Humour
*British cards overwhelm those of every other nation. Here we
value cards that have a direct reference to wartime conditions,
e.g. gas masks, blackouts, queues, Hitler, the home front, etc.
Collecting is normally by artist. Cards depicting Hitler attract
the higher values. See the fourth edition (p. 211–212) for lists
of artists.*

Price range   ..   .. 50p/**£1**/£4

■M19 Pub. Anon. Belg.
Artist Lili. Liberation/VE
Card. 1945 £1.50

Land Warfare
Armoured vehicles. Carriers, self-propelled guns, tanks, etc.

     ..   ..   **£1/£1.50/£2**

Combat scenes   ..   ..   **£1/£2/£2.50**

Damage. Atomic bomb   ..   ..   **£2/£3/£4**

Damage. Other ..   ..   50p/**£1**/£1.50

Débarquement en Normandie. Photo Gaby. Over 20 RP cards

     ..   ..   **£1/£1.75/£2.50**

Front line life   ..   ..   **£1/£1.50/£2**

Polish Army (Polski Korpus) Sepia o/s, posed battle scenes

     ..   ..   50p/**75p**/£1

Prisoners of War. In camp ..   ..   **£1/£1.50/£2**

Prisoners of War. Under escort   ..   ..   **£1/£1.50/£2**

Prisoner of War mail ex-Jap. camps. Value depends upon
     camp (rarest is Sandakan) and clarity censor mark ..   ..

     ..   ..   £7/**£8**/£10

Soft-skinned vehicles. Cars, jeeps, trucks, etc.   50p/**75p**/£1

Weapons ..   ..   **£1/£1.50/£2**

Munich
Price range   ..   ..50p/**£6**/£12

Official Cards
*The Germans used their fieldpost cards to carry propaganda
pictures and to raise money, thus there are entries in the
sections. Otherwise, apart from some American issues, official
cards tend to be dull and not highly valued.*

Air raid casualty. Card No. G. & S. 704   ..   ..   25p/50p

Divisional/Regimental cards   ..   ..   50p/**£1**/£1.50

Fieldpost—German

     Artists Hans O. Wendt   ..   ..   **£1/£1.50/£2**

     Others ..   .. **£2/£4/£5**

Fieldpost—Others   ..   ..   50p/**75p**/£1

US Army leave sections   ..   ..   **£1/£1.50/£2**

US Navy 'V' for Victory cards 25p/**50p**/75p

Patriotism/Propaganda/Sentiment
*During WW2, as in WW1, both sides made great use of aerial
propaganda. The British dropped leaflets over Germany the
day that War was declared, but when the first postcards were
used is not certain. The French dropped cards on the Germans
during the Phony War of 1940, the Germans on the French,
the British and Russians on the Germans. Although hundreds
of thousands of cards were dropped, very few have survived;
those that have are definitely collectors' items. See fourth
edition (pp. 213–214) for detailed listing.*

British   ..   ..75p/**£1**/£25

Dutch   ..   .. 50p/**£1**/£2

French   ..   ..   **£1/£1.50/£2**

German   ..   ..75p/**£4**/£50

USA ..   .. 50p/**£1**/£3

Peace/Victory
*As the Western Allies pushed the Germans back so Belgium,
Denmark, France and Holland were liberated. They issued*

*cards to celebrate. When the fighting ceased there were victory
parades and then the job of restoring Europe to health began.
It was called 'Restoration'. There were cards for that too and
also for the return of the fighting man to civilian
life—'Demobilisation'. As the date of a man's demobilisation
drew near he would count the number of 'days to do'. The
French celebrated '100 days to do' with* Père Cent *cards.*

Armistice. Photographic cards issued at Rheims on 7 July
    1945 showing signing of armistice at Rheims on 7 May
    1945. Stamped and date cancelled   ..   £15/**£25**/£30
Demobilisation ..   ..   £1/**£1.50**/£2
Père Cent ..   .. £1/**£2**/£4
VE Day scenes ..   ..   75p/**£1.50**/£3
VJ Day scenes ..   .. 75p/**£1**/£2

Pin-Ups
Magazines such as the American Yank *provided most of the
pin-ups for the forces. Postcard pin-ups are far fewer than in
WW1. However, film star photographic cards were very
popular.*

Déshabillé ..   .. £1/**£2**/£6

Glamour ..   .. 60p/**£1**/£2

Sea Warfare
*Good artistic impressions of ships and battles, or cards
showing clear photographic details are most highly valued.
Specific actions, such as the sinking of the* Graf Spee, *were
sometimes recorded by sets of cards.*

Graf Spee sinking. 12 cards in set   ..   ..   £2/**£3**/£6
Narvik   ..   .. £5/**£7**/£12
Pearl Harbour ..   ..   £1/**£2**/£5
Scapa Flow *Der Adler* series   ..   ..   ..   £2/**£3**/£4

Women at War
*The Germans used the theme of women's help for the war effort
as propaganda, the British and Americans still viewed the idea
with amusement.*

Men's Jobs
Humorous comment 25p/**50p**/75p
Photographic origin ..   ..   75p/**£1.50**/£3
Free French photo series ..   ..   ..   75p/**£1**/£1.50
Pub. Beals (US). Over 25 cards in series   ..   £1/**£1.50**/£2
Pub. Tuck. 'With the WAAF'. Over 25 cards in series ..   ..
   ..   .. 50p/**£1**/£2

As it is difficult to date a card precisely, a period
system has been used in this catalogue.
For a full explanation of the system see page viii.

VIETNAM WAR (1965–73) ■M 20

Within the USA there was great dissent against the war and public pressure finally forced President Nixon to withdraw US forces in 1973. Picture postcards have recorded the inner turmoil of America during this period as well as conditions in the firing area.

Protest cards	..	..	..	..	..	..	£1/**£1.50**/£3
Others	..	..	..	..	..	..	50p/**£1.50**/£2

■M20 Ger. Pub. Anon. Anti-Vietnam War Protest. Period 7 £1

FALKLANDS CONFLICT (1982) PERIOD 7 ■M 21

The Argentinian invasion of the British owned Falklands Islands on 2 April 1982, the sailing of the British Task Force and Landings from 21 May until the Argentinian surrender on 14 June, gave rise to many patriotic and anti-Government cards alike. A detailed listing here by publisher – in appropriate sections – is given in the section supplement.

Price range	..	..	..	..	..	25p/**50p**/£4.50

Three Band Pricing System

Left Hand Band: The lowest price you will probably be asked to pay for this card.
Middle Band: What you will normally be asked to pay for this card: its average, reasonable price.
Right Hand Band: The highest price you will probably be asked to pay for this card.
For a full explanation of the system see page ix.

SECTION SUPPLEMENT – MILITARY

FALKLANDS CONFLICT CARDS
Anti-Government/Thatcher
Eagle Editions
Reproductions of *Private Eye* Falklands cartoon covers   **25p**

Leeds Postcards
Anti-Belgrano sinking, etc. **25p**

S.A.S.
2 series of 8 anti-Falklands cards   ..   ..   ..   £2/£3
Individual anti-Falklands designs 25p/30p

Unofficial Royal Souvenir
'Thatcher': Queen of the Falklands **30p**

Various foreign anti-British issues
(incl. Fr. 'Le Monde Vécu' cards) 20p/**50p**/75p

Commemorative
Carousel
34. Tribute to the Task Force (2000 printed) **65p**

Faga
349. Falklands Island History.
   Blue on white coated board (2500) **60p**
   Brown on white coated board (200) **65p**
350. Task Force
   Navy on white coated board (7000) **£1**
   Brown on white coated board (500) **£1.50**
351. 150th Anniv. Brit. Rule 1983. Full col.
   on white coated board. (5000) **30p**
352. Mrs. Thatcher/Falklands. Red/blue on white coated
   board. Erroneous inscription (1000) **60p**
352. With error 'Arctic Circle' removed (1500) **45p**
354. Liberation of Falklands 1982. Red/Blue on white coated
   board. (1000) **60p**

■M21 Pub. Kenneth Mason for King George's Fund for Sailors. MS *Rangatira*, chartered to M.O.D. in 1982 for the Falklands campaign 30p

355. 150th Anniv. Brit. Rule. Light blue on white coated board (4000) **45p**

The value of the above issues is constantly rising.
Special stamps, FDI handstamps and cachets will add the following to these issues: .. .. .. £1.20/**£2.50**/£5.50

King Cards
Limited to 2000 printing.
201. Mrs Thatcher/Gen Galtieri/Map
202. Recapture of S. Georgia, 25 April 1982
203. Signing of Surrender Document of S. Georgia
205. 1st Anniv. British Victory

Price range .. .. 60p/**75p**/£1

Veldale
SE 13. Falklands Crisis with 'Argentine Forces Surrender June 14 1982' overprint **£1**
ditto without overprint (200) **£2.50**
ditto with special handstamps .. .. .. £1.10/£1.50

Task Force in Action/Personalities
Imperial War Museum
Official war artist Linda Kitson. Set of 8 b & w. Per set. **£8**

King George's Fund for Sailors
'The Falklands Collection' Pub. Kenneth Mason 1983. 118 ships which took part in Task Force.
Per card, unused **30p**
Used with Falkland Islands handstamps. Per card .. **£2**

Knight of Democracy
Hand printed cards in very small limited edition. Those with plain backs do not qualify as postcards, and are not listed here.

Maj.-Gen. Jeremy Moore portrait & facsimile signature **£1.50**

Noel Tatt
Artist Richard West. Col. set of 6 Falklands ships. Per set.
.. .. £1/£1.50

Pamlin Prints
8 b & w photos of Task Force ships **25p**

Precott-Pickup
2 sets of 63 col. cards of action/armour/landings/prisoners/ships/sinkings, etc.
1. Falklands Task Force
2. War in the South Atlantic.
Per set, unused **£12**
No. 2 set, all PU from Falklands .. .. £45/**£55**/£70
Launch of *Invincible*, single card, col. **25p**

Siphula
HMS *Hermes* being loaded with beer. April 1982.
B & w photo. (500) **£4.50**

BOOKS BY THE COMPILERS
TONIE & VALMAI HOLT

**PICTURE POSTCARS OF THE GOLDEN AGE: A Collectors'
Guide.** Invaluable for experts and beginners alike. THE Classic
....£6.50
TILL THE BOYS COME HOME: The Postcard of WW1.
Lavishly illustrated in col. and b.w. Incredible value at.. £10.00
**BEST OF FRAGMENTS FROM FRANCE by Capt. Bruce
Bairnsfather.** Immortal WW1 cartoons with modern
explanations...£6.50
**IN SEARCH OF THE BETTER 'OLE: The Life, Works and
Collectables of Bruce Bairnsfather.** Highly illustrated £14.00
**PICTURE POSTCARD ARTISTS: Landscapes, Animals &
Characters.** Full of interesting information for the collector £9.00
**GERMANY AWAKE: The Rise of National Socialism Illustrated
by the Contemporary Picture Postcard.** Superb pics. £10.50
HOLTS "BATTLEFIELD GUIDES" TO:
1. YPRES SALIENT..£1.75
2. NORMANY-OVERLORD £2.25
3. MARKET-GARDEN £3.25
4. THE SOMME..£3.25

All prices include P + P

Available from good postcard book retailers or direct from
the Authors, at
15 Market Street, Sandwich, Kent, CT13 9DA.
(Signed if desired).

CIGARETTE CARDS

1986 Catalogue, lists 8,000 sets ONLY £3.75
15,000,000 cards in stock on all major postcard
themes except topography.
Monthly Fairs in Central London.
Monthly auctions – next Catalogue 50p.
Acid-free albums for postcards and all
collectables. Send 35p for sample and current
price list (trade enquiries welcomed).
Speedy Mail Order Service to all parts of the
World – or why not call in at our shop. Open
Mon–Fri, 10.00 to 5.00

MURRAY CARDS
(INTERNATIONAL) LTD
51, Watford Way, London N.W.4.
Tel: (01)–202–5688

We do NOT sell postcards.

MODERN

The Postcards Produced During Period 7

Undoubtedly the fastest growth area in postcards during the past two years is in MODERNS. The major magazines, like *Picture Postcard Monthly*, now run regular articles on recent issues. Ron Griffiths produces a catalogue of Modern limited editions as well as regular modern sales lists. Other British catalogues now follow the lead set in this catalogue by including a Modern section and some of the French catalogues are even considered to be placing too much emphasis on current issues. More dealers stock modern cards and some specialise in them. Modern cards are being collected by more and more collectors and can definitely be deemed to have 'arrived'. The quality of some Modern productions (notably Dalkeith) remains consistently high.

Many worthwhile postcards are currently being produced by the big publishing companies, like Athena, Camden Graphics, E. T. W. Dennis, J. A. Dixon, Judges, J. Salmon, Skilton & Fry, etc., as well as by our major museums like the British Museum, V & A, Imperial War Museum, etc. As these are easily available from local and national book shops, newsagents, stationers, the museums themselves, they are not listed in this catalogue. Rather we have concentrated on informing readers about issues which are produced specifically for the collector (often in limited editions). These are normally available from specialist modern dealers like Ron Griffiths or direct from the publishers.

Abba

Manor House, 21, Schools Lane, Walton, Wakefield, WF2 6PA.
Designed and printed by Alan Bower from 1980. B & w cards on themes of local and national interest, commemorations, etc. Editions limited to 60, 100 or 200 numbered cards only.

Price range 15p/**20p**/75p

Art For Art's Sake

104, Brummond St, London, NW1.
Well-designed colourful cards, designed to be collected. All cards are numbered, and artist include Charles Stuart.

Price range 25p/35p

Benhams Silk Look Postcards

Benham, Westcliff House, Folkestone, Kent, CT20 1SZ.
Postcards issued mint and FDI to coincide with British Post Office stamp issues from 10 February 1982 onward. Total print run (mint and FDI) 9000. Sets of 3, 4 or 5.

Mint, per set   ..   ..   £1.50/**£2**/£2.50
FDI, per set   ..   ..   £4.50/**£5.20**/£6.50

Royal Engagement/Wedding series 1981 8 cards believed to have been designed

Per card.. .. .. £6/**£8**/£10

Papal Visit 1982. Set of 4 .. .. £4.50/**£6**/£8

■MOD 1 Pub. Postcard Traders Assoc. BIPEX Postcard No. 8 £1

Bipex ■MOD 1
Postcards issued by the Postcard Traders' Association each year for the annual British International Postcard Exhibition at Kensington Town Hall. All cards numbered.

1979 No. 1. Blue on white. Also season ticket designed by John Silvester **£1.50**
1980 No. 2. Navy on white. Daily ticket **£1.50**
Ditto Red on white. Season ticket **£1.50**
1981 No. 3. Red, blue, yellow on white. Hassall Skegness theme **£1**
1982 No. 4. Multicoloured. Boy scout theme **75p**
1983 No. 5. Multicoloured. *Entente Cordiale* **£3**
1984 No. 6. Multicoloured. 1st Provincial Bipex Harrogate
.. .. **40p**
1984 No. 7. Multicoloured Monoplane (Bleriot)/White Cliffs. Designed by Frank Burridge **50p**
1985 No. 8. Multicoloured Comet theme **£1**

Carousel Limited Editions ■MOD 2
Michael Dummer, 28 Ambleside Road, Kingsway, Bath, BA2 2LR.
Nos. 1–38 were listed in the second, third and fourth editions of this catalogue.
Subsequent issues are:
39. Birth of Prince Henry
40. Ditto .. .. Per pair **65p**
41. Christening of Prince Henry **35p**

■MOD 2 Pub. Carousel Limited Editions No. 39 Birth of Prince Henry 1984 35p

42. Queen Mother's 85th Birthday (1250 printed)
43. Ditto ..   .. Per pair **70p**
44. HMS Ark Royal. Royal commissioning 1 Nov. '85 (1500 printed) **35p**
45. 60th birthday of H.M. The Queen **35p**

Cath Tate
Cath Tate, 39 Kingswood Rd, London SW2 4JE.
Political protest cards from a socialist, anti-nuclear, anti-apartheid, anti-Royalist, etc. point of view. Various designs, b & w montages, etc. Cont. size.
See also Leeds Postcards
Per card **25p**

Chic Pix
27a Old Gloucester St., London WC1
Highly original postcards designed by Peta Coplans and Stanley Becker. Their technique varies from photomontage – to colourful highly decorated Kitsch 'Hollywood' pastiches. Themes range from good-natured anti-Royal satire to anti-nuclear, anti-American, anti-space programme protest. Their versatile avant garde *style borrows from the strip cartoon, 1930s* Art Deco, *and 1940s and 50s Hollywood style. They have also been commissioned to design publicity postcards for boutiques, studies, etc. resulting in some of their most visually pleasing, striking designs. Captions and quotes on reverse of card are often cryptic! Set of 3, 4 and 8 cards.*
See the third edition of this catalogue for earlier listings.

Recent-sets include:
One Woman's Story
Fall Out Charts
Per set ..   .. £1.50/**£4**/**£8**

■MOD 3 Pub. C.N.E.C. (Fr.   equivalent of P.T.A.) Salon of Sept. 1985 50p

---

CNEC ■MOD 3
Salon of the new *Chambre des Négociants et Experts en Carto-philie* (the French equivalent of the British Postcard Traders Association) organised by M. Mordente.
No. 1. 27–8 Sep 1985
 Unused **50p**
 Used with special 27 Sept 85 handstamp on F4f.50
  XII Congres de l'Union Postale Universelle 1947 stamp
 ..   .. **£1**

Collector Cards/Pamlin Prints ■MOD 4
73 Temple Rd, Croydon, Surrey, CR0 1HW.
Checklists of early series were printed in the second and third editions of this catalogue (pp. 146–147 and 188–189 respect-ively). Good quality photographic postcards. 1986 marks the company's 20th year of production, with over 20 million cards sold. Old England Series
New issues – Huddersfield; Scarborough
Re-issues – Crystal Palace; Epsom; Gloucester; Portsmouth; Wigan.

Social History
Issues covering all areas of the UK.

Railways
150th Anniv. Great Western Rly. 5 cards/6 card set for Reading Libraries
125th Anniv. of Victoria Station. 4 cards
Centenary of Hull & Barnsley Rly. 2 cards
50th Anniv. end of Selsey Tramway. 3 cards

Modern

Re-opening Chatham Dockyard Rly. 2 cards
Electrification of N. London Link
Last train to Tunbridge Wells West.
Buses and Trams
Merseyside Buses and Trams. 36 cards
75th Anniv. of Southdown Motor Services Ltd. 4 cards
Bus and Train cards for Bournemouth PTA/Museums.
Maritime
Cutty Sark Tall Ships at Chatham. 3 cards
HMS *Ark Royal*

Space
Giotto probe to intercept Halley's Comet

New Issues: Dec 1985/Jan 1986
M3355. N. Stafford Rly. TO–6–2 No. 2 1960
M3743. Costain's N.G. Ind. Rly. Croydon 1925
M3937. Sheffield Trams. Preserved tracks
M2170. 'Lady Ivy' Burrell Showman's Engine
C1595 Old Sidcup. 'Old Black Horse' 1913
C10131 Old Croydon. (S. End looking N) 1905
Per card **15p**

■MOD 4 Pub. Pamlin Prints. No. CV209 'Giotto. Halley's Comet Interceptor.' 1986 15p

Coral-Lee
PO Box 314 Rancho Cordova, CA 95670, USA.
Well produced photocards of topical personalities/events. Col.
Recent standard sized subject include:
Reagans in China 1984/Normandy June 1984/Olympic Games 1984/Reagan and King Hussein

Per card **30p**

New continental-sized issues include:
Van Halen/Prince/Lionel Ritchie/U.2/Cindy Lauper/Stevie

Wonder/Mr. T./Tina Turner/Sting/Richard Gere/Eddie
Murphy.

Per card **35p**

■MOD 5 Pub. Countercards (reprinted by Leeds Postcards).
Artists Brian Lewis and Andrew Waring. 'By British' 30p

Countercards ■MOD 5
17 Linden Terrace, Pontefract, W. Yorkshire.
*Four series of well designed and printed postcards by play-
wright Trevor Griffiths and writer Brian Lewis. Only 3000 of
each design were originally printed (though 'By British' has
been reprinted, see below) and value will increase as more
titles become out of stock. The cards all have a socialist/anti-
nuclear theme.*

Series A: The Featherstone Disturbance (from paintings of 'A
People's History of Yorkshire' Exhibition by Brian Lewis and
David Prudhoe).
A. 1 The Cage
A. 2 Soldiers and Owners
A. 3 Sergeant Sparrow
A. 4 Proclamation
A. 5 No one is innocent
A. 6 Featherstone 9.45 am
A. 7 Featherstone 10 am

Per card **15p**
Per set **£1.05**

Series B: Royals (Satirical cartoons from 'Designs for Prince
Charles' Wedding Cake' by Brian Lewis)
B. 1 Design for Prince Charles' Wedding Cake
B. 2 Rider
B. 3 Lady Di
B. 4 Royal Baby
B. 5 Princess Anne
B. 6 Eighty and Still Working

Per card **15p**
Per set **90p**

Series C: 7: 84 Theatre Company Posters. (Now out of stock except from the Theatre Company) 1971–81.

C. 1 The Ballygombeen Bequest
C. 2 The Cheviot, The Stag and the Black, Black Oil
C. 3 Little Red Hen
C. 4 Lay Off
C. 5 SUS
C. 6 Blood Red Roses
C. 7 Night Class
Per card **15p**
Per set **£1.05**

Series D: Protest and Survive
D. 1. 'Oi for England'. Poster design for Trevor Griffiths' Play
 .. .. **15p**
D. 2 Maggie Maggie Maggie **15p**
D. 3 'Blues' (Reagan & Thatcher) **15p**
D. 4 By British (CND) (later reprinted by Leeds Postcards)
 .. .. **30p**

Current Events/Issues/Personalities ■MOD 6

Today's modern postcard is beginning to emulate its Golden Age predecessor by recording events of local, national and International interest. They include reproductions of photographs and artist drawn. See also Leeds, J/V Postcards, TVH.

Acme Cards R.P. col. photos by Sally & Richard Greenhill of Punks/London & Provincial 'types'
Per set of 8 .. ..**£2.40**
Anti – Apartheid;-Nuclear;-Racism;-Sex Discrimination;-Smoking;-Vivisection;-War. others 10p/**20p**/30p
12th Franco – British Postal Speed Competition
Sep. 1984 .. .. **10p**

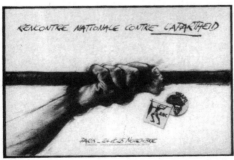

■MOD 6 Pub. Anti-Apartheid Campaign. Rally card. Fr. November 1985 10p

Le Monde Vécu Fr. Series Current Event cards. Per card **20p**
Liverpool's Financial Situation. Artist Ray French .. **20p**
Miners' Strike 1984 .. .. 25p/**50p**/75p
Postcard events – see COMPETITIONS/CRAZES/HOBBIES
York Minster Fire 1984 Various issues .. 15p/**50p**/75p
Others 15p/**25p**/50p

Dalkeith Publishing Co. ■A 13.
Railway Museum Building, Rear of 81 Old Christchurch Rd,
Bournemouth, BH1 1EW.
*Superbly designed, printed and presented postcards, on high
quality board, packaged in colourful, printed, hand-numbered
envelopes which describe the contents. Most series are stan-
dard-sized (14 × 9cm) sets of 6, but some 'PHQ' sized sets and
single cards have been added to the range. Frank Burridge,
curator of the Museum, does all the design and photography
of these magnificent cards himself.*
The first 102 designs of the *Railway* series were listed in the
third edition of this catalogue, pp. 189–190 (set nos. 1–17).
Nos. 103–192 (set nos. 18–32) were listed on p. 221 of the
fourth edition. The first 108 cards in the *Classic Poster* series
were listed on pp. 221–222 of the fourth edition. Listings of
both series are continued in the section supplement.

FAGA (Frederick G. Foley) ■MOD 7, MAP 2

Stockist: Ron Griffiths, 47 Long Arrotts, Hemel Hempstead,
Herts, HP1 3EX.
*The postcard production from 1961–84 of this highly collected
calligrapher, cartographer and designer were listed in the
second, third and fourth editions of this catalogue
(pp. 149–150, 191 and 222 respectively). For up-dated prices
for these cards, some of which have appreciated considerably,
consult the stockist above. Listed below are 1984 onwards
designs. Numbers printed are in brackets.*

367. Beaulieu. Multicoloured on coated board (2500) .. **25p**
368. The Year of the 3 Kings. Navy on White coated board
    (1000) **45p**
as above. Small trial print. Brown on white coated board. **£1**
369. Famous British Trains. 'Maxi' card. Blue on white matt
    board (650) **35p**
370. A Century of Motoring. Black on white coated board.
    German inscription (1000) **40p**
370A. A Century of Motoring. Black on matt white, no
    German inscription (2000) **40p**
371. Royal Princess. Blue & red on white coated board (1000)
    .. .. **80p**
372. Dibden Church. Brown on white coated board (600) **30p**
373. Battle of Bosworth. Blue and red on white coated board
    (1000) **40p**
as above Blue & red in error on thin yellow matt board. **30p**
374. Caxton and the Arthurian Legend. Black on white
    coated board (1000) **35p**
375. Southampton. Redesign of 1979 card. Black on white
    matt board (2000) **30p**
376. Hythe & New Forest map card **30p**

■MOD 7 'FAGA' Card No. 371. Naming of Royal Princess, 1984 80p

377.	50th Anniv. of Spitfire	**30p**
378.	Arthurian Legend	**30p**
379.	Lady of the Lake	**30p**
380.	25th Anniv. of Faga Cards	**30p**
381.	Wedding of Prince Andrew	**30p**
382.	50th Anniv. of Edward VIII abdication	**30p**

Halley's Comet ■MOD 1
See BIPEX; Rusnak, Ann; Paisley Productions; Pamlin Collectorcards; S.A.S.; Others

Stanley Gibbons
1980–2 Postcard Catalogue Publicity cards *each*		**40p**
1985 Figures of London—Postmen		**40p**
1985 Figures of London—Policemen		**£1**

■MOD 8 Pub. J/V Cards. No. 80C. Postcard designs by Brockington College pupils 25p

J/V Postcards ■ MOD 8

56 Church St, Donisthorpe, Burton-on-Trent, Staffs, DE12 7PY.

Started in 1982 by Peter Judson (J) and Arthur Veasey (V) with small print run view cards of local villages, J/V now covers most Midland Counties, Norfolk and Suffolk. Their high quality, col. and b & w photo cards also record local current events. Some early editions are now out of print (marked on the section supplement list) and command the highest valuation when obtainable.

Price range 25p/**50p**/75p

Leeds Postcards ■MOD 5

PO Box 84, Leeds, LS1 4HU.

Started part-time as a hobby by Richard Scott in 1979, it became a full-time occupation in 1981 and it is now planned to operate the business as a Workers' co-operative. Their shocking/amusing/controversial designs have a strong socialist/anti-nuclear/feminist tone. By Autumn 1985 2.6 million cards had been printed.

A list of the first issues (some of which are now out of print) appeared in the third edition of this catalogue, pp. 191–192.

Price range .. .. 25p/**50p**/£1

London Transport ■MOD 9

London Transport Museum Shop, 39 Wellington St, London WC2E 8PB.

Reproductions of posters for buses and underground from 1908 to the present day, including examples of some of the best contemporary Artists' work. Some of the earlier editions are now out of print and appreciating in value.

Price range 20p/**40p**/75p
London Transport Museum Cards **20p**
Recent issues Nos. LTM 132–169
   1985 Posters by Tom Ekersley **20p**

■MOD 9 Pub. London Transport. Official Sightseeing Bus 20p

Mannin Postcards
Published by Alan Kelly, 18, Inner Circle, Bray Hill, Douglas
I.O.M.
*B & W series. Standard size early issues limited to 250
numbered cards.*

1.	Bride Post Office 1909	**55p**
2.	Ballafesson PO 1910	**55p**
3.	Crosby Village & PO 1906	**55p**
4.	Union Mills Village & PO 1924	**55p**
5.	Port Soderick PO 1908	**50p**
6.	W. Baldwin Village & PO 1908	**50p**
7.	Groudle Miniature Rly. 1904	**40p**
8.	Ditto 1921	**40p**
9.	Port Soderick Rly Stn. 1907	**40p**
10.	Kirk Michael Rly Stn. 1912	**40p**
11.	Castletown Rly Stn. 1904	**40p**
12.	Port St. Mary Rly Stn. 1896	**40p**

Shipwreck series, b & w standard size. Limited to 500

13.	SS *Donegal* ashore 1908	**35p**
14.	SS *Mona* aground 1930	**35p**
15.	SS *Mayfield* aground 1909	**35p**
16.	SS *Argo* aground 1905	**35p**

I.O.M. T.T. named riders in action.
Sets of 6 col, cont size
Sets Nos. 1, 2, 3 .. .. Per set **£1.50**

T.T. Specials

1.	Joey Dunlop triple winner (3000)	**30p**
2.	Manx Int. Car Rally 1985	**30p**

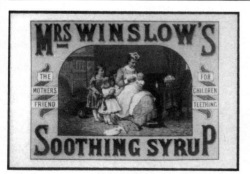

■MOD 10 Pub. Mumbles Railway Co. MRP 145 'Mrs.
Winslow's Soothing Syrup'. 20p

Mumbles Railway Co. Ltd. ■MOD 10
131A Western St, Swansea, SA1 3JX.
*The company began by publishing tramway and railway post-
cards, but now specialises in reproduction of old publicity
material. Productions include, (P) = photo):*

MRPO–MRP4	Swansea & Mumbles Rly. (P)
MRP5	SR West Country Loco (P)
MRP10	Castle & Pannier tank, Swansea (P)
MRP15–19	British Trams
MRP20–23	Blackpool Transport Posters
MRP25	Liverpool Overhead Rly Poster
MRP31–32	Blackpool Trams (P)
MRP35–36	Shipping Posters
MRP40–41	Theatre Posters
MRP45	Blackpool Poster
MRP50	S. Rly. Spain Poster
MRP6	Music Hall
MRP65–66	Bus Posters
MRP70	LT Tram, Brixton
MRP75	LMS loco at Swansea
MRP80–84	Old Advertising
MRP85	Golden Arrow
MRP90,92	Old Advertising
MRP100	Cab Yard, Night. John Bevan
MRP111	Peek Frean Ad
MRP115	Motor Tug *Margam* (P)
MRP120	WW2 'Swordfish' (P)
MRP130	Laurel & Hardy Poster
MRP145	Mrs. Winslow's Soothing Syrup Ad.
MRP150	Webb Bros. Clowns
MRP155	1912 Dieppe Grand Prix.
MRP165	Sunlight Soap
MRP166	Hudson's Soap
MRP167	Gossage's Magical Soap

1986 Issues (all col. cont. sized)

MRP50	Blackpool Car No. 4 at 1985 Illuminations (P)
MRP51	The Blue Train
MRP52	Southern Rly. Paris for weekend
MRP105	Moulin Rouge Poster. Artist Grün
MRP110	Peek Frean ad.
MRP112	Huntley & Palmer ad.
MRP113	Ship Canal. Biscuit ad.
MRP125	Cook's Tours 1900 brochure cover
MRP126	1900 Hotel Guide. 'Where to Stay'
MRP135	Cadbury's Cocoa ad.
MRP137	Rowntree's Cocoa ad.
MRP138	Terry's Chocolate ad.
MRP139	Cadbury's Cocoa ad.
MRP200	Mumbles Rly. Car No. 2 (P)

Per card **20p**

Murray King Postcard Collectors Series.
London-born Murray King moved to St Ives in 1960 and began publishing good quality, colourful picture postcards to depict the history, the romance and the beauty of Cornwall. Four designs were produced in the first year, with a print run of 5000 and the range of over 100 now includes good photographic views as well as artist drawn. All are continental size.

Legend and Lore Series: MK1–27 (though 8, 14 and 15 were not issued and MK 3 and MK10 are duplicated numbers)

Modern

Cornwall subjects: Col. artist drawn – 25 designs. From 1964 onwards.

MK28, MK112: Photographic. Cornish subjects.

Devon Character Cards: Devon subjects.

Others

Per card **25p**

Noel Tatt Ltd ■MOD 11
Nash House, Lyminge, Folkestone, Kent.

Collectors' Cards
Sets of 6 reproductions of works by well-known artists/
photographers on a variety of themes. Full colour on fine
board.

A. Watermills of Europe	Richard Ward
B. Wild flowers of the British countryside	Prunella Bibby
C. British Birds in their natural surroundings	Ken Wood
D. Great motorcars of a bygone era	Gordon C. Davies
E. His Majesty's Ship	Richard Ward
F. Cats	Sally Fawcett
G. The great Four Funnelled Liners	Richard Ward
H. Winter Landscapes	Prunella Bibby
I. When steam pulled the trains	Gordon C. Davies
J. Oast Houses of Kent and Sussex.	Ronald Dean, RSMA
K. My ponies	Gilly Meredith
L. Aerobatic Display Teams of Europe	Richard Ward
M. Animals, as I see them	Per Lindstrom
N. Famous Aircraft of the past	Gordon C. Davies
O. The most famous of landscapes	John Constable, RA
P. The Falklands Islands Task Force	Richard Ward
Q. Donkeys at play	Gilly Meredith
R. Nursery Scenes	Rene Cloke
S. Photographs of cats and kittens	Photokunst Groh
T. Popular breeds of dogs on camera	Photokunst Groh
U. Wartime aircraft of another era	Gordon C. Davies
V. Manor Houses of England	Richard Ward
W. Wild Ducks	Ronald Beavan
X. D-Day action	Gordon Davies
Y. 6th June 1944, the Longest Day	Richard Ward
Z. Military Aircraft in Action	Jonathon C. Margetts
2. Military Aircraft in Action	Jonathon C. Margetts

Per card **12p**
Per set **72p**

Limited Edition Postcards
1000 only printed on fine board from clients' own photographs.

Laminated finish. Continental size. Cost to customer £69 per 1000 cards.

Price per card **50p**

■MOD 11 Pub. Noel Tatt. 'High Street, Burnham-on-Crouch'. Limited edition for Colloryan 25p

Paisley Productions ■MOD 12
Don Malcolm, 105 Glenapp Ave, Paisley, Renfrewshire.
Commemorative postcards in limited editions. Recent productions include:

Eric Liddell
80 pairs (160 numbered cards) commemorating the 60th Anniv. of the 400 metres. Postmarked Peking and Paris
Per pair **£5**

George Orwell
250 pairs. Mint, commemorating his novel *1984*, featuring Isle of Jura and East Kilbridge.
Per pair **£1**

Lunardi's Visit to Paisley. 200th Anniv. 1983 250 pairs
Per pair **60p**

No. 5 International Astronomical Union 1985 Incl. Halley's
   Comet. **40p**

No. 6 175th Anniv. of Chopin's birth (250) **40p**

Plaistow Pictorial
3 New Plaistow Rd, London E15 3JA.
Well printed col. RP postcards with an aviation, military, naval or transport theme.
Standard sized (16 sets) .. .. Per set **£1.60**
Jumbo sized (49 cards) .. .. Per card **15p**

■MOD 12 Pub. Paisley Productions. George Orwell. 1984, Limited edition of 250 50p

Post Office

A listing of cards produced by the British PO was given in earlier editions, also cards issued by the Guernsey, Jersey, Isle of Man and US Post Offices. Interest in these cards is maintained by stamp collectors rather than postcard collectors and as only a very simplified listing could be given here it has been decided to exclude such cards from this edition. British PO PHQ cards (depicting stamp designs) are listed and priced in Stanley Gibbons *Collect British Stamps* checklist and *Great Britain Concise Catalogue*. National Postal Museum and Regional cards (of which there are now a great many, including numerous printings of some cards) are covered in the specialised publication *Collect Post Office Cards*, published by BP Publications and available from Stanley Gibbons.

Reflections of a Bygone Age ■MOD 13

Brian Lund, 15 Debdale Lane, Keyworth, Nottingham, NG12 5HT.

■MOD 13 Pub. 'Reflections of a Bygone Age'. Keyworth Life Series. No. 9 'Keyworth in Winter' 20p

Sport. Series of 6 b & w. Artist Russell Fisher (1000)
Per set **£1.50**

1983 Gen. Election. Set of 12 b & w (1500 numbered sets)
Per set **£2.50**

Keyworth Life. Set of 6 col. cont. size cards. Limited to 1000
Per set **£1**

Ronfol ■MOD 14
Ron Griffiths, 47 Long Arrotts, Hemel Hempstead, Herts, HP1 3EX.
Artist Jack Follows.
1. Wicked Lady. Black on yellow. (250) **30p**
2. National Postcard Week, June 1984. Black on white (500)
  ..   ..   **30p**
3. 25 Anniv. of death of Bruce Bairnsfather. Black on buff
(250) **30p**
3A. D. H. Lawrence. 1885–1930. Black on buff (250)   ..   **30p**
5. National Postcard Week, May 1986.   ..   ..   ..   **30p**

K.O.M. (King of Mods Postcard)
1. col. photo card of 'Derry Dog'. **25p**

Rusnak, Ann
American artist and postcard enthusiast, who after working as a teacher and in radio, began publishing her own postcards in 1980. Since then her cartoons have won several prizes. Rusnak cards are printed in small (max. 500) runs, with only 100 of her first two designs printed. These command a premium. The cards are cont. size and hand tinted.

■MOD 14 Pub. Ronfol. Artist Jack Follows. No. 3. 25th Anniv. of Bruce Bairnsfather's death in 1959 30p

'Lighter Side of History' series. (24 designs)

Per card   ..   ..   35p/**50p**/£3

'Timely Topics' series incl. Halley's Comet, Soccer Hooligans

Per card **35p**

■MOD   15   Pub.   J.   F.   Jehanno. Fr. Salon George V Postcard Fair. April 1981 £4

Salons George V ■MOD 15
Commemorative cards for Postcard Fair organised by J. Jehanno, Paris.
  1. Autumn 1975   Art Nouveau design by Philippe Fix
  2. May 1976   Postman design by Rétécé
  3. November 1976   Art Nouveau design by Pierre Legue
  4. April 1977   Repro. cover Fr. postcard magazine *La Carte Postale* design by E. Fromaget.
  5. October 1977   Magic carpet design by Mme. Jehanno
  6. April 1978   Design by Anne Nogard
  7. October 1978   Fantasy design by A. C. Nogard
  8. April 1979   Design by Claudine Hyza
  9. October 1979   Postcard back design by Buschet
 10. April 1980   Woman writing design by Villemot
 11. October 1980   Circus act design by Colombat
 12. April 1981   French Presidents design
 13. October 1981   Woman design by Coudry
 14. April 1982   Stylised design by Antoinette Goutier

Price range   ..   ..   £2/**£4**/£7

S.A.S. (South Atlantic Souvenirs/Seasonal Art Series)
■ MOD 16
Satyrical, political, social, anti-Tory themes, e.g. political cari-
catures. Col. cont. size. Recent issues include:

Many Happy Returns (Halley's Comet/Bill Halley)
Keep the Home Fires Burning
Have a Titanic Christmas
Have a Bumber Christmas
Greetings from the Bunker
We Three Kings
You won't be seeing much of me this Christmas
Christmas Future
Seasonal Hazards
Happy New Year, Prisoner
Others

Per card **25p**

■MOD 16 Pub. S.A.S. Seasonal Art Series 70. 'Keep
the Home Fires Burning'. 40th Anniversary 25p

Veldale Covers ■MOD 17
6 Comberton Park Rd, Kidderminster, Worcs, DY10 3DY.
Unfortunately the company ceased trading at the end of 1984.
Their well printed limited edition postcards produced from
1980 to complement Post Office stamp issues and to commem-
orate events and anniversaries, have been listed in the third
and fourth editions of this catalogue (pp. 196–197 and 225 –
226 respectively). The last issues are listed below.

■MOD 17 Pub. Veldale Covers. SE24 The Queen Opens new terminal at Birmingham Airport 1984 50p

CB Series
30/1 Europa
31/1 London Economic Summit
32/1 Greenwich Meridian
33/1 The Royal Mail
34/1 The British Council
35/1 Christmas 1984

SE Series
24/1 Queen opens Birmignham Int. Airport (1000)
25/1 D-Day
26/1 25 years of the Mini
27/1 Royal Birth. Prince Henry (1500)
28/1 Montage of 7 Veldale Royalty designs

Price range	..	..	..	..	..	..	35p/**50p**/£1
Early issues	..	..	..	..	..	..	.. £1/**£2**/£6

SECTION SUPPLEMENT – MODERN

1. DALKEITH PUBLISHING CO.

Set   *Railway Series*
No.

33.   Severn & Wye & Severn Br. Rly.
34.   GWR & LMS Joint Line Posters
35.   London, Chatham & Dover Rly.
36.   Pullmans
37.   Invergarry & Ft. Augustus Rly.
38.   More GWR Posters (Part 1)
39.   More GWR Posters (Part 2)
40.   Railway Guides (Part 1)
41.   Railway Guides (Part 2)
42.   Hundred of Manhood & Selsey Tramways

43.	Campbeltown & Machrinharsh Lt. Rly.
44.	London, Brighton & S.C. Rly.
45.	Metropolitan Rly. Posters
46.	Met. & Gt. Central Joint Rly.
47.	Badges & Buttons (Part 1)
48.	Badges & Buttons (Part 2)
49.	Christmas Rly. Posters
50.	Famous Trains
51.	Callander & Oban Rly.
52.	Southern Rly. Posters
53.	Gt. Northern Rly. Posters
54.	L.N.E.R. Posters (Frolics)
55.	Garstang & Knott End Rly.
56.	Rly. Posters of Dorsets & Hants
57.	Hull & Barnsley Rly.
58.	Salute to the Gt. Western
59.	Silver Jubilee Train
60.	Posters of the LMS
61.	Railway Golfing Posters
62.	Tribute to the Rly. Posters of Terence Cuneo
63.	Glyn Valley Tramway
64.	More S.R. Posters
65.	More L.N.E.R. Posters

Per Set **£1.50**

Set No.   *Classic Poster Cards (2000)*

19.	More Shipping Companies
20.	Propaganda
21.	Grasset & Berthon
22.	Follies Bergère
23.	More Parisian Music Hall
24.	Coach companies
25.	Domestic
26.	Recruitment
27.	Early cinema
28.	Travel in the 20s and 30s
29.	Lucian Bernhard

Per Set **£1.50**

2. J/V POSTCARDS

Key

'V'	= village cards. b & w views of villages and small towns.
'S'	= Special issues. (i.e. current events) b & w
'CS'	= Col. specials.
'M'	= Mini series. Initially small runs, sometimes reprinted.
'C'	= Col. view, sometimes produced for a client.
'X'	= Not an original J/V photo

Sizes: b & w are 9 × 14 cm. Col. are cont. 15 × 10.5 cm.

J/V No.	Title	No. Printed	County
49S	Uppingham Fatstock Show	500	Rutland
50S*	Vale of Belvoir Protest	500	Notts-Leics.
51S*	Hallaton – Medbourne Bottle Kicking & Hare Pie Procession	500	Leics.
72S*	Narborough Village Station	350	Leics.
80C	Postcard Designs, Brockington College	2500	Leics.
163V*	Market Day, Market Bosworth	630	Leics.
164S*	Cattle Market, Market Bosworth	630	Leics.
172S	Ashby Statutes Fair	500	Leics.
173S*	'The Modernaires' Bradford, 1948–50	600	Yorkshire
174S* } 175S*	To Commemorate the Closure of Snibston Mine, 1983	600	Leics.
178*	Explosion of Portagas, Desford	250	Leics.
179*	Fire at Loweth Wools, Leicester	250	Leics.
180S	Floods in the Soar Valley	500	Leics/Notts
181S	Hallaton Bottle Kicking	350	Leics.
182*	Nottingham Postcard Fair	500	Notts.
183CS	Village Cricket Club	100	Leics.
184CS	The Game Shop, Ashby-de-la-Zouche	500	Leics.
193	Kiss-a-Grams		Leics.
194*	Police and Pickets, Sheffield	500	Yorkshire
198S*	Miners' Wives & Pickets, Coalville, 1984	500	Leics.
199S*	Packington Morris & Pennyroyal Garland Dancers		Leics.
220S } 221S	Mining and the Coalville Times, 1892–1984	700	Leics.
222S	Earl Shilton Shopkeepers Protest	500	Leics.
254CS	Ruddington Requiem Railtour	1000	Notts.
255S	Allenton Flea Market	500	Derby.
256CS*	Ashby Lace Guild	1000	Leics.
318CS*	B. Blockley Village Stores, Ravenstone	250	Leics.

J/V No.	Title	No. Printed	County
319CS*	Bilsworth Tunnel Commemorative	3000	Northants.
320CS ⎫ ⎬ 321CS ⎭	Re-opening Blisworth Tunnel	(3000)	Northants.
324S ⎫ ⎪ 325S ⎬ 326S ⎪ 327S ⎭	Nottingham Goose Fair Set of 4	500	Notts.
334CS ⎫ ⎪ 335CS ⎬ 336CS ⎪ 337CS ⎭	Female Figure Set of 4	1000	
342M	The Weather's Hot . . .		
344S*	Scargill & MacGregor	1000	
345S	Hands Off Leics	1000	Leics.
347CS*	Dunwich Fishermen land World War Mine	500	Suffolk
352S	Sheep Shearing	500	Staffs.
372CS	Card Fair Notts	500	Notts.
373CS	Power Station	500	Notts.
374C	Charnwood '85 (Scout Camp)	3000	Notts.
375C	Charnwood '85 (Scout Camp Badges)	3000	Notts.
389S	Miners' Return	1000	Yorkshire
394M	'Before The Parade'		Lincs.
395M	Tractor Repairs		Staffs.
396M	Elm Tree		Northants.
397S	Greyhound Stadium	500	Leics.
398S	March to Molesworth	1000	Cambs.
412C	Narborough Railway Station		Leics.
432C	Turk's Head Pub		Leics.
506C	Mini-railway, traction engine		
510S ⎫ 511S ⎭	Signal Box, Coalville	500	Leics.
512S	Factory Fire, Wigston	500	Leics.
513S	Train Derailment, Stoke		Staffs.
515	Croft Quarry		Leics.
519S	Staff, Brockington College		Leics.

The Stanley Gibbons Postcard Department is at 399 Strand, London, WC2. Open Mon – Fri, 9.30 am – 5.30 pm; Sat. 10.00 am – 12.30 pm.

NOVELTY

A novelty postcard is one that deviates from the normal rectangular item made of standard board. It may have something stuck on it, may be made of unusual material or be of an unusual size or shape. It may also *do* something—squeak, smell or move—in which case it is a 'mechanical' postcard. Many novelty cards contravened existing Post Office regulations for postcards because of their irregular size, shape or material. They were then subject to letter or book rate (1*d*. instead of ¹/₂*d*. as for normal postcards in Periods 1 to 3). Some, like jewelled or tinselled items, had to be sent through the post in protective envelopes.

APPLIQUED MATERIALS

Buttons
Dried flowers
Envelope (to enclose a tiny letter)
Feathers (birds or hats)
Glass (eyes for animals)
Gutter (or tinsel)
Hair (on heads and other parts of the body)
Jewelling/glitter (usually mica)
Lace
Metal Models
Mirror (i.e. metal that reflects an image)
Photographs (inset personal portrait)
Pocket (to enclose a card or tiny hankie)
Pussy willow (to make the bodies of kittens)
'Real Japanese' (Tuck series with linen finish)
Sand paper (to strike matches)
Seeds (shamrock and others)
'Stickers' (for matches)
(Velvet and other materials (in the shapes of bloomers, flowers, hats, etc.)
Other materials
Price range   ..   ..   **£1/£3/£8**

■N1 Pub. 'D.R.G.M.' Embossed coins, national flag and exchange rate for Bulgaria. Period 2 £7

BANKNOTES/COINS/STAMP CARDS ■N 1
In Period 2 cards were printed to represent the banknotes and coins of various countries. Some of the gilded/silvered, embossed versions are most realistic.

Price range .. .. £2/**£4**/£6

BAS RELIEF
A deep form of embossing with a three-dimensional effect, often with 'jewelling'. Subjects are normally important personages. *See* ROYALTY. Publishers include Stengel & Co., and Sutton, Sharpe & Co.

Price range .. .. £1/**£1.50**/£2

BEER MATS
Period 7 cards produced by brewers in Britain and on the Continent (e.g. Munchner Hofbrau) often o/s.

Price range 25p/50p

COMPOSITE
A composite set is a number of postcards (from 2 upwards) which fit together to make a complete picture. See second edition for listing.

Price range .. .. £3/**£25**/£120

EMBOSSING
Many beautiful early Continental embossed designs exist. *See* GREETINGS. British publishers include DeLittle, Fenwick & Co., Hildesheimer, Ettlinger, Tuck ('Art' and 'Connoisseur' series).

Price range .. .. 75p/**£1.50**/£3

FANTASY
This is an imaginative, frequently surrealist, type of design, often with a *trompe l'oeil* element, sometimes using photomontage. Very popular are cards featuring heads composed of figures. These are known on the Continent as *Arcimboldesque* after the 16th century Italian painter, Arcimboldo, who devised the technique of using the shapes of animals, fish, fruit and other objects to form human portraits.

Girls in Neckties .. .. £10/**£20**/£30

Arcimboldesque Heads
For full listing, see edition four of this catalogue, p. 229.

Period 2: Composers, Personalities, Misc.

Price range .. ..£5/**£12**/£20

Period 7: French
Artist Jacques Lardie. Political figures .. 25p/**50p**/£1

HAND PAINTED/TINTED

Amateur artists..	50p/**75p**/£1.50
Commercially produced hand coloured	50p/**£1**/£2
Cont commercially produced water colours ..	75p/**£1.50**/£2.50
Japanese oil paintings	£1/**£2**/£3
Japanese water colours	75p/**£1**/£2
Photographic origin. Hand tinted	50p/**75p**/£1.50
Others	25p/**50p**/£1.50

HOLD TO LIGHT (HTL)/TRANSPARENCIES ■N 2

These are cards which, as their title implies, reveal a surprise
when held to the light. They came in two forms—cards that
appear quite standard until held to the light (transparencies)
and those that have cut out sections representing a source of
light—candles, moons, suns, windows, etc.—(cut outs).

Christmas and other greetings	£4/**£8**/£10
Cupples, Samuel (incl. World's Fair 1904)	£1/**£2**/£3
Exhibitions	£5/**£10**/£15
Hartmann transparency series	£2/**£3**/£4
Meteor transparencies (incl. Paris Exhibition 1900) .. ..
.. ..	£6/**£8**/£10
W.H. (Wittagelberg) Berlin (HTL and transparencies) ..
.. ..	£1.50/**£2.50**/£3
Others	£1/**£2**/£4

■N2 Pub. W. Hagelberg. HTL Christmas card. Period 2 £6

MECHANICAL

Postcards demanding some kind of action.

**Action Cards; Barometers; Blow Up; Cigarette Cards;
Cut Outs** Notably Tuck 'Birds and Butterflies on the Wing',
Dolls for Dressing, etc.; **Deeks Puzzle Cards** USA. Changing
pictures; **Girls' Own Paper Postcards** 1900. 2 sets of 4
postcards printed on one page to cut out; **Gramophone
Records** Modern; Pub. Ettlinger; Pub. Tuck; **Heat-activated
Cards** To show hidden pictures; **Jigsaw Cards** Notably Tuck
Picture Puzzle Postcards; **Kaleidoscopes** Pub. Alpha, at least
20 designs; **Reversible Cards** Showing a different picture
when turned upside down; **Scented Cards** With impregnated

pads to rub to release perfume; **Venetian Blinds** Roller Blinds; **Squeakers** Various publishers; **Windows** Or boxes that open to show another picture; **Wire Coils** Used for 'flying' butterflies, wagging tails, etc.; Others

Price range   ..   ..£3/**£10**/£25

PULLOUTS
The commonest kind of novelty card where a flap is raised to reveal a concertina of small pictures, usually views. Pullouts exist for most categories of postcards including ADVERTISING, ANIMALS, COMIC, ROYALTY, SOCIAL HISTORY, etc.

Artist drawn, signed ..   .. 75p/**£1**/£3
Artist drawn, unsigned   ..   ..   ..   50p/**75p**/£1.50
Photographic origin 25p/**50p**/75p
Collectable subjects (e.g. Teddy Bears, Hop-picking, Santas etc.) ..   .. £3/**£4**/£6

SHAPES
Cards were produced in a variety of unusual shapes, e.g. animals, circular, leaf, etc.
Price range   ..   .. 75p/**£1**/£3

SILK
This is the best documented type of novelty postcard (in the booklets of C. Radley). Three main types exist: embroidered, printed and woven.

Embroidered Silks

Period 2. Mostly Floral in Design
Price range   ..   ..£5/**£10**/£15

Period 3 See MILITARY – WWI

Periods 4, 5
Continuation of Continental sentimental Period 3 type designs incl. Tuck. 'Broderie d'Art series.
Price range   ..   .. £2/**£3**/£5
Year Dates   ..   .. £4/**£6**/£10

Printed on Satin/Silk
The least collectable type of silk card, though some fine Continental *Art Nouveau* designs exist and the British 'Fab' Patchwork series is interesting.

1900–1903. Ger. Pub. Krieger. Four Seasons series. Per set
  ..   .. £20/**£40**/£60
1900–1903. Various Continental designs   ..   £3/**£5**/£10
Period 2. 'Fab' Patchwork. Clan Crests/Flowers/Views   ..
  ..   .. £4/**£6**/£8
'Fab' designs for the USA market of State Capitals (Series 5)
  ..   .. £5/**£6**/£8

Others   ..   ..   75p/**£1.50**/£3
  N.B. Cards with plain backs (e.g. Cinema stars, Edith Cavell, etc.) are *not* postcards and are not listed.

Woven
These are the most artistic, skilfully produced and the most sought after of all the 'Silks'.

Alpha. Flags, greetings, etc.   ..   ..   ..   £10/**£20**/£45
American. St. Louis Exhibition (1904)   ..   £60/**£80**/£100
Others   ..   ..   £25/**£45**/£65
Austrian. Periods 2, 4   ..   ..   ..   £10/**£20**/£28
French. 1900. Pub. Benoiston, Paris Exhibition   £30/**£40**/£50
French. Period 2. Pub. Neyret Frères. *Art Nouveau*, Classical, Portraits, Views (the highest value is for col. *Art Nouveau*)
   ..   ..   £30/**£80**/£150
German. Periods 1/Early Period 2. Pubs. include Knuffmann and Krieger   ..   ..   ..   £20/**£35**/£50
Grant, W. H. & Co. Exhibitions, Greetings, Hands Across the Sea, Portraits, Ships, Subjects, Views (the highest value is for Exhibitions)   ..   ..   ..   £15/**£50**/£80
Japanese. 1908–1910. Admiral Togo, View of Amanohashitate
   ..   ..   £20/**£30**/£40
Stevens, Thomas. Exhibitions, Greetings, Hands Across the Sea, Portraits, Religious subjects, Ships, Subjects, Views (the highest valuation is for col. views and rare personalities) ..   ..   £20/**£60**/£200
Others   ..   ..£8/**£12**/£25

UNUSUAL MATERIALS

Postcards were manufactured from the most curious substances, which include aluminium, bark, celluloid, cork, ivory, leather, panel cards (on stout board), papyrus, peat, wood, others. The highest value is for postally used cards of unusual substances. One of the most original materials ever used was pulped paper currency in the USA—known as 'Macerated Money Cards'. Rare.

Price range   ..   .. £1/**£5**/£12

Three Band Pricing System

Left Hand Band: The lowest price you will probably be asked to pay for this card.
Middle Band: What you will normally be asked to pay for this card: its average, reasonable price.
Right Hand Band: The highest price you will probably be asked to pay for this card.
For a full explanation of the system see page ix.

POLITICAL/PROPAGANDA/ PUNISHMENT & JUSTICE

The postcard was a medium greatly utilised by civil, military and political commentators. Sometimes this was spontaneous comment by the artist, sometimes it was inspired or commissioned by governments and other bodies for their campaigns. This vehicle flourished in wartime, so consult also MILITARY. This is another section where artists reign supreme, although, sadly, much fine work is unsigned and as yet unidentified. To make the pointed barbs palatable to the collecting public, many political/propaganda drawings appear as cartoons. Therefore a high proportion of designers of political cards will also be found under COMIC. Several themes in this section also overlap with SOCIAL HISTORY.

Listed below are the main causes and themes of importance in this category. RPs will command highest values.

■POL 1 Pub. W.S.P.U. Ad. for *The Suffragette Weekly* edited by Christabel Pankhurst. Period 2 £20

Alsace-Lorraine (Periods 2, 3)	..	..	..	£3/**£5**/£8
Anti-British (*see* MILITARY)		..	..	..£5/**£15**/£25
Anti-Royalty. Q. Victoria, Boer War, Edward VII debauchery,				
George V, WW1	..	..	..	..£3/**£10**/£25
Anti-Semitic	..	..	..	..£5/**£15**/£60
Berlin Blockade (1948)	..	..	..	£15/**£25**/£30
Bolshevism/anti-Bolshevism	..	..	..	£5/**£10**/£30
Communism (incl. Period 7)	..	..	..	£3/**£8**/£10
Conscientious Objectors	..	..	..	£1/**£3**/£5
Edith Cavell (*see* MILITARY)		..	..	£1/**£3**/£6
Fascism	..	..	..	£3/**£5**/£15
Freemasonry ■CUR 3	..	..	..	£1/**£3**/£5
Irish Home Rule/Sinn Fein	..	..	..	£3/**£5**/£10
Lusitania (*see* MILITARY)	..	..	..	£1/**£3**/£5
Maternity benefit (1914)	..	..	..	£1/**£2**/£3
National Insurance Acts	..	..	..	75p/**£1.50**/£3
National Socialism (*see* MILITARY)		..	£3/**£7.50**/£15
Sidney Street Siege	..	..	..	£1/**£3**/£5
Socialism (throughout Europe)	..	..	..	£2/**£4**/£10

Spartakist uprising (1919)	£3/**£5**/£10
State Visits (e.g. Czar to France 1896) ..	..£7/**£15**/£25
Strikes (*see* SOCIAL HISTORY)	..£5/**£10**/£20
Suffragettes ■POL 1	..£5/**£10**/£20
Tariff Reform	75p/**£1.50**/£3

NOTABLE SERIES
More details were given in the fourth edition of this catalogue, pp. 234–235.

American
Pubs. include: Austen (Famous Men); Coral-Lee (Period 7); Sheehan, (U.S. Presidents)

Price range .. .. £1/**£2**/£3

British
Pubs. include: Birn Bros. (Suffrage series); Davidson Bros. (Fiscal Games/Political Dances/Chamberlain etc); Faulkner (Fiscal, John Bull, Suffragettes, etc); Hartmann (Eminent Men); Inter-Art ('Licker' – Nat. Ins Stamp); Jarrold (*Punch* cartoons); Millar & Lang (Fiscal, Freemason, etc); Tuck (Aesop's Fables, Empire, Fiscal, Game Birds, Politicians, etc); Valentine (Various); Wrench (*Punch* cartoons); others.

Price range .. .. £1/**£3**/£6

French
Many reproductions from satirical publications, like *Le Rire* (Musée des Sires, Musée des Souverains); *Le Burin Satirique*; *L'Assiette au Beurre*, etc., often in limited editions.

Price range .. ..£3/**£10**/£20

German
Notable are propaganda cards which chart the rise of Hitler's NAZI party. (see MILITARY).

Price range .. ..£5/**£12**/£25

Italian
Notable are propaganda cards which chart the rise of Mussolini's Fascist Party.

Price range .. ..£5/**£12**/£25

Portuguese
Revolutionary cards, Period 7 and others

Price range .. .. 50p/**£1**/£3

Others

Price range .. .. 50p/**£3**/£7

POLITICAL ARTISTS

The most important artists of this genre were listed in the fourth edition of this catalogue, pp. 235–236. They include: Boccasile (It); Camara, Léal de (Fr.); Carter, Reg; Corbello, Tito (It); Davey, George; Fredillo (Fr); Furniss, Harry; Ludovici, Anthony; Martino, A (It); Maurice, Reg; Mirko (It); Moreland, Arthur; 'Orens' (also 'Denizard', 'Godillot' – Fr.); Partridge, Bernard; Raemakers, Louis (Dutch); Raven-Hill, Leonard; Retrosi, Virgilio (It); Rostro (Fr.); Roubille, A. (Fr.); Roverini, M (It); Sancho, F. (Fr.); Spurgin, Fred; Thiele, Arthur (Ger.); Others.

Price range .. .. £3/**£8**/£25

POLITICAL LEADERS/PERSONALITIES ■POL 2

Heads of State, Members of Parliament, Presidents, Prime Ministers, Royalty. Favourite subjects are—*Britain*: Balfour, Campbell-Bannerman, Joseph Chamberlain, Churchill, Edward VII, Sir Edward Grey, Lloyd George and Queen Victoria; *France*: Clemenceau, Felix Faure, de Gaulle, Loubet and Poincaré; *Germany*: Bismarck, Hitler and the Kaiser; *USA*: Eisenhower, Kennedy, Lincoln, Nixon and Washington. Period 7 subjects include: Ayatollah Khomeini, Elizabeth II, Pope John Paul II, Margaret Thatcher, Pres. Mitterand, Pres. Reagan.

■POL 2 Pub. Hildreth & Chambers, Wolverhampton. 'Staveley Hill. MP for Kingswinford!' Message: We have got our man in magnificently. Majority 841. Last time 603, increase 238!!! Isn't it good?'. UB. PU 19 Jan. 1906 £3

Cartoons/Caricatures
Value according to quality of the artist.
Price range .. .. £2/**£5**/£20

Political Campaigns/Candidates/Election Results/ Groups of Cabinets/Governments
Artist drawn .. .. 75p/**£1.50**/£3
Photographic in origin .. .. £1/**£3**/£5

Straight Portraits
Artist drawn. Value according to quality of artist   £1/**£2**/£3
Photographic   ..   ..   75p/**£1.50**/£2

PUNISHMENT & JUSTICE

Famous Trials
Dreyfus Affair. *Jewish officer in the French Army who was convicted of treason and deported to Devil's Island. Subsequently he was re-instated and awarded the Légion d'Honneur when the case against him was proved to be fabricated. A detailed listing of cards covering the affair were listed on pp. 238–239 of the fourth edition of this catalogue.*

Price range   ..   ..£5/**£10**/£15

Haarmann the Mass Murderer (1924)   ..   ..   £2/**£4**/£6
Humpert-Crawford affair (1902)
    Artist drawn ..   .. £3/**£6**/£10
    Photographic ..   .. £3/**£6**/£8
Landru. Period 2. Artist Poulbot.†   ..   ..   .. £6/**£8**/£15
    Other artists ..   .. £2/**£3**/£5
Other trials. British and French. Periods 2, 7   .. £2/**£5**/£10

Punishments
Chain gangs/convicts/prisoners and prisons/slave ships. Clear
    photographs   ..   .. £1/**£2**/£4
Decapitation/flogging/hanging/various executions and punishments. Clear photographs   ..   ..   ..   £1.50/**£3**/£5
Tottenham Assassins. Privately produced, real photo cards of
    the siege and the suicides   ..   .. 75p/**£2**/£4

Unusual Punishments
Fr. Series of comic artist drawn penalties of gossip—hideously
    enlarged tongues. Period 2   ..   ..   ..   75p/**£1.50**/£3
Ger. Pub. Nister. col. artist drawn series which includes
    ducking, muzzling, neck collars, pillories, stocks, etc. Period
    2   ..   ..   75p/**£1.50**/£3

The Stanley Gibbons Postcard Department is at 399
Strand, London, WC2. Open Mon – Fri. 9.30 am – 5.30
pm; Sat. 10.00 am – 12.30 pm.

PUBLISHERS

We continue here the listing of cards of some of the most famous and important postcard publishers.

ALLEN, DAVID ■ C 1
See COLLECTIONS.

DAVIDSON BROS ■P 1
Famous for humorous cards by the best British artists. Tom Browne, their main artist, drew about 900 designs for them. Production began around 1902. A listing of the artists who drew for this publisher was given in the Second Edition (p. 168) *See also* COMIC.
Price range   ..   .. £2/**£4**/£12

■P1 Pub. Davidson. Artist Pyp. Series 6009. PU 1903 £2

S. HILDESHEIMER ■P 2
Hildesheimers began their business in London in 1876 producing greetings cards; their earliest postcards appear to have been sepia, court size, issued in 1899. Business developed rapidly and many artists were used to meet the demand for view cards. Soon a numbering system was introduced, but a higher number does not necessarily mean a later issue than a lower number. Perhaps the best known of Hildesheimer's work is the '5000 Series', a mixture of British and Foreign views (mostly artist drawn, but some photographic) with the occasional comic design. The series began *c.* 1904 and many cards are similar in concept and execution to the great Tuck *Oilette* series of views and scenes—possibly it was designed to rival the Tuck sets. Production appears to have ceased *c.* 1912.

Cards in the '5000 Series' in the number range 5038–5299 were listed in the third edition of this catalogue (pp. 214–215), numbers 5300–5399 in the fourth edition (pp. 251–252).

Price range   ..   .. 50p/**£1.50**/£4

■P2 Pub. Hildesheimer. Artist R. Gallon. No. 5456. Christ Church Gate, Canterbury. Period 2 £1

INTER-ART ■P 3

Over 8000 different designs are accredited to this company which began production in 1909. Its major artists were Spurgin and Donald McGill.

Checklist of cards issued to 1924 were given in the second and third editions of this catalogue.

Price range   ..   .. 25p/£1/£5

■P3 Pub. Inter-Art. Artist Gwen Hayward Young (Jotter's daughter) 'Comique' series. 6691. PU 1929 £1

JUDGES

In 1902 Fred Judge (*1872–1950*) and his brother Thomas Winn purchased and managed a Hastings photographic store. By August 1903 postcard views of Hastings and District—'The Judge Series'—were published using real photographic, collotype, photogravure and colour photogravure techniques.

By 1906 cards in a consecutively numbered *Main Series*, incorporating some renumbered special event cards, were available. Prior to No. 700 there are different negatives with the same number. By 1909 the *London Series* had appeared, and by 1914 the *Main Series* numbered over 4000. Photogravure, collotype and Fred Judge's sketched and initialed cards were produced as a cheap alternative to sepia in the 1920s and 1930s. In the mid 1950s b & w cards replaced sepia and the new current series of col. cards was introduced.

We have divided Judges output into 4 categories.

1. Early—non-Main Series
Series of local views (some printed in Germany), dated Hastings' events and flowers. Varied photographic and non-photographic cards; some col.
Price range   ..   ..   50p/**£1.50**/£4

2. Main Series
Consecutively numbered (50–22328) of British Isles topography, animals and floral studies. Mainly sepia (some hand-tinted) but also black/white, photogravure, sketch, collotype and col. Some duplicated numbers. Extensive reprinting; identifiable by back design. Also four-view topographical cards (4-1–4-806).
Price range   ..   ..   50p/**75p**/£2

3. London Series
Similar to Main series, consecutively numbered, L1–L799 (*possibly more*).
Price range   ..   ..   50p/**75p**/£2

A listing of these cards from Nos. 1–152 was given in the third edition of this catalogue (pp. 217–218) Nos. 155–332 in the fourth edition (pp. 253–254). The listing is continued in the supplement to this section.

4. Modern Cards
Col., consecutively numbered series, e.g. C6035, including retailers' special orders, e.g. C5573X. Also sketch, monochrome, unnumbered, col. and serrated ex-calendar cards.
Price range 25p/50p

LL (LOUIS LEVY)
In the Second Edition we published a full description of current knowledge and prevailing theories concerning LL together with a check list of London cards, Nos. 1–420. This check list was continued in the third and fourth editions (Nos. 499–670; 671–813).

Two additions can be made to these listings:

312. Tower of London (1910)
516. Hampton Court Palace. West Front

Valuations: Highest prices apply to *London Types* and then to active street scenes with clear detail of people/transport.
Period 2 pictures, published in Period 2   ..   ..   £2/**£4**/£8
Period 2 pictures, published in Period 4   ..   £1/**£1.50**/£2

REID, ANDREW
Andrew Reid established his printing business in Newcastle in 1845. Much early work was done for railway and shipping companies using both litho and letterpress techniques. His sons and grandsons carried on the business until the 1920s when it passed out of family management. The first postcards were produced in 1902. The shipping and railway cards are generally well printed chromo-litho products, particularly the UB vignettes, but amongst the local subject cards can be found some poorer examples of printing and colouring.
Price range

Railway cards	..	..	..	..	..	..£2/**£15**/£60
Shipping cards	..	..	..	..	..	£1.50/**£8**/£25

Listings of Railway and Shipping cards appeared in the third edition of this catalogue, p. 221.

J. W. RUDDOCK & SONS
J. W. Ruddock was born in New Malton, North Yorkshire in 1852. After apprenticeship he set up his own stationers and bookselling business in Lincoln in the 1880s. Postcard production followed later. The best known of Ruddock's cards are those in the *Artist* series probably begun in 1902. A 1907 catalogue refers to over 400 views in the series.

A listing of Ruddock view cards, arranged by artist was given in the third edition of this catalogue, p. 222.

Price range .. .. 50p/**75p**/£1.50p

TUCK ■AD 1, M 5, 6
Raphael Tuck & Sons Ltd. is probably the most famous of all postcard publishers. Founded in the 1870s by Raphael Tuck and continued by his son Adolph, the company developed such a reputation for the quality of its printing work that in 1893 it received its first Royal Warrant from Queen Victoria. Adolph Tuck led a campaign to persuade Parliament to allow British manufacturers to publish picture cards of the full Continental size. On 1 November 1899 that freedom was granted and the first dozen Tuck cards were quickly issued.
The company continued producing postcards until after the Second World War.

Celebrated Posters
Cards in this series were listed in the fourth edition of this catalogue, pp. 248–249.

Price range .. .. £15/**£25**/£60

The Empire Series
As the title implies, the subjects of these cards are patriotic—naval vessels, famous generals, etc.
The cards are individually numbered but also form series—e.g. Series 47 The Empire's Navy comprises cards 243–254. *See also* MILITARY.

Details of cards in series 47, 48, 49, 50, 55, 68, 69 and 70 were given in the third edition of this catalogue (p. 225).

Price range						
Celebrated Posters	..	..	..	..	..	£15/**£25**/£60
Empire Series	..	..	..	..	..	..£8/**£15**/£25
Others	..	..	..	..	..	£2.50/**£5**/£15

The Heraldic Series
These are amongst the most beautiful of Tuck postcards. Coloured embossed coats of arms on the left of the card are accompanied on the right by a fine monochrome view. Each series has a common coat of arms with differing monochrome views on its cards. Cards carry individual numbers or series numbers but apparently not both. It is, therefore, very difficult to correlate card and series numbers.
Details of the cards in series 150 (London), 152 (Glasgow), 153 (Manchester), 154 (Liverpool), 155 (Dublin), 156 (Edinburgh), 157 (Birmingham), 158 (Belfast), 159 (Bristol), 160 (York), 161 (Plymouth), 162 (Leamington), 163 (Brighton), 164 (Oxford), 165 (Cambridge), 166 (Aberdeen) and 167 (Bath) were given in the third edition of this catalogue (pp. 225–226).
Price range .. .. £3/**£6**/£12

Kings and Queens of England
This collection of 3 series (Nos. 614, 615 & 616) each of 12 cards, plus Edward VII (617), was described in the second edition of this catalogue (p. 109). There are 6 versions of Edward VII.

Per card	..	..	..	..	..	..	.. £6/**£8**/£10
Complete set of 42	..	..	..	..	.. £260/**£350**/£450		

Proof Limited Edition Sets
In May 1903 Tuck announced that they would, from time to time, issue special limited editions of their new postcards. Only 1000 copies of each set would be produced. All would have an individual Proof number in gold and would be printed on a special thick board. All purchasers would receive a certificate and be listed in a special register.

Sets numbered I–L were listed in the third edition of this catalogue, p. 226.

Price range .. ..£5/**£10**/£15

'United Kingdom' Postcard Series
A checklist is invited for this little-researched series, featuring photographic origin scenes on a green background, decorated with embossed, gilded symbols of the counties of the U.K.

Price range .. .. £2/**£4**/£6

L336	The Guildhall
L337	The Monument
SL338	Westminster, London
SL338	London, Westminster
L341	Waterloo Place
L342	Bow Church
L343	Southwark Cathedral
L344	Buckingham Palace
L345	Kensington Palace
L346	Australia House
L348	Regent Street
L350	St. Pauls and Ludgate Hill
L351	St. Pauls and Ludgate Hill
L353	St. Pauls Pigeons
L354	Flower Seller. Piccadilly
L355	Flower Seller. Piccadilly
L356	In Hyde Park
L358	Hyde Park Corner
L359	Old Bailey
L360	Law Courts
L361	Law Courts
L362	Law Courts
L363	St. James's Palace
L364	Changing Guard. St. James's Palace
L365	In Covent Garden
L366	Covent Garden
L368	Covent Garden
L369	Kew Gardens
L370	Kew Gardens
L373	River Thames at Kew Gardens
L375	Epping Forest
L376	Epping Forest
L379	Epping Forest
L381	West Front. St. Barts The Great
L382	North Door. St. Barts The Great
L383	Henry VIII. Gateway. St. Barts Hospital
L390	Harrow from the Football Ground
L391	Harrow from the Sixth Form Ground
L393	In the Dip. Hampstead Heath
L394	Bridle Path on Hampstead Heath
L395	Bridle Path on Hampstead Heath
L396	On Hampstead Heath
L397	Cheyne Walk Chelsea
L399	Chelsea Old Church
L400	Buckingham Palace
L401	The Lake St. James's Park, and Buckingham Palace
L402	St. James's Park
L404	In St. James's Park
L406	In St. James's Park
L407	The Tower of London
L409	Traitors' Gate, Tower of London
L413	Bloody Tower. Tower of London
L414	Gateway. Bloody Tower. Tower of London

L415	Middle Temple
L417	Fountain Court. Middle Temple
L418	Fountain Court. Middle Temple
L420	Pump Court. Middle Temple (*1926*)
L421	Sunday in Trafalgar Square
L422	A Demonstration in Trafalgar Square
L425	Westminster Cathedral
L426	Somerset House
L427	Royal Exchange and Bank of England
L430	St. Paul's from Ludgate Hill
L431	The Cenotaph
L434	Mrs. Ramsay MacDonald's Memorial Lincolns Inn Fields
L436	City of London War Memorial
L437	Royal Air Force War Memorial and County Hall
L438	St. Martins in the Fields (*1928*)
L439	St. Martins in the Fields
L440	Houses of Parliament
SL440	Houses of Parliament (*S*)
L441	Houses of Parliament
L443	Natural History Museum
L444	Imperial Institute
L449	Bush House
L450	Kingsway and Bush House
L451	The British Museum
L452	Tate Gallery
L453	St. Thomas's Hospital
L454	The Cavalry Monument Hyde Park
L456	Big Ben
L455	R. A. Memorial Hyde Park Corner
L457	Big Ben
L461	Dulwich Village
L463	Dulwich Village
L464	The Toll Gate. Dulwich Village
L465	Peter Pan
L467	Buckingham Palace
L468	Queen Victoria Memorial
L469	Regent Street
L470	Horse Guards Parade (*1928*)
L472	The Guardsman Horse Guards Parade
L473	St. Martin in the Fields
L476	Kingsway Night
L477	Kingsway Night
L478	The Lake Bushey Park
L483	St. Paul's Kitchener Memorial
L485	St. Martins in the Fields
L486	St. Martins in the Fields
L488	St. Martins in the Fields, The Crypt
L490	British Museum
L492	Ken Wood. The Lake
L493	Ken Wood. The Lake
L496	In Ken Wood
L497	In Ken Wood
L498	Ken Wood, The old duelling ground

To be continued

(*S*) = sketch form
Dates refer to postally used copies

1986/7 DATES
BLOOMSBURY CREST
HOTEL

Coram Street, Russell Square, W.C.1.

1986:
October 5
October 26
November 30
December 21

1987:
January 25
February 22
March 22

April 26
May 24
June 28
July 26
August 23
September 27
October 25
November 22
December 20

The internationally celebrated Bloomsbury Fair! The largest Postcard Fair held anywhere in the world. It has become a legend in its time. Every month we have over 100 dealers from all parts of Great Britain, with regulars from France, Belgium, Sweden and U.S.A. 170 stands packed with postcard stocks at any Bloomsbury Fair are estimated to be in excess of 1 million! Over 1000 attendance each month. If you collect postcards then Bloomsbury is the only place to be. A monthly get-together of all sections of the postcard world. Held in the magnificent 12,000 sq. ft. exhibition area of this luxury hotel, the finest venue in London. This is the international market place for everyone in our specialised collecting fields.

OPEN: 10.00 a.m.–4.30 p.m.

ADMISSION: 35p

Full catering facilities, plus hotel bar and restaurants. Nearest Tube: Russell Square.

For further information or bookings:
IPM Promotions
2 Frederick Gardens, Brighton BN1 4TB
Telephone 0273 675757
62 Greyhound Hill, Hendon, London NW4
Telephone 01–203 1772

RAILWAYS

This is the province of the specialist collector and values fluctuate wildly. Intense competitive interest can focus on particular cards thus pushing up the prices paid for them, but once that limited demand has been satisfied, prices can drop dramatically. Such action and reaction is not exclusive to this category of course but the novice railway collector would do well to look around a little before buying. The highest values in this section attach to poster-type designs and early vignette views. The continuing interest in local history RP cards make views of railway hotels and stations most desirable and map cards retain their popularity.

A more detailed introduction was given in the second edition of this catalogue (p. 177).

The listing here is given under the following headings:

Non-Official Cards. Thematic
Official Cards. Pre-1923 Companies
Official Cards. Post-1923 Companies
Minor Railways

Non-Official Cards—Thematic Listing

Accidents ■R 1

Gothard, W.—photographic series   ..   ..   £20/**£30**/£40
Other photographic/halftone/collotype cards. (Much of the
    value of these cards depends on their picture content and
    publisher interest) ..   ..£6/**£10**/£15

■R1 Pub. Warner Gothard, Leeds. 'Midland Railway Accident at Cudworth. January 19th 1905'. PU 1905 £25

Advertisements ■R 2

Reproductions of posters (see official cards)
    Periods 2–4   ..   ..   £25/**£35**/£60
    Period 7 ..   ..   25p/50p
French poster series. With/without references to railways in
    the British Isles   ..   ..£6/**£12**/£20
Poster type advertising (artistic cards from many countries)
    ..   .. £5/**£8**/£20

■R2 Pub. Orient-Express.
Artist Pierre Fix-Masseau.
Art Deco style. Period 7 50p

Foreign Railways (those other than in the British Isles).
Official cards (those issued with company crests or titles), e.g.
  America & Canada (various), Cape, Japan, Natal, Russia,
  Tasmania .. .. £4/**£6**/£10
Engines .. .. £1/**£2**/£3
General views of track etc. .. .. £1/**£2**/£3
Rolling stock, inside/external views .. .. £1/**£1.50**/£2
Stations .. .. £2/**£3**/£4

Funicular & Cliff Railways/Lifts
Great Britain .. .. £1/**£2**/£3
Foreign .. .. 75p/**£1**/£2

Locomotive & Rolling Stock—Pre-1923
Fleury, Paris—a series of many hundred cards of locomotives
of French Railways. Two different printings.
  Red captions .. .. £2/**£3**/£6
  Black captions .. .. £1/**£2**/£3
Hartmann (Series 3061) .. .. £1/**£2**/£3
JWB (Commercial series No. 312–12 No.) .. £1/**£1.50**/£2
Knight series .. .. £1/**£2**/£3
Locomotive magazine .. .. £1/**£1.50**/£2.50
Locomotive Publishing Co. (Early vignettes, both single and
  multi-col.) £15/**£20**/£25
Locomotive Publishing Co.—collotypes/half tone .. ..
.. .. £1/**£1.50**/£2.50
Locomotive Publishing Co.—photographic issues .. ..
.. .. £1/**£1.50**/£2.50
Locomotive Publishing Co.—col. series (Goffey 4–291) (F.
  Moore paintings) .. .. .. £1/**£1.50**/£2.50
Misch & Co.—'Noted Trains' series 331 and 332 .. £3/**£4**/£6
Parsons, F. J. .. .. £1/**£2**/£3
Pictorial Centre, Brighton (24 cards) .. .. .. £1/**£2**/£3

Pouteau—half-tone/photographic	£1/**£1.50**/£2
Railway photographs (photographic cards, no specific publishers)	£1/**£1.50**/£3
Smith, G.	£1/**£2**/£3
Smith, W. H.—'Kingsway series'	£1.50/**£2**/£3
Tuck, R. & Sons. 'Oilette' and other similar series (1904–1923). (6493, 9040, 9150, 9226, 9274, 9316, 9329, 9161, 9662, 9972, 9637, 8619, 9715, 9760) ..	£2/**£3**/£5
Tuck R. & Sons—Kerr Stuart series (4983, 4984) .. ..
.. .. £1.50/**£2.50**/£4
By Train (9186) and Villes de France (123, 124) £2/**£4**/£6
LCC Reward cards (12 No.) .. .. £2/**£3**/£4
Valentines series .. .. £1.50/**£2**/£3
Wildt & Kray (Series 1814, 1834) .. .. .. £1/**£2**/£3
Wrench series—uncol. (2280–2291, 4185–4193 & 4500–4512)
.. .. £1.50/**£2**/£3
Wrench Red Bordered series (10,089–10,106) .. £2/**£3**/£4

Locomotives & Rolling Stock—1923 Onwards

Allan, Ian—col./photogravure	75p/**£1**/£1.50
Chadwick views	75p/**£1**/£1.50
Dennis, E. T. W.	75p/**£1**/£1.50
Dixon, J. A. (col.)	75p/**£1**/£1.50
Judges (col.)	75p/**£1**/£1.50
Lake, G. H. (Eric Oldham paintings—10 cards) ..	£1/**£2**/£3
Locomotive Publishing Co.—col. series (Goffey 292–328)
.. .. £2/**£3**/£4
Mack, W. E.—(tinted cards)	£1.50/**£2**/£3
Photochrom Co.	£1.50/**£2**/£3
Pike	£1/**£1.50**/£2
Regent—photographic series	£1/**£1.50**/£2
Salmon, J. (col.)	£1/**£1.50**/£2
Tuck, R. & Sons. 'Oilette' and other similar series (1923–1936). (3541, 3547, 3569, 3570, 3593, 5303, 5304.)
Model Railway Engines (3404)	£2/**£3**/£4
Valentines series	£1/**£2**/£3

Locomotives and rolling stock were also well depicted on 'official' cards. *See below.*

Main and Local Lines (Standard & Narrow Gauge)

Branch lines owned or operated by major railway companies, or small independent companies promoted by Parliament or Light Railway Acts. A number of superb local published cards exist of these railways. Owing to publisher, social history or topographical interest they are often rated even higher in value than for their railway interest alone.
Main trunk railways (Periods 1 to 3) connecting major towns and cities such as London, Liverpool, Manchester & Glasgow. Within the British Isles, these railways became grouped together into four major concerns in 1923 (Periods 4, 5) and became State owned in 1948 (Periods 6, 7).

Bridges/Viaducts/Tunnels	50p/**75p**/£1.50
Hotels (views)	£3/**£4**/£6
Hotels (Poster ads)	£10/**£15**/£25

Level crossings and general trackside views ..	£2/**£4**/£8
Motor buses/road vehicles (railway owned) ..	£10/**£15**/£20
Official cards. *See below.*	
Railway staff. Uniformed/groups	£2/**£4**/£5
Rolling stock	£2/**£4**/£5
Stations, Town (interior/platform views) ..	£5/**£10**/£15
Stations, Town (exterior)	£3/**£5**/£10
Stations, Village (interior/platform views) ..	£8/**£15**/£20
Stations, Village (exterior)	£5/**£10**/£15

Miniature/Pleasure/Beach Railways—(Up to 38 cm Gauge)

Ravenglass & Eskdale. Photographic/col./collotype. Periods	
1–5	£1/**£3**/£5
Periods 6–7	25p/**50p**/£1
Romney, Hythe & Dymchurch. Photographic/col. Periods 3–5	
.. ..	£1/**£2**/£4
Periods 6–7	25p/**50p**/£1.50
Various pleasure/Beach railways	£1/**£2**/£3

Mountain Railways

Snowdon Mountain railway. Periods 1–5 ..	£1/**£2.50**/£4
Periods 6–7	25p/**50p**/£1
Foreign locations. Periods 1–5	£2/**£3**/£4

Official Cards—Pre-1923 Companies ■R 3, 4

'Official cards' is a term used to describe postcards issued/sold by railway companies to gain revenue and to promote all aspects of their business. Cards advertising railway hotels, ships and buses are excluded from this listing. Official cards have been issued from Periods 1 to 7 and are still being issued, although in ever reducing numbers.

■R3 Pub. Picture Postcard Co. 'Cambrian Railway. Snowdon'. Intermediate size vignette. UB. 1903 £20

Caledonian

Vignette/multi-view (early Period 2)	£10/**£15**/£25
Views (Glosso)	£3/**£4**/£6
Views (col.) (National, Valentine)	£4/**£5**/£6
Engines/Rolling stock (col.)	£4/**£6**/£8
Engines/Rolling stock (Glosso)	£3/**£4**/£5
Poster reproductions (col. photographic) ..	£40/**£50**/£70
Tartan-bordered views	£5/**£6**/£8

Ambulance train	£2/**£3**/£4
Sleeping Car—Reservation card	£10/**£15**/£20

Cambrian
Vignette-intermediate (Picture Postcard Company) .. ..
.. .. £15/**£20**/£25
Views—col. (Cambrian railways, Valentine, Photochrom)
.. .. £4/**£5**/£6
Correspondence/holiday advertising .. .. .. £6/**£8**/£10
Maps.. .. .. £15/**£20**/£25

Cork, Bandon & South Coast
Views—col. (Tuck 'Oilette', Sunnyside of Ireland) £2/**£4**/£6

Dublin & South Eastern
Correspondence/views .. .. £20/**£25**/£30

Dublin, Wicklow & Wexford
Views—vignetted .. .. £20/**£25**/£30
Celesque series .. .. £15/**£20**/£25

■R4 Pub. McCorquodale & Co. London & North Western
Railway Dublin-Holyhead steamer. Period 2 £6

East Coast Route (Great Northern, North Eastern, North
British Railways)
'Write-away' type Vignette (Andrew Reid) .. £12/**£15**/£18
Rolling stock/stations/views—col. .. .. £8/**£12**/£16
Flying Scotsman (Hildersheimer) .. .. .. £3/**£4**/£5

Furness
English 'Gruss Aus'—(chromo) (McCorquodale) £10/**£15**/£20
Views—col. (McCorquodale) .. .. £2/**£3**/£4
Views—col. (Heaton-Cooper paintings) (Tuck) £1.50/**£2**/£3
Engines/Rolling stock (photographic) (Tuck) .. £4/**£5**/£6
Poster reproductions—col. .. .. .. £50/**£55**/£60
Furness Abbey/Hotel (photographic) (Tuck) .. £2/**£3**/£4
Art studies—George Romney paintings (photographic) (James
Atkinson) .. .. £4/**£6**/£8

Glasgow & South Western
Vignette—col. (McCorquodale/Maclure MacDonald) .. ..
.. .. £15/**£20**/£25

Views—col. (Tuck 'Oilette') .. .. £3/**£4**/£5
Ambulances—WW1 .. .. £4/**£6**/£8

Great Central
Vignette—intermediate (Picture Postcard Company) .. ..
.. .. £15/**£20**/£25
Views—col. (Faulkner series) .. .. £4/**£5**/£6
Views—photographic (HHH series) .. .. .. £6/**£8**/£10
Engines/Rolling stock .. .. £6/**£8**/£10
Poster .. .. £50/**£55**/£60
Perforated engine card—col. (Central Advertising Co.) ..
.. .. £75/**£80**/£100
Restaurant car—'En Route' .. .. £6/**£8**/£15

Great Eastern
Views/correspondence/advertising .. .. .. £6/**£8**/£10
View/correspondence/advertising (col.) .. £10/**£12**/£15
View correspondence/advertising (Jarrolds series col. and
plain) .. .. £6/**£8**/£10
Views—col. (Tuck 'Oilette') .. .. .. £1.50/**£2**/£2.50
Trains/Stations—col. (Locomotive Publishing Co.) £2/**£3**/£4
Poster reproductions—(plain, col. incl. those by J. Hassall)
.. .. £50/**£55**/£60
Collotype series with crest—various subjects incl. locomo-
tives, steamers, Southwold bus and views) £2/**£2.50**/£3
Underground Railway Maps of London (incl. GER
advertising) .. .. £5/**£8**/£10

Great Northern
Vignette—intermediate (Picture Postcard Company) .. ..
.. .. £15/**£20**/£25
Vignette—London views (Picture Postcard Company) .. ..
.. ..£8/**£12**/£16
Views—col. (Photochrom) .. .. £1/**£1.50**/£2
Engines—col. (Photochrom) .. .. .. £1.50/**£2**/£2.50
Engines/Trains—col. (Locomotive Publishing Co.) .. ..
.. .. £1.50/**£2**/£2.50
Poster reproductions—col. (including Hassall's 'Skegness is so
Bracing') .. .. £50/**£55**/£60
Poster type advertising—Panoramic .. .. £12/**£15**/£18
Correspondence/view cards .. .. £6/**£8**/£10

Great Northern (Ireland)
Views/Correspondence .. .. £10/**£12**/£15
Shamrock—hotel advertising .. .. .. £15/**£20**/£25

Great North of Scotland
Views (Porter, Aberdeen) .. .. £6/**£7**/£8
Cruden Bay Golf Tournament .. ..£8/**£10**/£12

Great Southern & Western
Views—col. (Tuck 'Oilette', Sunnyside of Ireland) £3/**£4**/£5
Hotel multi-views .. .. £12/**£20**/£25
'Jotter' .. .. £2/**£4**/£5
'Parknasilla' Poster .. .. £30/**£40**/£60

Great Western
Vignette—intermediate (Picture Postcard Co.) £15/**£20**/£25

Vignette—London views (court size) .. .. £15/**£20**/£25
Views—sepia collotype/gravure/photographic .. £2/**£3**/£4
Views—col. .. .. £2/**£3**/£4
Engines/Rolling stock—collotype/gravure/photographic ..
.. .. £2/**£3**/£4
'Fishguard Harbour as a Port of Call' .. .. £4/**£5**/£6
Docks series (Autotype Co.) .. .. .. £4/**£5**/£6
Fishguard route .. .. £4/**£5**/£6
Poster reproductions—Series 3, col. (many are the work of
Alec Fraser) .. .. £50/**£55**/£60
Poster reproductions—col. (Acme Press, Andrew Reid) ..
.. .. £45/**£50**/£55
General interest—bridges, tunnels, stations etc. .. £2/**£3**/£4
Restaurant cars—'En Route' .. .. .. £12/**£15**/£20
Correspondence/view cards (single colour) .. .. £4/**£6**/£8
Wyndams series—correspondence cards (4 varieties) £4/**£6**/£8

Highland
Views—Railway title in red (Valentines) .. .. £6/**£7**/£8
Views—Railway crest in colour (Valentines) .. £4/**£5**/£6
Views—col. (Valentines) .. .. £5/**£6**/£7
Views—photographic (Valentines) .. .. .. £4/**£5**/£6

Lancashire & Yorkshire
Vignette (Picture Postcard Co.) .. .. .. £15/**£20**/£25
Views—plain .. .. £2/**£3**/£4
Views—col. .. .. £2/**£3**/£4
Engines/Rolling stock—plain .. .. £2/**£3**/£4
Engines/Rolling stock—col. .. .. £2/**£3**/£4

London, Brighton & South Coast
Vignette—including London views (Picture Postcard Co.)
.. .. £15/**£20**/£25
Views/general interest (Waterlow) .. .. .. £2/**£3**/£4
Bridges (Waterlow) .. .. £3/**£4**/£5
Poster reproductions—(single colour) .. .. £50/**£55**/£60
Correspondence .. .. £6/**£10**/£12

London, Chatham & Dover
Vignette—col. (court size) (Pictorial Postcard Syndicate)
.. .. £20/**£25**/£30
Vignette—single colour (court size) (Pictorial Postcard
Syndicate) .. .. £20/**£25**/£30
Vignette—single colour (court size) (Picture Postcard
Company) .. .. £20/**£25**/£30

London & North Western
St. Louis exposition .. .. £6/**£7**/£8

Tuck Cards
Engines and Rolling stock .. .. £1/**£2**/£3
Views and others .. .. £1/**£2**/£3

McCorquodale Cards
Views—plain/col. .. .. £1/**£2**/£3
Engines/Rolling stock—plain/col. .. .. .. £1/**£2**/£3
Ships plain/col. .. .. £3/**£4**/£6

| Poster reproductions—plain/col. .. | .. | .. | £50/**£55**/£60 |
| Maps—col. | .. | .. | £50/**£55**/£60 |

London & South Western

Vignette—(court size) (single colour) (Pictorial Postcard Syndicate) .. .. £20/**£25**/£30

Vignette—intermediate (col.) (Pictorial Postcard Syndicate)
.. .. £15/**£20**/£25

Vignette—intermediate (Picture Postcard Co.) £15/**£20**/£25

Vignette—London views (Picture Postcard Co.) £10/**£15**/£20

Poster reproductions .. .. £50/**£55**/£60

Correspondence/view .. ..£8/**£10**/£12

Orphanage (Locomotive Publishing Co.) .. .. £3/**£4**/£5

Midland

Vignette (Picture Postcard Co., British and Colonial Auto. Trading Co., Automatic General Stores—same views)
.. .. £15/**£20**/£25

Vignette—London views (Picture Postcard Co.) £10/**£15**/£20

Vignette—col. (Route to Scotland) (Andrew Reid) .. ..
.. .. £12/**£15**/£18

'Nearest Station'—views—col. .. .. .. £6/**£8**/£10

Views—col. (Photochrom, with/without 'bear' trademark)
.. .. £2/**£3**/£4

Rolling stock—col. .. .. £2/**£4**/£6

Engines—plain .. .. £1.50/**£2**/£2.50

Poster reproductions—Series (col.) .. .. £50/**£55**/£60

Poster reproductions (col.) .. .. .. £40/**£45**/£50

Maps (col.) .. .. £10/**£12**/£14

Heysham—Morecambe Electric Train (col.) £20/**£25**/£30

Exhibitions .. .. £15/**£18**/£20

North British

Views—plain with crest on front .. .. £6/**£8**/£10

Views—plain, col., tinted .. .. .. £3/**£4**/£5

Views—Edinburgh (col.) (Caledonian 129 series) £2/**£3**/£4

North Eastern

Views—photo Panoramic (series of 40) .. .. £6/**£7**/£8

Views—photo Panoramic (with map overprints) £10/**£12**/£15

Newcastle Electric trains (col./plain) .. .. £4/**£5**/£6

Poster reproductions (series of 20) (col.) (Photochrom) ..
.. .. £50/**£55**/£60

Industrial poster reproduction (series of 4) (col.) £55/**£60**/£75

Riverside Quay, Hull (col.) .. .. .. £6/**£8**/£10

North Eastern railway houses—(col.) .. .. £2/**£4**/£6

Exhibition .. .. £4/**£5**/£6

North Staffordshire

Views—collotype, gravure, col. enamelled, platemarked
.. .. £4/**£5**/£6

Views—as above (including scenes on the Leek and Manifold railway) .. .. £4/**£6**/£8

Portpatrick & Wigtownshire Joint

Views—single/multi-view, numbered series £15/**£20**/£25

Correspondence/views .. .. £20/**£25**/£30

South-Eastern & Chatham & Dover
Vignette—intermediate (col.) (Pictorial Postcard Syndicate)
.. .. £20/**£25**/£30
Vignette—intermediate (Picture Postcard Co.) £15/**£20**/£25
Vignette—London views (Picture Postcard Co./Automatic
General Stores) .. .. £10/**£15**/£20
Engines/Rolling Stock—col. (McCorquodale) .. £2/**£3**/£4
Trains/Stations—col. (McCorquodale).. .. .. £2/**£3**/£4
Poster reproduction (col.) .. .. £50/**£55**/£60
Maps (col.) .. .. £16/**£18**/£20
Maps/engines and trains (plain) .. .. .. £16/**£18**/£20
Correspondence/views (Photochrom) .. .. £10/**£12**/£15
Exhibition.. .. .. £4/**£6**/£8
Boulogne views—col. (Stevenard edit with overprints) ..
.. .. £4/**£6**/£8

West Coast Route (Caledonian and London & North Western)
Views—(plain/col.) .. .. £6/**£8**/£10
Rolling Stock (plain/col.) .. .. £12/**£14**/£16

West Highland
Views—col. (National) .. ..£8/**£10**/£12

Wirral
Pictorial route map .. .. £40/**£45**/£50

Official Cards—Post-1923 Companies

Great Western Railway
Views—col. (L. Richmond paintings) .. .. .. £2/**£3**/£4
Engines—gravure/photographic .. .. £1/**£2**/£3
Engines—col. .. .. £1/**£2**/£3
Poster reproductions .. .. £45/**£50**/£55
'King George V'—folded col. locomotive card £20/**£25**/£30

London Midland & Scottish Railway
Engines—col. .. .. £1/**£2**/£3
Holiday tickets/views—photographic with overprints .. ..
.. .. £3/**£4**/£5
Poster reproductions .. .. £30/**£35**/£40
Container services advertising .. .. .. £20/**£25**/£30

London & North Eastern Railway
Engines/Trains—photographic .. .. £2/**£3**/£4
Poster reproductions .. .. £30/**£35**/£40

Southern Railway
Engines—gravure/photographic .. .. .. £1/**£2**/£3
Engines/trains—col. .. .. £1/**£2**/£3
Poster reproductions .. .. £30/**£35**/£40
Correspondence .. .. £2/**£3**/£4
Harbours/West Country scenes (paintings by L. Richmond)
.. .. £2/**£3**/£4

British Railways

Trains—col.	£1/**£2**/£3
Poster reproduction (HST Services—Western Region)	
.. ..	£1/**£2**/£3
Poster reproduction (APT London/Glasgow) 1981	50p/**75p**
Gleneagles/Turnberry Golf Courses—col. ..	50p/**75p**/£1.50
Birmingham 'New Street Station'—photographic (London Midland Region)	£1/**£1.50**/£2
Kyle of Lochalsh Station (Scottish Region)	£1/**£2**/£3
Correspondence	£1/**£2**/£3

Minor Railways ■R 5
These include:
Bideford, Westward Ho! and Appledore; Campbeltown and Macrihanis; Corris; Festiniog; Freshwater, Yarmouth & Newport; Invergary and Fort Augustus; Isle of Wight; Joint S. Western and Brighton; Kent and East Sussex; Lynton & Barnstaple; Newport, Godshill and St. Lawrence; Vale of Rheidol; Wick and Lybster.

Periods 1/2 Vignettes	£15/**£20**/£30
Poster type ads	£20/**£40**/£75
Views	£6/**£8**/£12
Others	£5/**£10**/£20

■R5 Pub. E. T. W. Dennis. View on the Vale of Rheidol Railway. Period 5 £6

Three Band Pricing System

Left Hand Band: The lowest price you will probably be asked to pay for this card.
Middle Band: What you will normally be asked to pay for this card: its average, reasonable price.
Right Hand Band: The highest price you will probably be asked to pay for this card.
For a full explanation of the system see page ix.

RELIGION

It is the Roman Catholic countries, especially Italy, which
provide the most colourful and the greatest number of
postcards—through all the 7 periods. Also included in the
section are missions and associations like the YMCA and the
Salvation Army. For Jewish cards, *see* Social History.

ANGLICAN CHURCH
Cathedrals, churches—*see* 'Buildings' under Topographical.
Portraits of clergy 25p/**50p**/75p
Others 25p/50p

CHRISTIAN SCIENCE ■REL 1
Churches 25p/50p
Personalities 25p/**50p**/75p

■REL 1 Pub. First Church of Christ, Scientist, Boston, Mass.
Period 2 50p

GENERAL RELIGIOUS THEMES
Angels, Christmas and Easter Themes (*see* Greetings),
Colportage (distributors of bibles, tracts etc.) Old Testament
Texts, Reproductions of Religious Old Masters (*see* Art) etc.
Many of these postcards are beautifully produced, often
embossed and/or gilded. Publishers include Birn Bros.
(especially 'Guardian Angel' series), Ettlinger, Tuck, Wildt &
Kray.

Price range   ..   ..   50p/**75p**/£3

HINDUISM
Many beautiful coloured series of Indian cards showing Hindu
legends exist.

Price range   ..   ..   50p/£1.50/£3

MISSIONS/SOCIETIES

Church Lads' Brigade	50p/**75p**/£2
Church Mission to Jews. Personalities ..	50p/**75p**/£1
Ditto. Special overprints by Photochrom	25p/**50p**
International Society of the Apocrypha. Subscription reminders, etc.	25p/**50p**
London Society for Promoting Christianity to the Jews. Personalities	50p/**75p**/£1
Ditto. Special overprints by Photochrom	25p/**50p**
Scripture Gift Mission. Various issues	25p/**50p**
St. John's League of Mercy. Outings, etc. ..	25p/**50p**/75p
Society for the Propagation of the Gospel. Photographic origin issues showing good ethnic detail	50p/**75p**/£1
Others	25p/50p
South American Missionary Soc. Various issues ..	25p/50p
Universities Mission to Central Africa. Various issues	25p/50p
YMCA/YWCA (*see* MILITARY). Various ..	25p/**75p**/£1.50

NONCONFORMISM

Chapels—*see* 'Buildings' under SOCIAL HISTORY.	
Outings—cards of photographic origin ..	50p/**75p**/£1.50
Personalities	25p/**50p**/75p

PASSION PLAYS

Oberammergau: every ten years incl. 1980.	
Photographs of actors/stills	50p/**75p**/£1.50
General views	25p/50p
USA Pubs. Periods 2 to 4 incl. Bruckmann Trant, Commercial Color-type, Conwell, Crocker, Leo Schweyer	50p/**75p**/£1
Others	25p/**50p**/75p

REL 2 Pub. Anon. U.S.A. Lord's Prayer 'Lead us Not Into Temptation'. Col. Embossed. Period 2 £1

PRAYERS ■REL 2

Lord's Prayer. Ger. series of 6. Period 2. chromo-litho. Per set
.. .. £4/**£6**/£8
Lord's Prayer. USA Pub. Taggart. Series of 8. Per set ..
.. .. £3/**£5**/£15
USA Others. Per set .. .. £3/**£5**/£15
Others .. .. 25p/**50p**/£1

ROMAN CATHOLICISM

Events
The following list does not claim to be comprehensive, but gives a typical selection of religious events for which postcards are known, in chronological order, in Periods 1 to 7.

1897. It. 19th Eucharist Congress, Venice
1898. It. Exhibition of Sacred Art
      It. 20th Anniversary of Pope Leo XIII
1899. It. 800th Anniversary of St. John Baptist
1900. It. Celebrations of Holy Year
1903. It. Death of Pope Leo XIII
      It. Accession of Pope Pius X
1908. Fr. Lourdes Jubilee
1914. It. Accession of Pope Benedict XV
1922. Pope Pius XI
1925. It. Celebrations of Holy Year
1939. Accession of Pope Pius XII
1958. Accession of Pope John XXIII
Price range .. .. £2/**£4**/£10
1976. 41st International Eucharist. Vatican 'Maxi' Series
1978. John Paul I. Vatican Maxi series and other issues
      John Paul II. Various issues
1979. Visit of John Paul II to Ireland, Monte Cassino and other Italian locations, Poland, USA
      Various Vatican 'Maxi' series
1982. Visits of John Paul II to UK, Argentina
1983. Visits of John Paul II to Spain, Poland
1984–6 Visits—Various
Price range .. .. 25p/**£1**/£3

SALVATION ARMY

Gen. Booth. Various .. .. £1/**£2**/£2.50
Gen. Booth memoriam card Pub. Rotary 1912 .. £1/**£3**/£6
Mrs. Booth/other members of the Booth family £1/**£1.50**/£2
Various groups/meetings .. .. 50p/**£1**/£3
Period 7. International Staff Band **25p**

TEN COMMANDMENTS

Ger. Co. Period 2. Set of 10. Per set .. .. ..£7/**£10**/£12
Pub. Tuck. 2 versions: Catholic and Protestant (Nos. 163c and 163p). Per set .. .. £6/**£8**/£10
USA Pub. P.F.B. Per set .. .. £3/**£5**/£8

ROAD TRANSPORT

There is inevitable overlapping with SOCIAL HISTORY and TOPOGRAPHICAL, but here we have set out to list those themes which are more concerned with 'transporting', e.g. 'Omnibuses', than with 'activity', e.g. 'ploughing'. The highest values refer to RP cards with close-up detail. However, this is a field in which particularly good RP close-up examples can command prices beyond the valuations quoted here, especially if there is a strong social history connexion or local interest.

N.B. Values refer to Periods 1–2 unless otherwise stated.

Accidents
Periods 1, 2 .. ..£8/**£12**/£20
Periods 3–7 .. .. £2/**£4**/£6

Ambulances
Horse .. .. £5/**£10**/£15
Motor .. .. £5/**£8**/£10

Bicycling *see* COMPETITIONS/CRAZES

Buses & Coaches
Charabancs .. .. £1.50/**£3**/£5
Horse .. .. £10/**£20**/£35
Motor .. .. £8/**£20**/£35
Steam .. .. £10/**£25**/£35

Commercial Cabs/Carts/Delivery Vehicles
Handrawn.. .. ..£7/**£12**/£15
Horse .. .. £12/**£18**/£25
Motor .. .. £2/**£4**/£6

Fire Engines
Horse .. .. £10/**£20**/£30
Motor .. .. £8/**£15**/£25

Horse and Rider .. .. 75p/**£1**/£1.50

Lorries
Motor .. .. £6/**£9**/£12
Steam .. .. £10/**£20**/£30

Motor Cars
Periods 1, 2 .. .. £3/**£5**/£7
Periods 3–5 .. .. 75p/**£1.50**/£3
Period 6 .. .. 50p/**£1**/£2

Motor Cycles ■RT 1
General .. .. £1.50/**£3**/£6
Racing ads. .. .. £25/**£30**/£40

Motor Racing ■RT 2
Famous Cars
   Bluebird (Malcolm Campbell) .. .. £3/**£5**/£8

■RT 1 Pub. Motosacoche Association, Geneve. Artist Nizzolt. Invitation to a meeting. Period 4. Col £25

Golden Arrow (Major Seagrave)	£2.50/**£4**/£6
Others	£1.50/**£2**/£5

Fernel Series
Fernand Fernel, one of the *Collection des Cent* artists, drew a series of 10 cards *c.* 1903 called *Courses Automobiles* (Car Races). Different cards represent different races.
Price range .. .. £3/**£4**/£6

Hill Climbs. RP. Periods 5, 6 .. .. £2/**£3**/£5
Motor Magazine. Portrait series .. .. £1/**£2**/£4

■RT 2 Pub. Bros. Isenbeck, Wiesbaden. Gordon Bennett Race Course, 1904 £8

Personalities:
Allietz; Baras (Brasier); Bariller (Brasier); Boegge (Mercedes); Bonnier, Joakim; Brabham, Jack; Brooks, Tony; Cagno (Itala); Duchene; Fabry (Itala); Fangio, Juan; Gabriel (Bayard-Clement); Gregory, Masten; Hawthorne, Mike; Lancia (Fiat); Landon (Mors); Moss, Stirling; Nazzaro (Fiat); Porsche; Salvadori, Roy; Salzer (Mercedes); Seagrave, Major H. O. D.; Sisz (Renault).

Price range	..	..	..	..	..	..75p/**£3**/£10

Races

Gordon Bennett chromo-litho	..	..	..		£10/**£15**/£18
Gordon Bennett photo-origin (highest for RP)			..	£5/**£8**/£10
Gordon Bennett course maps	..	..	..		£3/**£5**/£8
Indianapolis (1910)		..	..	..	..£5/**£10**/£15
Isle of Man	..	..	..	..	..	£5/**£7**/£8
Nurburg Ring	..	..	..	..	..	£3/**£5**/£8
Peking-Paris	..	..	..	..	..	£5/**£8**/£10
Rennen (1907). 'Kaiser Prize'	..		..	£4/**£6**/£8

Seine-Inférieure Grand Prix 1908 (Pub. L'Hirondelle)

..	..	..	..	..	..	..	..	£6/**£8**/£12
Periods 1, 2 others	..	..	..	..		£3/**£5**/£8
Periods 3 to 6 others	..	..	..		50p/**£1.50**/£3

Valentine's Autocar series
Period 6 ..	..	..	..	..	..	..	£1/**£2**/£4

Motor Shows *See* ADVERTISING

Royal Mail
Carts and Vans. Periods 1–6		..	..	..	£4/**£8**/£10
Period 7. Pub. Post Office	..	..	..	..	25p/**50p**/75p
Carts and vans ..	..	..	..	..	..	£2/**£3**/£5
Postbuses. Period 7. Pub. Post Office	..	..	25p/**50p**/£65

Traction Engines
Accidents/Repairs	..	..	..	..	£10/**£18**/£22
Agricultural	..	..	..	..	..	..£8/**£15**/£20
Commercial	..	..	..	..	..	£10/**£18**/£20
Military	..	..	..	..	..	..£8/**£15**/£18
Show..	..	..	..	..	..	£15/**£20**/£40
Steam Rollers	..	..	..	..	£12/**£18**/£25

Trams

Price range	..	..	..	..	..	..£6/**£15**/£30

Trolley Buses (the higher value for close-up RPs) .. ..
.. ..£5/**£10**/£15

ROYALTY

This is a category which is inextricably bound with several others, notably:

MILITARY (In Victorian and Edwardian times Royal personages often led their countries' war efforts, at least as figureheads.)

POLITICAL (In Victorian and Edwardian times Royal personages—especially abroad—were often politically influential.)

SOCIAL HISTORY and TOPOGRAPHICAL (Royal visits were important events to the towns and cities where they took place.)

Royal cards are ideal for building up a collection throughout the 7 periods as they were amongst the first picture cards and are still being produced today.

BRITISH and FOREIGN cards are listed separately, in chronological order.

BRITISH ■ROY 1, 2

Periods 1, 2, 4, 6, 7.
See MILITARY *for Periods 3 and 5.*
See also MODERN *for Period 7.*

1897. Queen Victoria's Diamond Jubilee
Unused   ..   ..   £20/**£55**/£75
PU 1897 ..   .. £65/**£150**/£250
Other Pre-1900 GB Royal events   ..   ..   £15/**£20**/£25

1900
Pub. Tuck. 'Empire' postcards Souvenir of 1900 with Queen
   Victoria oval portrait   ..   .. £7.50/**£10**/£15
Pub. Tuck. 'Royal' postcard, ditto   ..   .. £7.50/**£10**/£15

■ROY 1 Pub. S. Krotoschin, Gorlitz. *Das Grosse Jahrhundert.* 'Victoria, Queen of Great Britain and Ireland, Empress of India'. UB £12

1901. Queen Victoria's Death
Pub. Faulkner, C. W. In Memoriam card produced within 15
  hours of her death .. .. £12/**£15**/£18
Edward VII Accession commemoration .. .. £4/**£6**/£8
Pub. Tuck. 'Empire' postcards Memoriam .. . .£8/**£15**/£20
Pub. Wrench. Memoriam cards published in Saxony and a
  week late in shops .. .. £8/**£15**/£18
Other Victoria mourning cards .. .. .. £5/**£7.50**/£12

1901. Voyage of the Duke and Duchess of Cornwall and York
Pub. Martin, B., Melbourne. 3 cards. Portraits of Edward VII,
  The Duke, The Duchess .. .. £5/**£8**/£10
Other Australian publishers .. .. .. £2/**£4**/£6
Pub. Tuck. 'Empire' Series 1649 .. .. .. £6/**£8**/£12
Pub. Wrench. 'Links of Empire' cards to commemorate the
Royal voyage in the *Ophir*. Postcards taken on board and
posted at ports of call: Series a. Ten cards. Portsmouth to
Australia via Gibraltar, Malta and Port Said; Series b. Ten
cards. South Africa, Canada and return to England.
  Unused .. ..£8/**£10**/£12
  PU from ports .. .. £10/**£15**/£25

1902. Coronation of Edward VII

*Set for 26 June 1902, postponed because of the King's illness
until 9 August. Cards to commemorate the coronation were
published by:*

Bird, Alfred & Sons (4 custard ads, UB vignettes) .. ..
.. .. £10/**£15**/£25
Blum & Degen; Dobbs; Downey; Galyons; Mansell; Pasualis
  Moss; Rotary; Russell; Others .. .. .. £1.50/**£3**/£5
Stead, W. T. Current Event postcards. Four designs (incl.
  postponement) .. .. £5/**£8**/£10
Stewart & Woolf. Set of 10 col., embossed showing V.I.P.s at
  the coronation (note mistake 'H.R.H. Princess of Wales' on
  Prince of Wales card) .. .. £4/**£6**/£8
Tuck. Kings & Queens of England (*see* PUBLISHERS: Tuck).
  Six cards of Edward with diff. Shakespeare quote. (Date
  erased when coronation postponed) .. .. .. £6/**£8**/£10
Tuck. 'Coronation' series. Embossed, gilded, circular design
.. .. £5/**£8**/£10
Tuck. 'Empire' postcards 1462, 1451/1453 .. .. £5/**£8**/£10
Tuck. Other designs .. .. £1.50/**£3**/£5

1902–1910. Reign of Edward VII
*Many cards showing the Royal Family visiting towns, cities,
seaside, races, etc. to open public buildings, review the fleet or
inspect troops, sail or attend the races, etc. See* SOCIAL HISTORY.

Price range .. .. 75p/**£1.50**/£6

1903
Tuck. Series of 10 cards to commemorate King's visit to Paris,
  issued in France .. .. £2/**£3**/£5
Voisey, Chas. Set of 15 cards to commemorate King's visit to
  Paris .. .. £2/**£3**/£5

1904–1907. Queen Alexandra's photographs
Pub. A. V. N. Jones. Fascinating snapshots of the British Royal Family on Royal Yacht cruises, visiting foreign royalty, celebrities, etc. Also published in book form. Over 40 cards .. .. £1/**£2**/£2.50

1907
Historic meeting of Crowned Heads, Windsor Castle. Several Pubs. .. .. 75p/**£1.50**/£2

1908
Pub. Southwood. Empire Day 'Greeting from the Motherland'. Artist E. J. Walker .. .. 75p/**£1.50**/£3

1910. Edward VII's Death

Memoriam cards, many silvered, in purple or in plain black/ Coronation Souvenirs/Procession/Queen Alexandra's Message. Publishers include Beagles; Downing; East London Printing Co.; C. W. Faulkner; Hutson Bros.; Millar & Lang; Louis Levy; Lillywhite; Philco; Ritchie; Rotary and Tuck.

Price range .. .. 75p/**£1.50**/£6

1910. Proclamation of George V
Pub. Mark Cook of Chester; Judges; others 75p/**£1.50**/£2

1910. George V's First Court
Pub. Tuck. Artist Harry Payne .. .. £3/**£5**/£6

1911. Coronation of George V

The event was covered almost as thoroughly as his father's by many publishers including Davidson Bros.; Inter-Art (incl. Spurgin designs); Louis Levy; Vivian Mansell; McKenzie; Millar & Lang; Rotary; Russell; Schwerdtfeger; Taylor and Tuck.

Price range .. .. £1/**£1.50**/£4

1911. Investiture of Prince of Wales
Various pubs. .. .. £1/**£1.50**/£3

1911. Crowning of George V as Emperor of India at Delhi Durbar
Price range .. .. £1/**£2**/£4

1913. Marriage of Prince Arthur of Connaught and the Duchess of Fife
Various pubs. .. .. 50p/**75p**/£1.50

1919. Marriage of Princess Patricia of Connaught and the Hon. Alexander Ramsay
Various pubs. .. .. 50p/**75p**/£1.50

1922. Marriage of the Princess Royal and Viscount Lascelles
Various pubs. .. .. £1/**£1.50**/£2.50

1922. Marriage of Lord Louis Mountbatten and Lady Edwina Ashley
Various pubs.   ..   ..   £1/**£1.50**/£2.50

1923. Marriage of Duke and Duchess of York
Price range   ..   ..   £1/**£1.50**/£3

1924. Marriage of Princess Alice and Prince Alexander of Teck
Various pubs.   ..   ..   50p/**75p**/£1.50

1924. Royal Family at the Wembley Exhibition
Price range   ..   ..   50p/**£1.50**/£3

1934. Marriage of Duke of Kent and Princess Marina
Various pubs.   ..   ..   75p/**£1**/£2.50

1935. Silver Jubilee of George V
Various pubs.   ..   ..   £1/**£2**/£4

1935. Marriage of Duke of Gloucester and Lady Alice Montague Douglas-Scott
Various pubs.   ..   ..   50p/**75p**/£1.50

1936. George V's Death
Mourning and Memoriam cards by various pubs.   £1/**£2**/£3

1936. Edward VIII
Coronation (which did not take place, because of Abdication)
..   ..   £1/**£2**/£4
Visits in UK   ..   ..   £3/**£5**/£8
Visits abroad (e.g. Vimy Memorial)   ..   ..   £2/**£4**/£6
Wedding to Mrs Simpson   ..   ..£8/**£10**/£15
Various portraits before Abdication   ..   ..   ..   £1/**£2**/£3
With Mrs Simpson/Duchess of Windsor   ..   ..£5/**£10**/£15

1937. Coronation of George VI
Various designs ..   ..   £1/**£1.50**/£4

1938. Visit of George VI and Queen Elizabeth to France
Various designs ..   ..   75p/**£1.50**/£2

1947. Betrothal of Princess Elizabeth and Philip Mountbatten
Various designs ..   ..   50p/**75p**/£2

1947. Marriage of Princess Elizabeth and Prince Philip
Various designs ..   ..   50p/**75p**/£2

1952. George VI's Death
Mourning cards by various pubs.   ..   ..   ..   £1/**£2**/£4

1953. Coronation of Elizabeth II
Various Pubs.   ..   ..   50p/**75p**/£2

1960. Marriage of Princess Margaret and Antony Armstrong-Jones
Various Pubs.   ..   ..   50p/**75p**/£1.50

1969. Investiture of Prince of Wales
Various Pubs. .. .. 75p/**£1**/£3

1972. Silver Wedding of Elizabeth II and Prince Philip
Various Pubs. .. .. 50p/**75p**/£1

1973. Marriage of Princess Anne and Capt. Mark Phillips
Various Pubs. .. .. 50p/**75p**/£1
Post Office PHQ card **£12**

1977. Silver Jubilee of Elizabeth II
Post Office PHQ cards. Set of 5 .. .. **£12**
Pub. Carousel. City of Portsmouth Souvenir Postcard HMS
    Victory **£1.50**
Pub. Postcard Association of Great Britain. col. **£1**
Others .. .. 50p/**75p**/£1.50

1978. Silver Jubilee of Queen's Coronation
Post Office PHQ cards. Set of 4 .. .. **£2**

1980. 80th Birthday of Queen Elizabeth, the Queen Mother
Post Office PHQ card **50p**
Others .. .. 25p/**50p**/£2

1981. Wedding of Prince of Wales
Post Office PHQ cards. Set of 2 .. .. **95p**
Guernsey Post Office PHQ cards. Set of 7 .. .. ..**£1.60**
Prescott-Pickup. Set of 60 .. .. **£15**
Others .. .. 25p/**50p**/£3

1982. 21st Birthday of the Princess of Wales
FAGA and others .. .. 25p/**50p**/£1

1982. Birth of Prince William of Wales
Veldale/Carousel and others .. .. .. 25p/**50p**/£1

■ROY 2 Pub. Skilton & Fry. Engagement of Prince Andrew and Miss Sarah Ferguson, 1986 25p

1982. Christening of Prince William
Carousel and others ..   ..   25p/**50p**/£1

1983. 30th Anniversary of Queen's Coronation
Carousel and others ..   ..   50p/**75p**/£1

1983. Royal Tours of Australia/New Zealand and Canada
Prescott-Pickup. Australia/NZ 30 cards **£6**
Prescott-Pickup. Canada 15 cards **£3**

1984. Birth of Prince Henry   ..   ..   ..   25p/**50p**/£1.50

1984. Christening of Prince Henry   ..   ..   25p/**50p**/£1.50

1985. 85th Birthday of Queen Mother ..   ..   25p/**50p**/£1.50

1986. 60th Birthday of the Queen 25p/50p

1986. Engagement and Wedding of Prince Andrew   25p/50p

FOREIGN ■ROY 3, 4
A comprehensive listing of Foreign royalty postcards in chronological order was given on pp. 280–283 of the fourth edition of this catalogue. A summary appears below.

Price range
Period 1	£7.50/**£15**/£30
Period 2	.. £2/**£8**/£25
Period 3	..£5/**£10**/£15
Period 4	.. £2/**£4**/£6
Period 5	.. £1/**£2**/£5
Period 6	50p/**£1.50**/£3
Period 7	25p/**75p**/£1.50

■ROY 3 Pub. Philco Pub. Co. Series S 460E. 'The Late Crown Prince of Portugal (Luis Felipe). Assassinated February 1st 1908'. RP £2

■ROY 4 Pub. Russian Red Cross. Tzar Nicholas and Tzarina Alexandra Feodorovna of Russia at Riga, 1913, on the 300th Anniv. of Romanov Dynasty £10

SHIPPING

One of the most attractive areas in this section is in the chromo-litho adverts of shipping lines large and small, in Period 1 and early Period 2, sometimes sold, sometimes issued free for promotional purposes. This section in general has inevitable over-lapping in MILITARY, SOCIAL HISTORY and TOPOGRAPHICAL. High prices are attached to close-up RP photos, poster-type ads and early chromo-litho printing. Additional valuation accrues from railway and island connexions, 'Paquebot' or 'Posted at Sea', etc. postmarks and cachets.

Advertising
Many early cards showing liners (in particular) are advertising cards produced by the Line concerned.

Period 1 and early Period 2, chromo-litho vignettes, UB
.. .. £5/**£12**/£20
Period 2, 3. Col. art, not vignettes, e.g. Allan Line, Blue Funnel, Cunard, Canadian Pacific, P & O, Red Star, White Star, etc. .. .. £3/**£6**/£10
Poster types .. .. £7.50/**£15**/£30
Other periods .. .. 50p/**£1.50**/£4

■S1 Pub. 'H.M & Co.' (Henry Moss). Series 4364. Artist R. J. Martins. 'Off to the Fishing Grounds'. PU 1906 £3

Artists ■S 1
Bannister, A. F. D. (*Periods, 4, 5*) .. .. .. 75p/**£1**/£2
Black, Montague, B. .. .. £1/**£2**/£3
Burgess, Arthur (*Periods 2–4*) .. .. .. £1/**£2**/£2.50
Cassiers, Henri (*notably 'Red Star' posters*) .. £6/**£8**/£10
Chilley, A. (*sailing ships*) .. .. 50p/**75p**/£1.50
Cummings, Neville .. .. £1/**£2**/£3
Dixon, Charles (*Period 2 Lines*) .. .. £1/**£2**/£3
Eckenbrecker, T. von (*e.g. Nord-Deutscher*) .. £4/**£5**/£6
Forrest, A. S. (*e.g. Booth line*) .. .. .. £1/**£1.50**/£2
Fry, John. .. .. £1.50/**£3**/£4
Gabriel, E. .. .. £2/**£4**/£5

Lacy, Chas. de	£1.50/**£3**/£4
Mann, J. S.	.. £1/**£2**/£4
Martins, R. (*sailing ships*)	.. 75p/**£1**/£3
Mason, Frank (*Pub. F. T. Everard*)	£1/**£1.50**/£2
Meade – Gibbs	£1/**£1.50**/£2
Mitchell, W. Fred (*Titanic etc*)	.. £2/**£3**/£5
Montague, R. (*Tuck 'Oilettes'*)	75p/**£1**/£1.50
Rosenringe, O.	£1/**£2**/£4
Shoesmith, Kenneth (*Norwegian views*) ..	.. £2/**£4**/£6
Stower, Willi (*Periods 2–4*)	£3/**£5**/£7.50
Thomas, Walter..	.. £2/**£3**/£4
Welsh, William	£1/**£2**/£3
Others	75p/**£1.50**/£3

Docks/Harbour/Shipyard Scenes
Good general detail	75p/**£1.50**/£5
Launchings	.. £2/**£5**/£10
RPs	.. £8/**£15**/£25

Hovercraft
Periods 6/7	25p/**50p**/£1

Japanese Ship Advertising
Often with Art Nouveau *borders.*
Price range	.. £2/**£4**/£6

Life at Sea/Sailors
Oilette types, e.g. 'Britain's Bulwarks' ..	50p/**75p**/£1
Pub. Gale & Polden	25p/**50p**/75p
Others, e.g. Pub. John Walker	.. 25p/50p

Menu/Souvenir Cards ■S 2
Chromo-lithos	£1.50/**£3**/£5
Others	£1/**£1.50**/£2

Naval Ships (*see* MILITARY)
Period 1. Chromo-litho	£5/**£6**/£8
Gale & Polden 'Wellington' series. Col. art. battleships ..	
.. ..	£1/**£1.50**/£2

■S2 Pub. White Star – Dominion Line. *Souvenir de Voyage* of RMS *Canada*. Sailed from Liverpool to Quebec, 3 June 1911 £1.50

Tuck 'Empire' series .. ..£6/**£10**/£12
Tuck Oilettes. Our Navy, e.g. HMS *Australia*, HMS *Queen Mary*, HMAS *Sydney*, etc. .. .. .. £1.50/**£2**/£2.50

Paddle Steamers ■S 3

This section is concerned with photographic origin and real photographs. RP types are most highly valued, particularly with close-up people detail. Artist-drawn cards should be valued under the *Passenger and Merchant Ships* heading.
Price range .. .. £1/**£2**/£8

Passenger & Merchant Ships

This section overlaps with SOCIAL HISTORY and TOPOGRAPHICAL and covers a broad spectrum of passenger and merchant vessels, e.g. ferries, trawlers, tugs, etc. Higher values are associated with clear RP cards, or where appropriate, fine chromo-litho UB examples. Local interest can raise values beyond these bands.
General. Period 2 .. .. £1.50/**£3**/£6
General. Periods 3, 4 .. .. £1/**£1.50**/£3
Sailing ships .. .. £1/**£3**/£6
Others .. .. 75p/**£1.50**/£3

Piccadilly Hotel (Ship Cards)

Price range .. .. 75p/**£1**/£1.50

Publishers ■R 4

Most famous postcard publishers, like Salmon, Tuck and Valentine's, produced pleasing ship series. Notable series were published by the following publishers:

MacBrayne, David
Glasgow & Highland Royal Mail Steamers, chromo-litho vignette. Printer McCorquodale, UB .. .. ..£8/**£12**/£20

Reid, Andrew
Chromo-litho vignettes for The America Line; Belfast Steam Ship Co.; P. & O.; Pacific Steam Navigation Co. (Orient Line); Pacific Line; Ullswater Navigation & Transit Co., etc.
Ships include:
SS Arabia; SS Graphic; SS Heroic; SS Himalaya; SS India; SS Macedonia; SS Magic; SS Malwa; SS Marmord; SS Mongolia; SS Moolton; SS Moormond; SS Oravia; SS Orcana;

■S3 Pub. for New Palace Steamers Ltd. by J.J.K. & Co. (J. J. Keliher). P.S. *Royal Sovereign*. Period 2 £8

SS Orellana; SS Oropesa; SS Oroya; SS Raven; SS Sardinia; SS Simla; SS St. Louis.

Price range . . . . £1.50/**£8**/£25

McCorquodale & Co.
Col. scenes for Royal Mail routes (e.g. Holyhead–Dublin).

Price range . . . . £3/**£4**/£6

Stuart, F. G. O.
Ships series, e.g. RMS *Adriatic*, RMS *Amazon*, RMS *Aragon*, RMS *Briton*, SS *Armdale Castle*, SS *Avondale Castle*, SS *Durham*, SS *Goorkha*, SS *Kenilworth Castle*.

Price range . . . . £1/**£2**/£2.50

Shipwrecks

Abertay (Cornwall, 1912)
Alaska
Bardic (Lizard, 1924) RP
Berlin
    Pub. Hartman. Set of 12
    Pub. Rotary RP
    Pub. Philco RP
Cecile Herzogin (Salcombe, 1936)
Coopland
Crescent City
Elizabeth (Bude, 1912)
Gladiator, HMS (1908). Pub. Broderick
Hilda (St. Malo, 1905)
La Gascogne (St. Nazaire)
Le Chili (Bordeaux)
Mahratta, SS (on Goodwins, 1909). Pub. Glencairn Craik, Deal
Mermaris (River Tigris)
Montagu, HMS (Lundy, 1906). Pub. Twiss Bros., Ilfracombe
Phoenix, HMS (Kowloon, 1908). Pub. M. Sternberg
Pisagna (Dover, 1912)
Queen Elizabeth (Steamboat) (Kew, 1904). Pub. Walter Pearce, Brentford
Scotia (1909). Photo S. Thorn, Bude
Thyra (Duncan's Bay, 1914) RP
Price range
    Artist drawn/photo origin . . . . £2/**£3**/£4
    RP . . . . £5/**£10**/£15

Silks

Woven types, incl. Grant & Stevens, e.g. RMS *Adriatic*, RMS *Edinburgh Castle*, RMS *Empress of Britain*, RMS *Carmania*, RMS *Ivernia*, RMS *Mauretania*, RMS *Royal George*, RMS *Titanic*, SS *Haverford*, etc. See NOVELTY.

Price range . . . . £12/**£20**/£25

Titanic

Much interest has been renewed in this ill-fated White Star liner following the filming of the wreck in 1985. See fourth edition for more detailed listing.

Artist-drawn . . . . £4/**£8**/£12
Commemorative/Memoriam . . . . . . £10/**£15**/£25
RP . . . . £8/**£10**/£15

SOCIAL HISTORY

The strong interest in social history which has developed in recent years has made this one of the most popular of collecting categories. There is a clear distinction to be made between Social History and Topographical. Normally the collector of social history cards is seeking a pictorial record of a particular historical aspect—perhaps cards showing workers in particular occupational settings, buildings of a particular type (e.g. fire stations), etc. The geographical location of the subject is of less importance than the subject itself.

The collector of topographical cards on the other hand is normally only interested in cards showing people/scenes in a particular location—sometimes a county, but more usually in a particular town or even village. There is often a 'conflict' of values between the two collectors—someone interested in views of fire stations in general might be prepared to pay £5 for a particular card, but the topographical collector of the district in which that fire station is situated (if it can be identified) might pay £20. It is quite impossible in a general catalogue of this nature to cater adequately for the topographical collector, prices here refer to the subject matter of cards rather than to local interest.

AGRICULTURE/FISHING/RURAL

Included in this section are cards which show rural and fishing occupations, especially those which no longer exist (or which modern technology has completely altered), agricultural machinery and fish processing.

The higher price range applies to clear RP cards showing active scenes with good detail of people and equipment.

Agricultural Shows/Markets
RP .. .. £2/**£4**/£6
Others .. .. 75p/**£1.50**/£3

Equipment/Machinery (Periods 2 to 4)
Horsedrawn carts/ploughs. RP .. .. £2/**£4**/£6
   Others .. .. 50p/**75p**/£1.50
Other machinery. RP .. .. £2/**£4**/£8
   Others .. .. 75p/**£1.50**/£3

Occupations
Period 1 General .. .. £2/**£4**/£6

Animal-Tenders (Periods 2 to 4)
Cowherds/Pigmen/Shepherds, etc.
RP .. .. £1.50/**£2**/£4
Others .. .. 50p/**75p**/£1

Arts/Cottage Industries/Crafts (Periods 2 to 4)
Blacksmiths/Dairy workers/Forge workers/Lace-makers/
Spinners/Weavers/Wheelwrights, etc.
RP .. ..£3/**£10**/£15
Others .. .. 75p/**£1.50p**/£3

Fisher Folk (Periods 2 to 4)
Scenes at markets/fish halls/on board/landing the catch,
coracle or Curragh fisher men, etc.
RP .. .. £2/**£4**/**£8**
Others .. .. 50p/**75p**/£1.50

Harvesters (Periods 2 to 4)
Grain/Tobacco, etc.
RP .. .. £1.50/**£4**/**£6**
Others .. .. 50p/**£1**/£2.50

Hops (*Periods 2 to 4*)
Young & Cooper cards
Lettered cards, A to K. b & w .. .. £1/**£2**/£4
Numbered cards, 1 to 25. col. .. .. .. £1.50/**£3**/£5
Others .. .. £1.50/**£3**/£8

Pickers (Periods 2 to 4)
Flowers (incl. lavender)/'Fruit'/Hops/Vegetables, etc.
RP .. .. £1/**£3**/£5
Others .. .. 50p/**£1**/£3

Rural Scenes (Periods 2 to 4)
Crops/grazing herds/landscapes/views.. .. 25p/**50p**/75p
Scenes of Village Life. RP .. .. £1/**£3**/£6
　Others .. .. 25p/**50p**/£1
Tuck named series, e.g. 'Rapholette glossy', 'Oilettes'
(including 'Cottage Gardens', 'Country Charms', 'Rural
England', 'The Simple Life', etc.) .. .. 25p/**75p**/£1.50

AMUSEMENT PARKS
RP .. .. £1.50/**£3**/£6
Others .. .. 75p/**£1**/£2

ARCADES
RP .. .. £1.50/**£3**/£8
Others .. .. 50p/**75p**/£2

ASSOCIATIONS/ORGANISATIONS
See also RELIGION.
Bands .. .. 50p/**£1**/£3
Boys Brigade .. .. £1.50/**£3**/£6
Church Army .. .. £1/**£2**/£4
Dr. Barnado .. .. 75p/**£1.50**/£3
Evangelism .. .. £1.50/**£2**/£4
Jewish .. .. £2/**£3**/£6
Political .. .. £2/**£5**/£8
Red Cross .. .. 75p/**£1**/£3
St. John Ambulance .. .. 75p/**£1**/£3
Salvation Army .. .. £1/**£1.50**/£5
YMCA/YWCA .. .. 50p/**75p**/£1.50
Others .. .. 50p/**£1**/£3

278

COALMINING (Periods 2–6)
Highest valuation for Gothard/RPs.

Artist-drawn/photographic origin	£2/**£4**/£6
Disasters/Memoriam	£18/**£20**/£35

Mines

Pithead	£3/**£6**/£8
Underground	£4/**£5**/£10
Miners	£6/**£8**/£10
Strikes (see also MODERN)	£15/**£20**/£35

■SH1 Pub. Hildesheimer. Messrs. Peter Robinson. 'One of the Show Rooms'. Period 2. Sepia £4

COMMERCIAL/INDUSTRIAL ■SH 1
This section deals with picture cards which can readily be associated with a particular commercial or industrial enterprise. The highest valuations are for clear RP with good people activity.
Breweries, Bridges, Chimneys, Engineering activities, Factory buildings. Exterior/Interior, Mills (Water and Wind), Salt works, Shop fronts, Shop interiors, Tin mines, Zinc mines, Workshop scenes, Others

Price range RP	£3/**£8**/£15
Others	50p/**£1.50**/£3

CRAFTS/OCCUPATIONS/SERVICES/TRADES ■SH 2
This section covers all forms of work except those included in 'Uniformed Public Services' below. All cards must have a subject contemporary to the period in which they were published, i.e. 'historical' types are not included. The major interest lies in skills or activities now out of date. See also 'Agriculture/Fishing/Rural' above.

The following list of occupations does not pretend to be exhaustive but only indicative of what may be found:

Barber; Barrel organist; Birdman; Cabbie; Chauffeur; Chimney Sweep; Clerk; Cobbler; Deliveryman; Dentist; Doctor; Egg Seller; Errand Girl; Flower Girl; Horn Blower; Lamplighter; Letter writer; Match Girl; Message Boy; Milkman; Newsvendor; Pavement Artist; Porter; Rat Catcher;

Refuse Collector; Road Sweeper; Sandwichboard Man; Servants; Schoolteacher; Shoeblack; Shopkeeper; Snake Catcher; Street Trader; Town Crier; Waiter; Window cleaner; Others.

Price range

RP ..	..	..	..	..	..	..	..	.. £3/**£8**/£20
Others	..	..	..	..	..	..	..	£1.50/**£3**/£5

■SH2 Pub. D. Constance Ltd. New Donald McGill Comic No. 1009. Period 4 75p

DISASTERS
This section deals with 'Acts of God' such as epidemics, fires, floods, landslides and storms rather than obviously man-made catastrophes like rail or road accidents, except where the latter assumed disaster proportions. Probably every area of the country has had its own disaster. See also AVIATION, RAILWAYS, ROAD TRANSPORT. *A listing of well-documented, named disasters was published in the fourth edition of this catalogue, p. 306.*

Avalanches; Crashes (Aeroplane, Motor Cars, Trains, Trams); Earthquakes; Epidemics; Explosions; Fires; Floods; Storms;

others.	..	..	..	..	..	..	.. £2/**£6**/£15
Pub. Gothard, Warner		..	..	..	..	£18/**£25**/£45

•

ETHNIC ACTIVITIES/CHARACTERS/GROUPS ■SH 3
By 'ethnic' we mean that the subject matter is directly concerned with a particular race. The reference may be humorous (e.g. endless Irish/Scottish/Welsh jokes) or observant of activity or dress. The most highly valued cards are those of photographic origin. A detailed listing of types appeared in the fourth edition of this catalogue, p. 294. Higher values apply in the country of origin of the subject.
Africa; Britain; European Mainland; Far East; India; Middle East; North America, South America; others.
'Coons', Cowboys; Gypsies; Indians; Jews; Opium smokers; etc.

■SH3 Pub. R. O. Fusslein, Johannesburg. Artist H. Egersdorfer. 'Sketches of South African Life'. Series VI. 'Trekking'. Period 2 £3

Artist-drawn
Well-known (e.g. H. Egersdorfer – S. African Types; Ellam–Japanese types; John Innes– Wild West; Mortimer Menpes – Japanese and other types; Others) .. .. £1/**£2**/£4
Lesser known or artist anon .. .. .. 50p/**75p**/£1.50
Pub. Tuck 'Wide-Wide-World' series and other 'Oilettes' of 'Native Life in . . .' .. .. 75p/**£1.50**/£2.50
Others .. .. 50p/**75p**/£1.50
Photo-origin (highest valuation for close-up RP) £1.50/**£5**/£10

LEGEND & LORE
Many areas have their own folk history, often based on historical events. These cards are normally of non-photographic origin. However, sometimes local pageants and processions may re-enact a legend and photographic cards of that event were published. Such photographic origin examples should be valued under 'Local Events/Gatherings' below.

Customs/Proverbs	50p/**75p**/£1.50
Ducking Stools	25p/**50p**/75p
Dunmow Flitch	£1/**£2**/£3
Folk dances, Maypoles, Morris men, etc. ..	75p/**£1.50**/£3
Ghosts	50p/**75p**/£1.50
Gretna Green	25p/**50p**/75p
Lady Godiva (not silk)	50p/**75p**/£1.50
Local Legends:	
Wiltshire Moonrakers	50p/**75p**/£1.50
Others	25p/**50p**/£1
Pillories/stocks	25p/**50p**/75p

LOCAL EVENTS/GATHERINGS
The cards in this section are of photographic origin. Under 'Edwardian Life' we include all those Edwardian activities which attracted the attention of the professional or amateur photographer. Very many splendid 'posed groups' may be found—amateur theatrics, families, nurses and just people gathered together for some special occasion. Although, frequently, neither place nor person can be identified, the card can be a valuable social record.

Auctions; Bear baiting/performing—see ANIMALS; Beating bounds/Crying marches; Carnivals (mostly Continental); Edwardian life; Elections; Fairs; Fêtes; Flower festivals; Fund-raising; Goose fairs; Inaugurations. (Hospitals, libraries, etc.); Markets; *Oktoberfest* (Ger. Munich *Bierfest*); Ox/Pig roasts; Pageants; Parades; Rag days; Regattas; *Sommerfest* (Ger.); Unidentified gatherings; Well dressings; Works outings; Others

Price range

RP..	..	..	..	..	..	..	..	.. £3/**£8**/£15
Others ..	..	..	..	..	..	..	50p/**£1.50**/£3

■SH 4 Pub. R. Barthelemy, Paris. World Jamboree of Peace. France 1947. PU with special stamp and postmark. Limited edition (No. 0409) £15

SCOUTS AND GUIDES ■SH 4

A highly collectible theme as many collectors have fond youthful memories of their days in the organisation. The movement inspired many postcards—photographic and artist drawn—of the leaders, scout and guide groups and meetings etc. There are many comic cards by well-known artists.

Comic designs
Artists Jagger, Reg Maurice, Gilson, etc. .. .. £1/**£3**/£6
Jamborees
1923–85 .. .. 25p/**50p**/£25
Leaders
Baden-Powell, Prince of Wales as Chief Scout of Wales, Princess Elizabeth, Princess Margaret, Princess Mary as Girl Guides, etc.

Artist drawn ..	..	..	..	..	..	75p/**£1.50**/£4
RP.. ..	..	..	..	..	..	.. £1/**£3**/£5

Scouts & Guides
Artist drawn
Well-known artists/series (e.g. Harry Payne/Pub. Tuck. 'Our Boy Scout' series, etc.) .. ..£8/**£15**/£40
Lesser-known, artist anon. .. .. .. £1.50/**£3**/£5
RP (Life in camp, etc.) .. .. .. £1.50/**£4**/£6
Others .. .. 75p/**£1.50**/£3
1985. 75 Years of Guiding 25p/**50p**/75p

SEASIDE ■SH 5
Photographic origin cards with close-up detail are the most
highly rated.

Bathing Beauties
Pub. Editions du Panorama de Paris. Series of coloured cards
   of photographic origin, UB   ..   ..   ..   £1/**£2**/£4

Artists
Abeille, Jack. Period 1	£10/**£15**/£20
Wennerburg, B. Period 2 UB	£2/**£4**/£8
Other signed artists. Period 1	£3/**£5**/£10
Other signed artists. Periods 2, 3	£1/**£2**/£3
Other signed artists. Periods 4, 5	50p/**75p**/£1
Unsigned artist drawn. Period 1	£1/**£2**/£3
Unsigned artist drawn. Periods 2, 3	75p/**£1**/£2

Bathing Machines
Photographic Origin/R.P. Periods 1 to 3
Close-up, sharp picture with detail of people ..	£1/**£2**/£4
In distance, but with detail of people	50p/**£1**/£2

■SH 5 Pub. W. A. Wells. 'The Beach, Dovercourt', complete
with bathing machines. Period 2 £3

SIEGES/STRIKES/RIOTS
see also POLITICAL

Price range
RP	..£6/**£15**/£30
Others	.. £2/**£6**/£12

UNIFORMED PUBLIC SERVICES
Higher values are for clear photographic origin cards.

Customs & Excise	£3/**£4**/£6
Fire Service	£2/**£3**/£5
Nursing/Medical staff	£1/**£1.50**/£4
Police	£1/**£2**/£5
Postmen. Comic drawings. F.S., etc. ..	.. 75p/**£1**/£3
Postmen. Photographic origin	£1/**£1.50**/£5
Postmen. Others	75p/**£1.50**/£5
Prison	£1/**£2**/£5
Railway (*see* RAILWAYS)	£2/**£4**/£6
Others	£1/**£1.50**/£5

SPORTS

We list below the best known artists for cards in this category, followed by alphabetical entries for each sport.

Artist Drawn. Named Artists
The Sport/Series for which they are best known is given in brackets.

Browne, Tom†	£1.50/**£3**/£5
Carter, Reg† (*Sporting Chinamen. Chromo-litho series 364*)	
.. ..	£2/**£3**/£3.50
'Crackerjack' (*Hockey*)	75p/**£1**/£1.25
Crombie, Charles (*Golf*)	£1/**£1.50**/£2
Elliott, Harry (*Horse sports*)	£2/**£3.50**/£4.50
Hebblethwaite (*Cricket*)	75p/**£1**/£1.25
Kinsella, E. P.† (*Cricket, Cycling, Football, Tennis*)	
.. ..	£1.50/**£3**/£5
Parett, Harry† (*Roller-skating*)	75p/**£1**/£1.50
Payne, Harry†	.. £4/**£6**/£10
Pirkis, A. G.† (*Tennis*)	75p/**£1**/£1.50
Quinnell, Cecil (*Sporting glamour studies*) ..	£1/**£2**/£2.50
Rowland, Ralph (*Hockey*)	£1/**£1.50**/£1.75
Rowlandson, G. D. (*early chromo-lithos*)	£3/**£4**/£5
Sager, Xavier† (*Bowling at le Bal Tabarin*) ..	£6/**£7**/£8
Schönpflug, Fritz† (*Boxing, Football*)	£1/**£3**/£4
Spurgin, Fred† (*Cycling*)	£1/**£1.50**/£2
Thackeray, Lance† (*many sports*)	£3/**£4**/£5
Thiele, Arthur† (*Bowling, Dancing, Tennis*) ..	£3/**£5**/£8

Angling

Price range	50p/**75p**/£1.50

Archery

Price range	£1/**£1.50**/£2

Athletics

Athletes	50p/**75p**/£1.50
Meetings RP	75p/**£1.50**/£3

Badminton

Price range	75p/**£1**/£1.50

Ballooning

Artist drawn	£1.50/**£2.50**/£4
Photo-origin (higher value for RP)	£3/**£5**/£8

Baseball

Comic

Baseball Illustrated. Pub. Davidson Bros. Series 2618/9. Artist Tom Browne .. .. £4/**£5**/£6

Baseball Kidlets. Pub. Ullman Series 195 .. £2/**£3**/£4

Others .. .. 75p/**£1.50**/£2

General

Baseball Series. Pub. The Rose Co. .. .. 75p/**£1.50**/£2

Baseball Terms Illustrated. Pub. Frederickson. Artist Dewey .. .. 75p/**£1.50**/£2

Others .. .. 50p/**75p**/£2

Players
    Baseball Hall of Fame. Pub. Cooperstown, N. F.   ..   ..
   ..   .. £1.50/**£2.50**/£4
    Baseball Players. Pub. Pomand. Chromolitho ..   ..   ..
   ..   .. £1.50/**£2.50**/£4
    Others   ..   .. 75p/**£1.50**/£2

Basketball/Netball
Price range   ..   .. 75p/**£1**/£1.50

Bicycling
See COMPETITIONS/CRAZES

Billiards/Snooker
Artwork by Tuck. Pub. J. V. A.
Caricatures   ..   .. £2/**£3**/£3.50
Billiards rooms ..   .. 75p/**£1.50**/£3
Others   ..   .. 75p/**£1**/£1.50

Board Games
Price range   ..   .. 50p/**£1.50**/£3

Boating/Canoeing
Comic   ..   .. 50p/**£1**/£2
Scenes   ..   .. 50p/**75p**/£1

Bowls
Price range   ..   .. 75p/**£1.50**/£3

■SP1 Pub. The Dana Studio (Photographers) USA. 'Jack Johnson'. 20 June 1912. RP £5

Boxing ■SP 1
Pub. Beagles. 'Famous Boxers' series ..   ..   .. £1/**£2**/£3
Pub. Lilywhite. 1919. Carpentier versus Joe Beckett. Twelve
    cards in set   ..   .. £2/**£2.50**/£3.50
Others   ..   .. 50p/**£1.50**/£5

■SP2 Pub. Purger, Munich. 'Spectators at a Bull Fight'. UB.
PU 1904 £1.50

Bullfighting ■SP 2
Price range   ..   ..   50p/**75p**/£1.50

Card Games
Price range   ..   ..   50p/**£1**/£2

Cricket
Perhaps the most documented sport on the postcard. Postcards
fall into the following categories. The earlier the Period, the
higher the valuation.

Comic   ..   ..   £1/**£2**/£4
Players
Amateur ..   ..   50p/**75p**/£1.50
Professional (County/International)   ..   ..   £2.50/**£4**/£5

Teams
County   ..   ..   £3/**£5**/£8
Local..   ..   ..   50p/**£1.50**/£5
Touring (MCC/International)   ..   ..   ..   £2/**£3.50**/£5

Artist-drawn
Illustrated 'phrases' ..   ..   75p/**£2.50**/£5
Others   ..   ..   50p/**£1**/£2

Publishers
For an alphabetical list of the main cricket publishers, see
the fourth edition of this catalogue, p. 301.

Croquet
Comic   ..   ..   50p/**75p**/£1
Scenes   ..   ..   75p/**£1**/£1.50

Curling
Artist drawn 25p/**50p**/75p
Photo-origin   ..   ..   75p/**£1**/£1.50

Dancing
Many famous artists, e.g. Reg Carter, Mela Koehler, Thiele,
Usobal, etc. did 'Dance' series.
Well-known artists   ..   ..   £1/**£3**/£15
Others   ..   ..   50p/**75p**/£1

Sports

Diabolo—*see* COMPETITIONS/CRAZES

Fencing
Comic	75p/**£1**/£1.50
Photo-origin	50p/**75p**/£1

Football—Association
Comic—general	25p/**£1**/£1.50
Comic—named artists	£1/**£3**/£8
Commemoratives	£3/**£5**/£6
Crowd scenes	£1/**£2**/£2.50
Grounds/scenes	75p/**£1.50**/£3
Players—amateur	75p/**£1.25**/£2
professional	50p/**£2**/£6
Teams—amateur	£1/**£2**/£3
military	50p/**75p**/£1
professional pre-1939	£3/**£6**/£8
professional post-1939	75p/**£2**/£4

Football—Rugby League
Players	£2/**£4**/£6
Teams—amateur	£1/**£2**/£3
professional/touring	£3/**£5**/£10

Football—Rugby Union
Comic	75p/**£1**/£1.50
Grounds, scenes	£1/**£1.50**/£2
Pub. Tuck. Oilette	75p/**£1**/£1.50
Teams—city	£1/**£2**/£3
touring	£2/**£3**/£5
town/village	£1.50/**£3**/£4

Foxhunting—*see* ANIMALS: Horses

Gambling/Playing Cards—*see* CURIOUS/MISCELLANEOUS

Golf
Comic—general	£1/**£1.50**/£2.50
Comic—named artists	£1/**£3**/£6
Courses/Club houses	£1.50/**£2.50**/£3
Players	£2/**£4**/£8
Tournaments	£1.50/**£3**/£6

Gymnastics
Price range	50p/**75p**/£1.50

Hockey
Comic	50p/**75p**/£1.50
Teams	£1/**£1.50**/£2
Others	25p/**50p**/75p

Horse racing—*see* ANIMALS: Horses

Motor Racing—*see* ROAD TRANSPORT

Mountaineering
Artist drawn. Period 1/Early Period 2	£1/**£2**/£4

Comic	..	..	..	..	..	..	..	50p/**75p**/£1
Pub. Abrahams, Keswick	..	..	..	..	50p/**75p**/£1
Others	..	..	..	..	..	..	..	25p/**50p**/75p

Olympic Games
20th Anniversary of re-establishment of the Games (1914)
.. ..£6/**£10**/£12
Paris (1924). Artist Pauteuberge   .. .. ..£8/**£10**/£12
Berlin (1936). Col. designs .. .. £12/**£15**/£20
Monotone officials   .. .. £1.50/**£3**/£5
Garmish Partenkirchen (Winter Games) (1936)   £7/**£10**/£12
Moscow (1980). Official cards. Artist drawn. Garish colour.
   Printed 1978 .. .. 25p/**50p**/75p
Los Angeles (1984). Various   .. .. .. 25p/**50p**/£1
Others
   Period 4 .. .. £4/**£7**/£10
   Period 6 .. .. 50p/**75p**/£1

Polo
Price range   .. .. 75p/**£1**/£1.50

Roller Skating—*see* COMPETITIONS: Rinking

Rowing
Price range   .. .. 25p/**75p**/£3

■SP3 Pub. Misch and Stock. On front, col. picture of sailing boats. Reverse shows that this Period 2 postcard was 'Carried in Parmela Yacht Race' 28 Aug. 1979, celebrating the 150th Anniv. of Western Australia. Period 7 £5

Sailing/Yachting ■SP 3
Crews, races, regattas, sailing ships .. .. .. £1/**£2**/£3
Cards used with special commem. handstamps .. £3/**£5**/£10

Shooting
Game   .. .. 50p/**£1**/£1.50
Target   .. .. £1/**£1.50**/£3

Show-jumping (Horse Shows)
General scenes .. .. 75p/**£1**/£1.25
Olympia Horse Show. General   .. .. £1/**£3**/£5
   Poster ads.   .. .. £3/**£5**/£8

Skating

Artist-drawn	..	..	..	..	..	..	50p/**£1.50**/£5
Comic	..	..	..	..	..	..	50p/**75p**/£1
Others	..	..	..	..	..	..	25p/**50p**/75p

Sports Days & Events
Price range .. .. 75p/**£1.50**/£3

Swimming
Price range .. .. 50p/**£1.50**/£3

Table tennis (Ping Pong)

A listing of table tennis cards appeared in the third edition of this catalogue, pp. 136–137
Price range (value according to Period, Artist, etc.) .. ..
.. .. 25p/**£2.50**/£12

Tennis

Artist drawn (value according to artist)	.. ..	£1/**£3**/£5
Comic (value according to artists)	.. ..	50p/**75p**/£3
General scenes ..	.. ..	25p/**50p**/75p
Players. Pre-1939	.. ..	£3/**£4**/£5
Periods 5–6 ..	.. ..	£1.50/**£2.50**/£3
Period 7 ..	.. ..	**25p**/50p
Wimbledon scenes	.. ..	25p/**£3**/£4

Tobogganing
Price range .. .. 50p/**75p**/£1.50

Trophies
Price range .. .. 50p/**£1**/£1.50

Walking
Racing .. .. £1/**£1.50**/£3
Round the World, see CURIOUS

Water Polo
Price range .. .. 75p/**£1**/£1.50

Winter Sports

Chromo-litho	..	..	..	..	..	£1/**£1.50**/£4
Others	..	..	..	..	..	25p/**50p**/75p

Wrestling
Price range .. .. £2/**£3**/£4

Three Band Pricing System

Left Hand Band: The lowest price you will probably be asked to pay for this card.
Middle Band: What you will normally be asked to pay for this card: its average, reasonable price.
Right Hand Band: The highest price you will probably be asked to pay for this card.
For a full explanation of the system see page ix.

TOPOGRAPHICAL

The hardy perennial debate of the distinction between SOCIAL HISTORY and TOPOGRAPHICAL cards continues. It is indisputable that in many cases the two factors are inextricably represented on a particular postcard.

The *Chambers Dictionary* definition of *Topography* is 'Detailed study, description, or features of a limited area'. In pursuance of this concept, and to reinforce the rationale explained in the introduction to SOCIAL HISTORY, we have moved to that section any postcards which relate to personalities and events in a district. Under this heading of TOPOGRAPHICAL are postcards which relate purely to landscapes and street scenes and whose *raison d'être* is to record how that scene looked when the drawing or photograph of it was made – not any event, that was taking place in it. In other words – view postcards.

As in SOCIAL HISTORY, cards showing local events are worth a great deal more to the collector living in, or particularly interested in, that particular area. So TOPOGRAPHICAL cards showing local views often have a geographically limited appeal. This means that definitive pricing is almost impossible in this section. Cards in this section fall into two main categories: artist-drawn postcards of the 'Oilette' variety and cards of photographic origin. In the latter category the work of local publishers is the most highly valued. Period 2 cards are still the most sought after, but the cards of Periods 4–6 are beginning to be collected.

BUILDING/STRUCTURES

Interest continues to grow in what was once an underestimated theme, as local historians recognise the value of the picture postcard as a record of much changed towns and villages. An Ecclesiastical postcard club has even been formed. This section concentrates on the buildings themselves, but human figures often identify the building (e.g. schoolchildren). An interesting event in that building would, of course, take the postcard into the SOCIAL HISTORY section.

Bandstands, Barracks, Casinos, Churches, Cinemas (see also ENTERTAINMENT), Factories, Fire Stations, Historical buildings/structures, Hospitals, Hotels (see also ADVERTISING), Municipal buildings, Police stations, Post Offices, Public houses, Railway stations (see also RAILWAYS), Restaurants, Schools, Skyscrapers (Chrysler Building, Flat Iron Building, New York, etc.), Theatres (see also ENTERTAINMENT), Village halls, others.

Price range

RP..	..	..	..	..	..	..	..	.. £3/**£8**/£15
Others	..	..	..	..	..	..	..	75p/**£1.50**/£3

CAVES/GROTTOS (SPELEOLOGY)

An increasingly popular theme, including explorers, tourist attractions and novelty cards. Researcher Dave Irwins has discovered some 20,000 different cards.

British Caves

Alum Pot; Blue John Mine; Cox's Cave; Dan-yr-Ogof;

Eastwater Cavern; Eldon Hose; Gaping Ghyll; Goatschurch Cavern; Gough's Cave; Goydon; Juniper Gulf; Lamb Leer; Peak Cavern; Sell Ghyll; Skirwith; Speedwell Mine; Stump Cross; Swildon's Hole; Victoria Cave; Wookey Hole; Yerdas.

Period 2	..	..	..	..	..	..	75p/**£1.50**/£4
Periods 3–7	..	..	..	..	..	..	25p/**50p**/£1.50

Foreign Caves

Adelsberg Grotto (Yugoslavia); Betharrem Caves (France); Blue Grotto (Capri); Cango Caves (S.A.); Carlsbad Caverns (USA); Charlottenholhle (Ger); De Haan Grotto (Belg); Dechenhohle (Ger); Howe Cave (USA); Jenolan Caves (Australia), Mammoth Cave (USA); Sloup (Czech); Wiatomo Cave (N.Z.); Others.

Period 1.UB. Gruss Auss type	..	..	..	..	£1/**£3**/£5
Period 2. Pub. Tuck 'Wide, Wide World' Series, Artist					
Fullwood/Others	..	..	..	..	50p/**£1.50**/£3
Periods 3–7	..	..	..	..	25p/**50p**/£1

INLAND WATERWAYS
Highest values apply for scenes with activity/traffic.

Bridges; Dams; Ferries; Fords; Lakes; Rivers; Village Ponds; Weirs; Others

RP	..	..	..	..	..	..	£2/**£4**/£6
Others	..	..	..	..	..	..	25p/**75p**/£1.50

Canals
Narrow Canals

British RP: Barges/Construction/Disasters	..	£7.50/**£15**/£30
General views/Locks/Tunnels	..	£2/**£3**/£5
British others	..	£1.50/**£3**/£4
Foreign	..	75p/**£1.50**/£3

Ship Canals

British	..	..	..	..	..	..	£2/**£4**/£6
Foreign	..	..	..	..	..	..	£1/**£2**/£3

LANDSCAPES/STREET SCENES ■T1–3
City centres; City suburbs; Inland towns; Landscapes/Rural Views; Seaside towns; Villages.

The highest valuations are for highly animated scenes, especially of scarce village views. British scenes rate higher for UK collectors (as of course do 'Foreign' cards in their country of origin).

Artist Drawn

Well known artists (see also ARTISTS*) including:* Wilfrid Ball; Baness; Marjorie Bates; W. H. Borrow; A. de Bréanski; H. Cassiers; Harry Colls; C. Essenhigh-Corke; Sidney Endacott; J. Finnemore; Charles E. Flower; John Fulleylove; Robert Gallon; Prof. van Hier; 'Jotter' (Hayward-Young); Elmer Keene; Luigi Loir; E. Longstaffe; A. Mailick; Wm Mathison; M. Morris; K. Mutter; Parsons Norman; Arthur Payne; Harry

Payne; Reginald Phillimore; A. R. Quinton; Manuel Wielandt; Henry Wimbush; Sepping Wright, etc.

Price range .. .. £1.50/**£2.50**/£6

Lesser known or Anon artists

Price range 25p/**50p**/75p

Publishers of the above include:
Boots (the chemist); Faulkner, C. W. ('Rough Seas', Various Views Series); Hildesheimer, S. & Co. ('5000' series q.v.); J. Salmon (notably by Essenhigh-Corke and Quinton); Ruddock, J. W. (notably E. Anglian area); Tuck (notably the prolific 'Oilette' range; also 'Aquarette'; 'Connoisseur'; 'Oil-facsim'; 'Rough Seas'; 'Turneresque'; 'Views'; 'Watercolour' and many others).

■T1 Pub. J. Salmon. Artist A. R. Quinton. 'The Admiralty Arch', London. No. 1204. Period 2 £3

■T2 Pub. 'Wyndham Series'. Victoria Parade, Deal, Kent. Photo-origin. UB. Early Period 2 £6

Photographic Origin
These are postcards which originated from a photograph which is then mass produced by a traditional printing process involving the transfer of ink, often in the form of dots (See Picture Postcards of the Golden Age by Tonie and Valmai Holt for more details of printing processes). The quality of such products varies from superb to extremely poor. 'Fuzzy' views

■T3 Pub. Anon. 'Council offices, Barry'. RP. Period 4 £3

*are worth less than the following valuations; local collectors
will pay more than the following valuations, but condition is
all important in this section.*

Animated sharp scenes by local publishers ..	.. £3/**£6**/£12
Non-animated scenes by local publishers ..	75p/**£1.50**/£3
Animated sharp scenes by National publishers	75p/**£1.50**/£3
Non-animated scenes by National publishers	25p/**50p**/75p

Real Photographic
*These are postcards which are reproduced from an original
photograph by a photographic process. They will often be
labelled 'Real photograph' and normally have a glossy finish.
Unfortunately they are prone to fading and cracking. The well-
preserved, sharp, detailed real photo by a local photographer/
publisher is (apart from the cards of highly prized artists) the
rarest, most precious and sought after postcard today.
Comments on condition, etc. as for photo-origin above.*

Animated sharp scenes by local publishers ..	..£5/**£10**/£15
Non-animated scenes by local publishers ..	.. £1/**£2**/£4
Animates sharp scenes by National publishers ..	£3/**£5**/£8
Non-animated scenes by National publishers	50p/**75p**/£1

Publishers of the above include (as a small representative
sample of the literally thousands that existed in Edwardian
times):
Local (see also PUBLISHERS)
Anthony of Ypres; Broom, Mrs. Albert, Fulham; Colliers of
Reading; Jackson & Son, Grimsby; King, John, of Southall;
Lawrence, William, Dublin; Martin, Charles, London area;
Muir & Moodie, Dunedin, N.Z.; Peel, Robert, Oxford; Rattar,
J. D., Berwick; Smith, E. Gordon, London area; Spalding,
Fred, Chelmsford; Welch, J. Portsmouth, etc.

National
Delittle, Fenwick & Co.; Dennis, E. T. W.; Frith, Francis;
Hartmann; Judge's; 'LL' (British & Continental); Photochrom;
Pictorial Stationery Co. (Peacock series); Ritchie, Wm;
Rotary; A & G Taylor; Tuck (scores of differently named
series); Valentine's (most major areas of U.K.); Woolstone
Bros., etc.

INDEX TO THEMES

294

Index to Themes

Index to Themes

Index to Themes